EXPERIMENTS IN PHYSIOLOGY AND BIOCHEMISTRY

Edited by G. A. KERKUT

Department of Physiology and Biochemistry, University of Southampton, Southampton, England

Volume I

ACADEMIC PRESS
London and New York
1968

ACADEMIC PRESS INC. (LONDON) LTD
Berkeley Square House
Berkeley Square
London, W.1

U.S. edition published by
ACADEMIC PRESS INC.
111 Fifth Avenue
New York, New York 10003

Library of Congress Catalog Card Number: 67–30765

PRINTED IN GREAT BRITAIN BY
ADLARD & SON LIMITED, DORKING, SURREY

EXPERIMENTS IN PHYSIOLOGY AND BIOCHEMISTRY

Volume I

Contributors

H. L. ATWOOD, *Department of Zoology, University of Toronto, Canada* (p. 307)

L. BARTON BROWNE, *C.S.I.R.O., Division of Entomology, Canberra, A.C.T., Australia* (p. 189)

P. J. BENTLEY, *The Mount Sinai Graduate School of Biological Sciences, City University of New York, New York, U.S.A.* (p. 161)

SUSAN P. BONNER, *Department of Biology, Rice University, Houston, Texas, U.S.A.* (p. 1)

JAMES W. CAMPBELL, *Department of Biology, Rice University, Houston, Texas, U.S.A.* (p. 1)

DAVID H. CHEN, *Insect Physiology Laboratory, Entomology Research Division, ARS, U.S. Department of Agriculture, Beltsville, Maryland, U.S.A.* (p. 201)

EVERETT DOUGLAS, *Scripps Institution of Oceanography, University of California, La Jolla, California, U.S.A.* (p. 371)

W. A. L. EVANS, *Department of Zoology, University of Wales, Cardiff, Wales* (pp. 63 and 395)

ERNST FLOREY, *Department of Zoology, University of Washington, Seattle, Washington, U.S.A.* (p. 221)

W. S. HOAR, *Department of Zoology, University of British Columbia, Vancouver, Canada* (p. 125)

G. HOYLE, *Department of Biology, University of Oregon, Eugene, Oregon, U.S.A.* (p. 269)

A. K. HUGGINS, *Department of Biochemistry, University College London, England* (p. 25)

G. A. KERKUT, *Department of Physiology and Biochemistry, University of Southampton, England* (pp. 111 and 353)

THOMAS W. LEE, *Department of Biology, Rice University, Houston, Texas, U.S.A.* (p. 1)*

S. H. P. MADDRELL, *Department of Zoology, University of Cambridge, England* (p. 209)

X. J. MUSACCHIA, *Department of Physiology, University of Missouri, Columbia, Missouri, U.S.A.* (p. 379)

E. M. PANTELOURIS, *Department of Biology, University of Strathclyde, Glasgow, Scotland* (p. 101)

* Present address: Science Department, Central Connecticut State College, New Britain, Connecticut, U.S.A.

I. PARNAS, *Department of Zoology, Hebrew University, Jerusalem, Israel* (p. 307)

GEORGE V. PICKWELL, *U.S. Navy Electronics Laboratory, San Diego, California, U.S.A.* (p. 371)

C. B. SEDDEN, *Department of Physiology and Biochemistry, University of Southampton, England* (p. 347)

A. SHAPIRA, *Department of Physiology and Biochemistry, University of Southampton, England* (p. 353)

M. W. SMITH, *Department of Physiology, Institute of Animal Physiology, Babraham, Cambridge, England* (p. 177)

P. STANBURY, *School of Biological Sciences, University of Sydney, N.S.W., Australia* (pp. 59 and 389)

ANTHONY T. TU, *Department of Chemistry, and Interdepartment Curriculum in Toxicology, Utah State University, Logan, Utah, U.S.A.* (p. 85)*

R. J. WALKER, *Department of Physiology and Biochemistry, University of Southampton, England* (p. 331)

* Present address: Department of Biochemistry, Colorado State University, Fort Collins Colorado, U.S.A.

Preface

The easiest way of learning how to perform an experiment is to watch someone else demonstrating it and then, using the same equipment, to try and copy the procedure. If one fails the first time one can watch again then repeat the process; any further failures can be corrected by being shown precisely what has gone wrong. For most experiments this is the best method of learning; however, it is often impossible to follow this procedure because the specific methods are not easily available in the laboratory where one is working.

Another system is to read through a series of instructions and attempt to follow them out. This is more difficult because the writer often infers practical experience not possessed by the reader. Furthermore, there may be minor practical details that are not immediately appreciated either by the reader or the writer. Nevertheless, this is the most commonly used method of learning how to conduct an experiment, and the work published in the scientific journals provides the necessary information and stimulus.

However, it is often difficult to follow experimental procedure from the published account in a scientific paper. This is frequently the fault of an editorial system which considers the "materials and methods" to be less important than the "results and conclusion", and most authors are persuaded to present these sections in a very condensed form.

The present volume is the first of a series in which it is hoped to supply sufficient practical details to enable the reader to follow and carry out the experiments for himself. The information is presented in detail, though possibly there may be too much detail for some people and not enough for others. Initially, only those experiments that could be performed in three hours were selected for the present volume. However, it was felt that there were also many experiments that would take longer in time but which could be broken down into smaller periods and so fit in with a rather more liberal practical programme. It is intended that at a later date the three-hour class type of experiments will be collected from this and subsequent volumes and published separately.

I should welcome suggestions from authors for future contributions. A detailed scheme for the arrangement of material is presented on p. xi. Such a lay-out is only tentative and can be modified according to the particular needs of individual experiments.

It is hoped that the body of practical information to be presented in this series will help to spread skill and experience from one Laboratory to another.

DEPARTMENT OF PHYSIOLOGY AND BIOCHEMISTRY   G. A. KERKUT
UNIVERSITY OF SOUTHAMPTON
ENGLAND

March 1968

Note on Vivisection

All experimentalists should note that most countries have rules and regulations concerning that performance of experiments on living animals.

In England, Scotland and Wales it is necessary that any experiments carried out on vertebrate animals should be performed in a Government licensed laboratory, by persons licensed to carry out the experiments, under the supervision and guidance of licensed persons. Failure to do this may bring about legal proceedings against the experimentalists.

The exact legal situation differs according to the country where the experiments are being carried out, but in all cases students are advised to ask their instructors for specific information.

Guiding Principles in the Care and Use of Animals

Approved by the Council of the American
Physiological Society

Only animals that are lawfully acquired shall be used in this laboratory and their retention and use shall be in every case in strict compliance with state and local laws and regulations.

Animals in the laboratory must receive every consideration for their bodily comfort; they must be kindly treated, properly fed and their surroundings kept in a sanitary condition.

Appropriate anesthetics must be used to eliminate sensibility to pain during operative procedures. Where recovery from anesthesia is necessary during the study, acceptable technic to minimize pain must be followed. Curarizing agents are not anesthetics. Where the study does not require recovery from anesthesia, the animal must be killed in a humane manner at the conclusion of the observations.

The postoperative care of animals shall be such as to minimize discomfort and pain and in any case shall be equivalent to accepted practices in schools of Veterinary Medicine.

When animals are used by students for their education or the advancement of science such work shall be under the direct supervision of an experienced teacher or investigator. The rules for the care of such animals must be the same as for animals used for research.

BRAND NAMES

Often in the experiment, a piece of equipment will be referred to by its trade, manufacturer's or supplier's name. It may be that you do not have this specific piece of *named* equipment in stock but that you have an equivalent or alternative make. In almost all cases there is nothing "magic" about the specified brand. It is mentioned because the author used it. When in doubt, it is advised that you carry out a trial experiment on your own equipment. This may be preferable to ordering the equipment BRAND X from your suppliers and finding when it is delivered some three months later that it is more expensive and worse than the model that you already have in the laboratory.

Suggestions for Future Contributors

These volumes will provide full details of methods and specific experiments on the biochemistry and physiology of animals. It is intended that they will fill the gap that has been made by the restricted amount of space that journals provide to the "Materials and Methods" section of papers.

Where possible each account should provide very full experimental details so that:

(1) Research workers and advanced students will be able to perform the experiments with the minimum of difficulty.

(2) Technicians will know what equipment to set out and which chemical solutions will be required.

It will help if the material can be presented as a series of separate but linked experiments so that the reader will realise the precise task involved in each experiment. In some cases it may be necessary to give details as to how to construct a piece of equipment and how to test it. This would then be equivalent to an "experiment".

A *suggested* plan of the account is as follows though the authors can, where necessary, alter the layout to suit the particular case.

(1) Title of experiments.

(2) General principles that the experiments and methods will illustrate.

(3) Title of specific experiment.

(4) Apparatus required.

(5) Animals required.

(6) Chemical solutions required. Please give solutions in terms of g/ml instead of molarity of solutions.

(7) Experimental details. These should be very full, in numbered paragraphs, with diagrams where this will help show specific equipment, dissections technique, manipulative methods, etc. The authors should not assume too much "know-how" on the part of the reader. The reader may be an expert, but in a slightly different field and these experiments are to help him extend his technique.

(8) Sample results. These should be edited labelled traces, titration readings, tables, graphs, etc. together with full calculation of the result. The worker should see from these records exactly the sort of result that he should be able to obtain for himself.

(9) Trouble shooting. Notes about what can go wrong with the experiment. What to check first if the experiment is unsuccessful.

(10) Further ideas about experiments that can be carried out with this equipment.

(11) Bibliography. Further reading with notes as to the significance of the selected references. Full titles to papers and books should be given together with first and last page references.

There is no strict limitation as to number of words or figures, though authors are asked to be as concise as is concomitant with clarity.

Contents

xiv CONTENTS

1 | Enzymes of Arginine and Urea Metabolism in Invertebrates

JAMES W. CAMPBELL, SUSAN P. BONNER* and THOMAS W. LEE**

Department of Biology, Rice University, Houston, Texas, U.S.A.

ANIMALS AND APPARATUS

ANIMALS

The methods described for the assay of ornithine transcarbamylase (OTC), arginase, and urease have been used successfully with members of several invertebrate phyla including the flatworms, annelids and molluscs. Because terrestrial pulmonate gastropods are widely distributed and contain all three enzyme activities, experiments with the land snail, *Otala lactea*, are described in detail. The methods apply equally well to other land snails (*Helix pomatia* or *H. aspersa*, for example) which may either be locally collected or purchased from suppliers of edible snails.

Land snails may be kept in the laboratory in a state of estivation under dry conditions for several months. Several days prior to use, they should be placed under moist conditions and fed on lettuce or cabbage to assure complete tissue hydration.

APPARATUS

1. Tissue homogenizers (any of the several commercially available types).

2. A refrigerated centrifuge capable of forces of $5\,000 \times g$ (preferably to $15\,000 \times g$).

3. Water baths (two): one thermostatically controlled for temperatures around 25°C and one a covered boiling-water bath.

4. Ammonia diffusion vials (Fig. 1). These may be inexpensively constructed from shell vials.

5. A colorimeter (any of several commercially available with settings or filters for readings at 420, 490, 540 and 660 mμ).

* National Science Foundation Undergraduate Research Participant.
** Present address: Science Department, Central Connecticut State College. New Britain, Connecticut, U.S.A.

6. Measuring pipettes of various sizes including 0·1 to 5 ml.

7. Dissecting equipment. Large and small scissors and fine forceps, preferably eye forceps.

8. Balance suitable for weighing 0·1–2 g.

9. Stopwatch or other suitable interval timer.

10. Thick-walled conical centrifuge tubes (12–15 ml), 18 × 150 mm test tubes, and plastic centrifuge tubes (polyethylene, polycarbonate, cellulose nitrate, etc.).

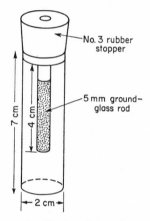

FIG. 1. Ammonia diffusion vial used in urease assay.

CHEMICAL SOLUTIONS

All solutions are to be prepared with a high grade, glass-distilled or deionized water.

REAGENTS FOR ARGINASE ASSAY

1. 0·1 % Cetyltrimethylammonium bromide (CTAB).*

2. 0·5 M Sodium glycinate, pH 9·5. Dissolve 3·754 g glycine in about 80 ml water, adjust to pH 9·5 with conc. NaOH, and dilute to 100 ml. Refrigerate.

3. 0·02 M Sodium glycinate, pH 9·5. Dilute 1 ml of 0·5 M to 25 ml.

4. 0·85 M L-arginine, pH 9·5. Dissolve 9 g L-arginine hydrochloride in approx. 40 ml water. Add 1·5–1·6 ml CO_2-free 50% (w/w) NaOH to adjust to pH to 9·5 and dilute to 50 ml. Refrigerate.

5. 0·005 M $MnCl_2 \cdot 4 H_2O$. Dissolve 0·099 g in water and dilute to 100 ml.

6. 0·5 M $HClO_4$. To 800–900 ml water, add slowly and cautiously 42·5 ml of conc. $HClO_4$ (70%) and dilute to 1 liter.

---

* Available from Distillation Products Industries, Rochester, New York, U.S.A. (Division of Eastman Kodak Co.) or through several commercial supply houses.

7. Urea acid reagent. Mix 1 vol of conc. H_2SO_4 with 3 vol 85% H_3PO_4. To each liter of the acid mixture, add 1 ml 1% $CuSO_4 \cdot 5 H_2O$. Store in a brown bottle and allow to age 1 month. Any precipitate which forms will settle in this time, but if the reagent is required before aging, this precipitate may be removed by centrifuging.

8. 4% Ethanolic 1-phenyl-1,2-propanedione-2-oxime (PPO)*. 4 g of PPO dissolved in 95% ethanol. Refrigerate.

9. 0·001 M Urea standard solution. Prepare stock solution (0·01 M) by dissolving 0·601 g urea in water and diluting to 1 liter. Accurately dilute 10 ml of this to 100 ml for the working standard.

REAGENTS FOR ORNITHINE TRANSCARBAMYLASE ASSAY

1. 0·1% CTAB.

2. 0·2 M L-ornithine, pH 8·0. Dissolve 1·686 g L-ornithine hydrochloride in about 40 ml water and adjust to pH 8·0 with NaOH. Dilute to 100 ml. Refrigerate.

3. 0·9 M Sodium glycylglycinate, pH 8·4. Dissolve 11·889 g glycylglycine in about 80 ml water and adjust to pH 8·4 with NaOH. Dilute to 100 ml. Refrigerate.

4. 0·2 M Carbamylphosphate, dilithium salt. Prepare just before use and keep at 0°C. Dissolve 204 mg 75% dilithium carbamyl phosphate (may be obtained from the Sigma Chemical Co., St. Louis, Missouri, from 75 to 90% purity) in 5 ml cold water.

5. 2 M $HClO_4$. Add 17 ml conc. $HClO_4$ (70%) to 70 ml water and dilute to 100 ml.

6. Citrulline acid reagent. Mix 50 ml conc. H_2SO_4 and 150 ml 85% H_3PO_4. Add this mixture slowly and cautiously to about 200 ml water. Dilute to 500 ml after adding 0·1 ml 1% $CuSO_4 \cdot 5H_2O$.

7. 3% 2,3-Butanedione-2-oxime in water.*

8. 0·001 M Citrulline standard. Prepare stock solution (0·01 M) by dissolving 0·1752 g citrulline in water and diluting to 100 ml. Accurately dilute 10 ml of this to 100 ml for the working standard. Refrigerate both solutions.

REAGENTS FOR UREASE ASSAY

1. 0·005 M Ethylenediaminetetra-acetic acid, disodium salt (EDTA). Dissolve 1·681 g in water and dilute to 1 liter.

2. 0·5 M Tris (hydroxymethyl) aminomethane (Tris), pH 9·0. Dissolve 6·055 g Tris base in about 80 ml water. Adjust to pH 9·0 with HCl and dilute to 100 ml.

* See footnote, p. 2.

3. 0·05 M Urea. Dissolve 3·003 g in water and dilute to 1 liter. Refrigerate.

4. 1 N H₂SO₄. To 600–700 ml water are added slowly and cautiously 27·8 ml conc. H₂SO₄. Dilute to 1 liter.

5. 5 N H₂SO₄. Dilute 138·9 ml conc. H₂SO₄ to 1 liter as above.

6. Saturated K₂CO₃.

7. Folin-Wu or Koch and McMeekin Nessler's reagent.† May be purchased commercially. Discard when cloudy.

8. Ammonium sulfate standard solution containing 10 μg N/ml. Dissolve 0·472 g (NH₄)₂SO₄ which has been dried in a desiccator for several days in 0·1 N H₂SO₄ and make up to 100 ml with the 0·1 N acid. Accurately dilute 10 ml to 100 ml for the working standard.

REAGENTS FOR PROTEIN DETERMINATION

1. Solution A. Dissolve 0·4 g soldium tartrate in water. Add 0·2 g CuSO₄.5H₂O and stir until dissolved. Dilute to 1 liter.

2. Solution B. Dissolve 40 g Na₂CO₃ in 0·2 N NaOH and dilute to 1 liter with 0·2 N NaOH.

3. Solution C. Mix equal volumes of solutions A and B just prior to use.

4. Folin-Ciocalteau phenol reagent.† May be purchased commercially as the conc. reagent (2 N). Dilute 1 : 1 or to 1 N for use.

5. Crystalline bovine serum albumin standard containing 20 μg/0·1 ml. Prepare stock solution by dissolving 100 mg albumin (may be obtained from the Sigma Chemical Co.) in 10% NaCl and diluting to 100 ml with 10% NaCl. Dilute 1 : 4 for use.

IDEA AND PRINCIPLE

A study of the enzymes arginase, urease, and ornithine transcarbamylase in *Otala* was chosen because their presence in land snails poses several presently unsolved questions concerning their functional significance in these and other invertebrates. The enzymes arginase and urease have been known to occur in invertebrate animals since the early 1900s, and both have been the subject of numerous investigations in comparative biochemistry. Interest in the distribution of arginase has been mainly in the context of its functional role in the Kreb-Henseleit ornithine cycle (Fig. 2) and in the distribution of urease in terms of its role in the uricolytic sequence (Fig. 2). Since land snails are generally considered to be uricotelic, the presence of both of these enzymes represents exceptions to or incompatibilities with two

† References for the detailed preparation of these reagents are as follows: For Nessler's reagent, Folin and Wu (1919) and Koch and McMeekin (1924); this reagent may be stabilized by the addition of 976·7 mg KCN per liter of the solution as described by Minari and Zilversmit (1963). For the protein phenol reagent, see Folin and Ciocalteu (1927).

of the early generalizations in comparative biochemistry. The hepatopancreas of some land snails is one of the richest sources of arginase, although the "rule of Clementi" states that arginase does not occur in the livers of uricotelic species (this is, however, invalid even among the vertebrates where it was originally proposed because of the occurrence of arginase in avian and reptilian livers). The occurrence of urease in the tissues of land snails appears

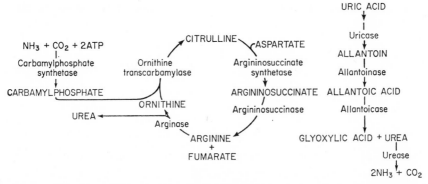

FIG. 2. Role of ornithine transcarbamylase and arginase in the synthesis of arginine and the urea cycle and role of urease in the uricolytic pathway.

not to coincide with its function in the uricolytic sequence, a function attributed to it in other invertebrates, since, according to the "rule of Przylecki", uricolytic enzymes (specifically the urico-oxidase system) do not occur in uricotelic species. Ornithine transcarbamylase, first demonstrated in the land snail in 1962, is also widely distributed among invertebrates, occurring in several members of at least three phyla. Its only known function in animals is in the synthesis of arginine (Fig. 2), and only recently has this role begun to be investigated in invertebrates.

The procedures described here for the assay of arginase and ornithine transcarbamylase and for urease are essentially modifications of methods originally described by Brown and Cohen (1959) and Simmons (1961). These procedures have been used successfully with several species of flatworms, annelids and molluscs and may be used to investigate other species of invertebrates for special student projects.

EXPERIMENTAL DETAILS

GENERAL

Since this may represent the student's first experience in the determination of enzyme activity, certain general considerations are appropriate. The two most commonly used methods for the direct determination of enzyme activity are those in which the amount of product formed or substrate utilized is measured during a given time interval under specified conditions of pH and temperature and substrate, enzyme, and, in some cases, co-factor concentrations. The former method will be used here to measure the enzymes which catalyze the reactions shown in equations (1–3).

$$\text{L-Arginine} + H_2O \quad \xrightarrow[\text{Mn}^{2+}]{\textit{Arginase}} \quad \text{L-ornithine} + \text{urea} \qquad (1)$$

$$\text{L-Ornithine} + \text{CAP} \quad \xrightarrow[\textit{transcarbamylase}]{\textit{Ornithine}} \quad \text{L-citrulline} + P_i \qquad (2)$$

$$\text{Urea} + H_2O \quad \xrightarrow{\textit{Urease}} \quad 2\,NH_3 + CO_2 \qquad (3)$$

The products which will be measured are urea, citrulline, and NH_3 for equations (1), (2) and (3), respectively. Alternative procedures can, and have been, used for each of these reactions.

In general, enzyme activity is determined by initiating the reaction through the addition of the enzyme (tissue extract) to a reaction mixture containing substrate, buffer, and, if necessary, the appropriate co-factors. In some cases, such as with OTC, the reaction mixture contains the enzyme and the reaction is initiated by the addition of one of the substrates, carbamylphosphate (CAP). The reaction is then allowed to proceed for a definite time interval at constant temperature. It is stopped by "killing" the enzyme. This is done by the addition of protein denaturants such as perchloric ($HClO_4$), trichloroacetic or mineral acids. The product formed is then measured (see Analytical Procedures, p. 14). The choice of the actual procedure followed is dictated by several factors, each specific to the particular enzyme in question.

When determining enzyme activity with crude tissue preparations, there are several variables which must be controlled in order to conclude definitely that enzyme activity is present. The control preparations used and their rationale are as follows.

(a) *Zero time control.* This control is used primarily to show that there is an increase in the product of the enzyme reaction with time of incubation. It gives the amount of endogenous product at the start of the reaction. It also serves to check the effectiveness of the reagent used to "kill" the enzyme since this is added prior to the addition of the enzyme.

(b) *Minus enzyme control.* This control contains no enzyme (tissue extract) and is used to determine spontaneous, or non-enzymatic, formation of product.

(c) *Minus substrate control.* This control gives a measure of the amount of endogenous substrate present in the enzyme preparations.

(d) *Heat-inactivated control.* This control consolidates the above since it is prepared prior to the incubation period and accounts for endogenous product as well as spontaneous reactions. In addition, it serves as a critical indicator of enzyme activity since it is only in exceptional cases that heating (100°C) fails to destroy enzyme activity.

Since the volume must be kept constant, the omission of any component from a reaction mixture is compensated for by the appropriate amount of water as indicated in the protocols given later for the enzyme assays. The preparation and use of these controls will become clear as the experiment progresses.

DETERMINATION OF ARGINASE ACTIVITY

1. *Preparation of reaction mixtures*

A series of 12 or 15 ml conical centrifuge tubes, preferably heavy-walled, is marked according to the protocol given in Table I. With the exception of the tissue extract, the components may be added to tubes 1 through 4A as indicated. Nothing is added to tubes 5 and 5A since these serve as the *heat-inactivated* controls and require special preparation. Five ml of 0·5 M $HClO_4$ may be added to tubes 1 and 1A since they serve as the *zero time* controls (*extreme caution should be exercised when pipetting the $HClO_4$*). Before proceeding to the preparation of the tissue, make sure the incubation bath is adjusted to 25°C and prepare a beaker for boiling water.

2. *Tissue preparation*

The anatomy of *Otala* is similar to that of *Helix* which is illustrated in Borradaile *et al.* (1961) and Barnes (1963). The shell is removed from the animals with the aid of dull scissors and forceps by carefully cutting along the upper edge of the whorls starting at the aperture and progressing counter-clockwise toward the apex. The exposed body of the snail may be uncoiled by severing the columellar muscle. All four lobes of the hepatopancreas (= digestive gland, liver, etc.) may be excised rather easily but care must be taken to prevent rupturing or including portions of the intestine. The cream-colored gonadal tissue is embedded in the apical lobe and this should be removed with the aid of fine forceps if tissue purity is required. The excised tissue should be kept cold (placed on a watchglass kept on crushed ice) until sufficient material has been collected for the enzyme preparation (conveniently about 1 g). With large *Otala* or *Helix*, 0·3 g or more may be obtained from one individual. Blot the tissue lightly with filter paper and weigh on a suitable balance. *Do not place the tissue directly on the analytical balance pan—*

TABLE I

Protocol for the assay of arginase activity in the hepatopancreas tissue of Otala

Tube no.	Description	Arginine soln (0·85 M, pH 9·5; ml)	Glycine buffer (0·5 M, pH 9·5; ml)	MnCl₂ soln (0·005 M; ml)	H₂O (ml)	Enzyme soln* (ml)
1,1A	Zero time control	0·1	0·1	0·1	0·5	0·2
2,2A	Experimental	0·1	0·1	0·1	0·5	0·2
3,3A	Minus enzyme control	0·1	0·1	0·1	0·7	—
4,4A	Minus substrate control	—	0·1	0·1	0·6	0·2
5,5A	Heat-inactivated control	0·1	0·1	0·1	0·5	0·2

* A 1 : 49 dilution of the crude homogenate. Added last to start reaction (see text).

The final concentration of components, in 1 ml vol, is: arginine, 0·085 M; glycine, 0·05 M; and McCl₂, 0·0005 M.

use tared glassine weighing paper or its equivalent. *Record the weight of the tissue.*

Place the weighed tissue in a glass homogenizer and add 9 vol (9 ml for each g tissue) 0·1% CTAB at room temperature. Place the homogenizer in the crushed ice bath and homogenize with about twenty excursions of the pestle. With *Otala* or *Helix* hepatopancreas tissue, the arginase activity may be high and dilution of the homogenate is required (see comments under Trouble-shooting, on determining different levels of activity, p. 21). This dilution is made by adding 4·9 ml of cold 0·02 M sodium glycinate, pH 9·5, to 0·1 ml of the homogenate in a test tube. The diluted extract should be kept cold and used as soon as possible. *Save a portion of the homogenate for protein determinations.* This is done by accurately pipetting 0·1 ml portions into each of two test tubes, sealing them with Parafilm, rubber stopper, etc., and placing them in the deep freeze.

3. *Enzyme assay*

Pipette 0·2 ml portions of the 1 : 49 diluted enzyme into tubes 5 and 5A and place these tubes in the boiling-water bath (beaker) for 10 min. Place the remainder of the tubes in the 25°C bath and allow to equilibrate at this temperature (5–10 min). Tubes 1 and 1A, the zero time controls, may be completed at this time by the addition of 0·2 ml of the enzyme solution to each. *Do not, however, contaminate the enzyme pipette or solution with the $HClO_4$ contained in these tubes.* Tubes 5 and 5A are cooled (crushed ice) and the reaction mixture components added. These tubes are also placed in the 25°C bath.

Start the reactions in tubes 2, 2A and 4, 4A by adding 0·2 ml of the diluted enzyme solution *seriatim* to each tube at 30 sec intervals. Thoroughly mix the contents of each tube after the addition of the enzyme by shaking. Incubate undisturbed at 25°C for 30 min and stop the reaction by adding 5 ml 0·5 M $HClO_4$ to each tube (Table II).

TABLE II

Tube	Time enzyme added to start reaction (min)	Time $HClO_4$ added to stop reaction (min)
2	0	30
2A	0·5	30·5
3	—	31
3A	—	31·5
4	2	32
4A	2·5	32·5
5	(incubate approx. 30 min)	
5A		

After the addition of the $HClO_4$, cover the tubes (Parafilm, Saran Wrap, marbles, etc.) and place in the refrigerator or cold room. If sufficient time remains (2 h or more), urea analyses may be performed as described under Analytical Procedures, p. 15. If not, the tubes may be kept for several days prior to being analyzed.

DETERMINATION OF ORNITHINE TRANSCARBAMYLASE ACTIVITY

1. *Preparation of reaction mixtures*

Following the directions given above in the arginase assay, prepare a series of tubes according to the protocol in Table III. The components, except the enzyme and CAP, are added to tubes 1 through 6A as required. Tubes 7 and 7A will serve as the *heat-inactivated* controls. One ml of 2 M $HClO_4$ may be added to the *zero time* controls, tubes 1 and 1A.

2. *Tissue preparation*

Dissect the tissue according to the directions given above in the arginase assay. Homogenize the weighed tissue in 9 vol 0·1% CTAB and transfer the homogenate to a chilled centrifuge tube (polyethylene, polycarbonate, cellulose nitrate, etc. *but not glass*). Prepare a counterbalance tube of exactly the same weight to balance the centrifuge. Centrifuge in the refrigerated centrifuge at 5 000 × g for 15 min. Carefully decant the supernatant fluid into a chilled test tube and keep in the crushed ice bath. Because of the low level of enzyme activity, no dilution of this is required. *Save duplicate 0·1 ml portions for protein determinations.*

3. *Enzyme assay*

Pipette 0·1 ml of the enzyme solution (supernatant fluid) into tubes 7 and 7A and place these in the boiling-water bath for 10 min. Pipette 0·1 ml of the enzyme solution into tubes 1 through 6A except 3 and 3A which are the *minus enzyme* controls (*do not contaminate the enzyme solution or pipette with the $HClO_4$ in tubes* 1 *and* 1A). If these tubes are to be held for more than 10–15 min, place them in an ice-water bath. Weigh out 204 mg of CAP (dilithium salt of 75% purity) into a screw-top tube and keep at 0°C. Cool tubes 7 and 7A and add the reaction mixture components (except CAP). Place the tubes at 25°C and allow to equilibrate. During the equilibration period, dissolve the CAP in 5 ml ice-cold distilled water. *Make sure it is completely dissolved.*

Start the reactions in tubes 1 through 7A by adding 0·1 ml CAP solution *seriatim* to each tube (except tubes 5, 5A and 6, 6A which are *minus CAP* controls) at 30 sec intervals. It is suggested that a time schedule be written out for the addition of the CAP and $HClO_4$ prior to starting the assay (see

TABLE III

Protocol for the assay of ornithine transcarbamylase activity in the hepatopancreas tissue of Otala

Tube no.	Description	Ornithine soln (0.2 M, pH 8.0; ml)	Glycylglycine buffer (0.9 M, pH 8.4; ml)	H$_2$O (ml)	Enzyme* soln (ml)	CAP soln† (0.2 M; ml)
1,1A	Zero time control	0.1	0.1	0.6	0.1	0.1
2,2A	Experimental	0.1	0.1	0.6	0.1	0.1
3,3A	Minus enzyme control	0.1	0.1	0.7	—	0.1
4,4A	Minus ornithine control	—	0.1	0.7	0.1	0.1
5,5A	Minus CAP control	0.1	0.1	0.7	0.1	—
6,6A	Minus CAP and ornithine control	—	0.1	0.8	0.1	—
7,7A	Heat-inactivated control	0.1	0.1	0.6	0.1	0.1

* 5 000 × g supernatant fluid from crude homogenate.
† Added last to start reaction (see text).

The final concentration of components, in 1 ml vol, is: ornithine, 0.02 M; glycylglycine, 0.09 M; and CAP, 0.02 M.

schedule for arginase assay). Thoroughly mix the components of each tube after the addition of the CAP by shaking. Incubate at 25°C for 15 min and stop the reaction by adding 1 ml 2 M HClO$_4$ *seriatim* to each tube (except tubes 1 and 1A to which the HClO$_4$ had previously been added.) Because of the spontaneous reaction of CAP and ornithine in this assay, it is essential that the *heat-inactivated* and other controls be incubated for the exact length of time as the experimentals in order to use them as corrections.

After the HClO$_4$ has been added to the tubes, they are covered and placed in the refrigerator until the citrulline determinations (see Analytical Procedures) are performed. They may be kept for several days prior to these analyses.

DETERMINATION OF UREASE ACTIVITY

1. *Preparation of reaction mixtures*

The reaction mixture components are pipetted into a series of diffusion vials as required according to the protocol given in Table IV and with reference to the procedures used in the arginase assay. Vials 5 and 5A serve as the *heat-inactivated* controls, and 1 and 1A as the *zero time* controls.

2. *Tissue preparation*

The weighed tissue is homogenized in 9 vol 0·005 M EDTA in a glass homogenizer kept in a crushed ice bath. This 10% homogenate may be used directly in the assay system or it may be transferred to a chilled plastic centrifuge tube and centrifuged in the refrigerated centrifuge at 15 000 × g for 15 min. *Balance the centrifuge*. The supernatant fluid is carefully decanted and kept at 0°C. *Save 0·1 ml portions of the homogenate or supernatant for protein determinations*.

3. *Enzyme assay*

Following the detailed procedure given for the arginase assay, pipette 0·1 ml of the enzyme solution (homogenate or supernatant fluid) into vials 5 and 5A and place them in the boiling-water bath for 10 min. Add 0·2 ml 5 N H$_2$SO$_4$ to the zero time controls (1 and 1A). Cool vials 5 and 5A and add the reaction mixture components. Place all tubes in the 25°C bath and allow them to equilibrate.

Start the reactions in vials 2, 2A and 3, 3A by adding 0·1 ml of the enzyme solution *seriatim* at 30 sec intervals. Incubate at 25°C for 20 min and stop the reactions by the *seriatim* addition of 0·2 ml 5 N H$_2$SO$_4$. Vials 5 and 5A are incubated for approximately 20 min prior to adding the H$_2$SO$_4$.

After the addition of the H$_2$SO$_4$ to all the vials, proceed directly to the determination of the NH$_3$ formed as described under Analytical Procedures, p. 16.

TABLE IV

Protocol for the assay of urease activity in the hepatopancreas tissue of Otala

Vial no.	Description	Urea soln (0·05 M; ml)	Tris buffer (0·5 M, pH 9·0; ml)	H₂O (ml)	Enzyme soln* (ml)
1,1A	Zero time control	0·1	0·2	0·6	0·1
2,2A	Experimental	0·1	0·2	0·6	0·1
3,3A	Minus substrate control	—	0·2	0·7	0·1
4,4A	Minus enzyme control	0·1	0·2	0·7	—
5,5A	Heat-inactivated control	0·1	0·2	0·6	0·1

* 15 000 × g supernatant fluid from crude homogenate. Added last to start reaction (see text). The final concentration of components, in 1 ml vol, is: urea, 0·005 M and tris buffer, 0·1 M.

ANALYTICAL PROCEDURES

GENERAL

The products of the reactions are measured by colorimetric procedures in which they are reacted with specific compounds to give colored complexes. The optical density (absorbance) of the resulting complexes are proportional to the concentration of the reaction products according to the Lambert-Beer law. By preparing a standard curve for each product, the relationship between optical density and amount of product may be obtained. Figure 3 illustrates such a relationship obtained with urea, citrulline, and protein

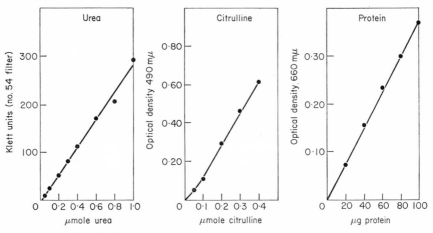

FIG. 3. Relationship between optical density of colored complex and amount of material present. The colorimetric procedures used are described under Analytical Procedures. A Klett colorimeter was used for urea and a Coleman Junior for citrulline and protein.

(bovine serum albumin). The optical densities of the reaction mixture samples are located on such a graph, and the corresponding amount of product is obtained directly on the abcissa. Because of the lack of reproducibility from one batch of reagents to another of the standard curves for both urea and citrulline, a series of standards should always be included with each determination of these products.

The colored products formed in the urea and citrulline determinations are light-sensitive and must be protected during the heating and cooling periods. The use of low-actinic tubes is convenient, but not essential for this.

The color development in these two procedures is also affected by several compounds which may be present in tissue extracts or in the reaction mixtures themselves. For example, the amount of Mn^{2+} present in the arginase reaction mixture markedly affects the color development in the urea determination. In the procedures given, failure to correct for this generally introduces an error of less than 10%. For critical work, or when other compounds are added to the reaction mixtures to determine their effect upon the action of the enzyme, the urea or citrulline standards should be prepared to contain the exact amount of the reaction mixture components which are present in the portion taken for analysis. This is conveniently done by preparing an excess of the *zero time* control. Thus, if, in the arginase assay, 1 ml portions are taken for urea analysis, then 1 ml of this *zero time* mixture (containing $HClO_4$) should be added to each of the urea standards. A procedure is given by McLean *et al.* (1965) to correct for the effect of urea in the citrulline determination.

To maintain a constant volume during the heating period used in the urea and citrulline determinations, the tubes are stoppered either with marbles or with rubber stoppers provided with capillary tubing *open to the atmosphere*.

UREA DETERMINATION (ARGINASE REACTION)

The reaction mixtures are centrifuged at about 1 500–2 000 rev/min for 20–30 min to sediment the denatured protein. A portion (up to 5 ml) of the supernatant from each tube is pipetted into 18×150 mm test tubes and brought to 5 ml with water. A set of urea standards is also prepared as shown in Table V.

TABLE V

0·001 M urea (ml)	H_2O (ml)	μmole urea
0	5·0	0 (blank)
0·1	4·9	0·1
0·2	4·8	0·2
0·4	4·6	0·4
0·6	4·4	0·6
0·8	4·2	0·8
1·0	4·0	1·0

To each tube is added 2 ml of the urea acid reagent, followed by 0·4 ml of 4% 1-phenyl-1,2-propanedion-2-oxime. The tube contents are *thoroughly mixed*, stoppered (make sure, if rubber stoppers are used, that they are fitted with capillary tubes open to the atmosphere), and placed in a boiling-water bath which is covered and essentially light-proof. They are kept in the boiling-water bath for 60 min and then cooled by being placed in a water bath at room temperature which is also protected from light. After cooling for 5–10 min, the optical densities are read at 540 mμ (or with no. 54 Klett filter). The colorimeter is adjusted to zero with the blank tube of the standard series.

CITRULLINE DETERMINATION (OTC REACTION)

The reaction mixtures are centrifuged at 1 500–2 000 rev/min for 20–30 min. A portion (up to 1 ml) of the supernatant from each tube is pipetted into 18 × 150 mm test tubes and brought to 1 ml with water. A set of citrulline standards from 0 to 0·4 μmoles (0·05–0·1 μmole intervals) is prepared from the 0·001 M citrulline solution according to the protocol given in Table V for the urea standards, except that the final volume is 1 ml. To each of the tubes add 5 ml of the citrulline acid reagent, followed by 0·25 ml of 3% aqueous 2,3-butanedione-2-oxime. The tube contents are thoroughly mixed, stoppered or capped, and placed in the covered boiling-water bath (lightproof). Heat in the boiling-water bath for 30 min, cool (protect from light) 5–10 min, and read the optical densities at 490 mμ. The colorimeter is adjusted to zero with the blank tube of the standard series.

AMMONIA DETERMINATION (UREASE REACTION)

The NH_3 formed by the action of urease is in solution as $(NH_4)_2SO_4$ in the reaction mixtures. It is volatilized by making the reaction mixtures alkaline and is trapped as $(NH_4)_2SO_4$ on the ground-glass stick (containing H_2SO_4) of the diffusion vial. The NH_3 is then determined by its reaction with Nessler's reagent.

Place about 35 ml of 1 N H_2SO_4 in a 50 ml beaker. Do each vial in turn. Add approximately 1 ml of the saturated K_2CO_3 to the reaction mixture. Quickly immerse the ground-glass portion of the stick in the 1 N H_2SO_4, shake off the excess acid, and touch the tip of the ground-glass stick momentarily to filter paper. Carefully insert the ground-glass stick and stopper into the diffusion vial and stopper tightly. *Care must be exercised to assure that the H_2SO_4-containing ground-glass stick does not come in contact with the alkaline reaction mixture nor any K_2CO_3 present on the sides of the vial.* Place the vials in a rack or protect them from the danger of being tipped over. Leave them for 8 h or overnight. Do not leave for greater periods as the alkali causes NH_3 liberation from the protein present in some of the vials. If a multipurpose rotator is available, a diffusion time of only 1 h is required.

At the end of the diffusion period, carefully remove the ground-glass stick from the vials. Wash the ground-glass stick with exactly 4 ml water, collecting the wash in a test tube marked to correspond to the vial. This may be used directly in the Nesslerization procedure or, if the total amount of NH_3-N exceeds about 25 μg, a smaller portion may be used if the volume is brought to 4 ml with water. Prepare a series of standards from 0 to 25 μg with the $(NH_4)_2SO_4$ standard which contains 10 μg N/ml.

To each tube, add 2 ml Nessler's reagent and allow to stand 15 min after thoroughly mixing the contents. Read the optical densities at 420 mμ (no. 42 Klett filter). The instrument is adjusted to zero with the blank of the standard series.

PROTEIN DETERMINATION

The 0·1 ml portions of the crude 10% homogenates and/or their supernatant fluids which have been kept in the deep-freeze are thawed by the addition to each of 9·9 ml water. Thoroughly mix and centrifuge for 15 min at 1 500–2 000 rev/min. Pipette portions of each (up to 0·5 ml, in duplicate) supernatant into test tubes. Prepare a series of protein standards containing from 0 to 100 μg protein with the serum albumin standard which contains 20 μg per 0·1 ml. Use 20 μg intervals. Adjust all volumes to 0·5 ml. To each add 3 ml of protein solution C which has been freshly prepared by mixing equal volumes of protein solutions A and B. Mix and allow to stand 30 min. To each tube add 0·3 ml of the Folin-Ciocalteau phenol reagent (diluted to 1 N) and immediately mix thoroughly. Allow to stand 30 min and read *seriatim* in the same order as the addition of the phenol reagent at 660 mμ (no. 66 Klett filter). Adjust the instrument to zero with the standard blank. Make sure the volume of 3·5 ml is sufficient for the colorimeter used.

RESULTS

EXPRESSION OF RESULTS

Enzyme activity is generally expressed as the amount of product formed (or substrate utilized) under specified assay conditions per amount of tissue. While arguments can be made for the various different units employed, both for product and tissue, we have found it convenient to use two designations. The *tissue activity*, which is defined as the μmoles product formed (or substrate utilized) per g fresh weight tissue per h at 25°C, is the more physiological expression of enzyme activity since it relates directly to the tissue's enzymatic potential. This is a useful expression when relating this potential to the actual amount of the product produced by the tissue *in vivo*. Tissue activity is influenced, however, by factors which affect the weight of the tissue such as hydration-dehydration. This is a far more pronounced effect with invertebrates than with vertebrates. Land snails, for example, undergo cyclic hydrations-dehydrations amounting to as much as 50% of their weight. For this reason, *specific activity*, which is defined as μmoles product per mg protein per h at 25°C, is also used. This is the more precise statement of activity since the denominator, the tissue protein content, is normally subject to less variation than the fresh weight.

The standard unit of enzyme activity, proposed by the Commission on Enzymes of the International Union of Biochemistry, is μmoles per mg protein per min at 25°C. This may be obtained from the specific activity used here simply by dividing by 60.

CALCULATIONS OF RESULTS

1. *Arginase*

One ml, of the total of 6 (1 ml reaction mixture + 5 ml HClO$_4$), of each of the deproteinized reaction mixtures was used in the urea determinations. The optical densities (as Klett units) given by these, as well as the urea standards, were read and recorded. Readings of 53 and 50 Klett units were obtained for the samples from tubes 2 and 2A, respectively. The readings in all the control tubes were negligible, the highest being about 6 Klett units. From a graph prepared by plotting Klett units *v.* μmoles urea standards (Fig. 3), these readings were found to correspond to an average of 0·2 μmole urea in the samples from tubes 2 and 2A and an average of approximately 0·03 μmole for the highest control samples. Calculations were made as follows.

$$\text{Tubes 2, 2A} = \text{average of } 0\cdot20 \ \mu\text{mole/ml}$$

$$\begin{aligned} (\times) \ \ &\underline{6} \ \ \text{(total vol of sample)} \\ = \ &1\cdot20 \ \mu\text{mole} \end{aligned}$$

$$\begin{aligned} (-) \ &\underline{0\cdot18} \ \text{(control value, } 6 \times 0\cdot03) \\ = \ &1\cdot02 \ \mu\text{mole} \end{aligned}$$

Thus, 0·2 ml of the 1 : 49 diluted homogenate formed 1·02 μmole urea per 30 min or 2·04 μmole/h at 25°C.

Since each ml of the 10% homogenate is equal to 0·1 g tissue, 0·2 ml of the 1 : 49 dilution is equivalent to 0·0004 g:

$$\frac{0\cdot0004 \text{ g}}{2\cdot04 \ \mu\text{mole}} = \frac{1 \text{ g}}{x \ \mu\text{mole}}$$

$x = 5\ 100$. The tissue activity is thus equal to 5 100 μmole urea per g per h at 25°C.

From the protein determination, the protein content of the 0·2 ml portions of the 1 : 49 diluted homogenate was 0·054 mg. Thus,

$$\frac{0\cdot054 \text{ mg}}{2\cdot04 \ \mu\text{mole}} = \frac{1 \text{ mg}}{x \ \mu\text{mole}}$$

$x = 37\cdot8$ μmole. The specific activity is $37\cdot8$ μmole per mg protein per h at 25°C.

2. *Ornithine transcarbamylase*

Citrulline determinations were made with $0\cdot5$ ml portions of the deproteinized reaction mixtures. The optical densities and corresponding μmoles of citrulline from the standard curve were as shown in Table VI.

TABLE VI

Tube	Optical density 490 mμ	μmole Citrulline
1 1A	$\dfrac{0\cdot021}{0\cdot019} > 0\cdot020$	0·021
2 2A	$\dfrac{0\cdot232}{0\cdot233} > 0\cdot233$	0·168
3 3A	$\dfrac{0\cdot020}{0\cdot015} > 0\cdot018$	0·018
4 4A	$\dfrac{0\cdot007}{0\cdot010} > 0\cdot009$	0·009
5 5A	$\dfrac{0\cdot008}{0\cdot006} > 0\cdot007$	0·007
6 6A	$\dfrac{0\cdot005}{0\cdot009} > 0\cdot007$	0·007
7 7A	$\dfrac{0\cdot029}{0\cdot025} > 0\cdot027$	0·028

Calculations were as follows:

Tubes 2, 2A $= 0\cdot168$ μmole per $0\cdot5$ ml

$(\times)$ 4 (total vol of sample $= 2\cdot0$ ml)

$= 0\cdot672$ μmole

$(-)0\cdot112$ (control 7, 7A; $4 \times 0\cdot028$)

$= 0\cdot560$ μmole

Thus, 0·1 ml of the 5 000 × g supernatant of the homogenate formed 0·56 μmole citrulline per 15 min or 2·24 μmole/h at 25°C. Since each 0·1 ml of the supernatant is equal to 0·01 g tissue, the tissue activity is 224 μmole/g/h at 25°C.

The protein content of the 0·1 ml portion of the supernatant was 0·41 mg. The specific activity is thus 5·46 μmole per mg protein per h at 25°C.

3. *Urease*

Each wash (4 ml) from the ground-glass sticks of the diffusion vials was used directly in the Nesslerization procedure. Following the directions described above, the average amount of NH_3-N formed in vials 2, 2A was 2·52 μg. A value of 0·75 μg was found for control tubes 1, 1A (zero time), 3, 3A (minus substrate), and 5, 5A (heat-inactivated). Calculations were as follows.

$$\text{Vials 2, 2A} = 2\cdot52 \ \mu\text{g } NH_3\text{-N (total formed in reaction)}$$
$$(-)0\cdot75 \text{ (control value)}$$
$$= 1\cdot77 \ \mu\text{g N}$$

Since each 60·06 μg urea contains 28·016 μg N, 60·06/28·016 = 2·24: 2·14 × 1·77 = 3·79 μg urea. This corresponds to 3·79/60·06 or 0·063 μmole urea.

Thus, 0·1 ml of the supernatant fluid from the homogenate hydrolyzed 0·063 μmole urea per 20 min at 25°C or 0·189 μmole/h. Since the 0·1 ml of the supernatant is equivalent to 0·01 g tissue, the tissue activity is 18·9 μmoles urea hydrolyzed/g/h.

The 0·1 ml contained 0·56 mg protein so the specific activity is 0·33 μmoles urea hydrolyzed per mg protein per h at 25°C.

For comparison, a 0·1 ml portion of the crude homogenate (prior to centrifuging) was also used. The tissue activity determined with this was 19·8 μmole/g/h and the specific activity, 0·17 μmole/mg/h. Note the increase in specific activity.

TROUBLE-SHOOTING

In all three assays, the amount of product measured in the final samples must fall within a fairly narrow range for the colorimetric procedures (0·05–1 μmole for urea; 0·05–0·4 μmole for citrulline; 5–25 μg for NH_3-N). Thus, the amount of tissue chosen for assay must be such that the amount formed, considering all dilutions, is within these limits. Choosing either too much or too little enzyme solution is generally one of the most common difficulties. The amounts used in the OTC and urease assays are adequate for *most species* of land snails which have these activities. The amount to use in the arginase assay is an especially perplexing problem with some land snails, in which the levels of activity vary tremendously and unpredictably. In such cases, it is suggested that a series of tubes be substituted for 2, 2A (Table I) in which 0·1 ml portions of the following homogenate dilutions are used: 1 : 9, 1 : 24, 1 : 49 and 1 : 99. When species are used for which no data on the level of activity are available, a 0·1 or 0·2 ml portion of the crude homogenate should also be included. Adequate controls (zero time or heat-inactivated) must also be included in the protocol. In the arginase assay, a control may be used to demonstrate that the increase of color is actually due to the formation of urea. To one tube containing all of the components of the reaction, add 0·5–1 mg of urease. Owing to the degradation of urea by the urease, no color should develop with this sample. When species with fairly constant and known levels of activity are used (such as vertebrate) it is possible to calculate the level of enzyme solution to be used from the literature values for tissue activity.

A common source of error in the determination of NH_3-N used in the urease assay is contamination of the H_2SO_4-containing ground-glass stick with saturated K_2CO_3. This neutralizes the acid and no NH_3 is trapped. This is avoided by exercising care in carrying out the directions given. A good grade of distilled water must be used in the Nesslerization procedure to avoid the colloid breaking (cloudiness) when the reagent is added to the sample. If glass-distilled water is not available, the reagent of Koch and McMeeking, stabilized with KCN, may suffice.

Further Ideas

Only minimum protocols are described for showing the presence of the enzyme activities and their approximate levels. Special projects could logically take either of two directions. They could, for example, involve the use of the described methods by the student to gain more information concerning the action of enzymes. The effect of time of incubation, enzyme or substrate concentration, pH, temperature, etc., may be determined for any of the enzymes. On the other hand, the methods may be used in a strictly comparative study in which a series of invertebrates (or vertebrates) is investigated for the presence or absence of the enzyme activities. Since the levels of activity are important in such studies, each species must be standardized so that measurements are done under optimal conditions for enzyme activity. For the purposes here, this standardization would involve mainly choosing the correct amount of tissue to be assayed for each species.

REFERENCES

Folin, O. and Ciocalteu, V. (1927). *J. biol. Chem.*, **73**, 627–650.
Folin, O. and Wu, H. (1919). *J. biol. Chem.*, **38**, 81–110.
Koch, F. C. and McMeekin, T. L. (1924). *J. Am. chem. Soc.*, **46**, 2066.
Minari, O. and Zilversmit, D. B. (1963). *Analyt. Biochem.*, **6**, 320–327.

BIBLIOGRAPHY

METHODS

Barnes, R. D. (1962). "Invertebrate Zoology", pp. 238–320. Saunders, Philadelphia·
[Illustrations of molluscan anatomy, including *Helix*.]
Borradaile, L. A., Potts, F. A., Eastham, L. E. S. and Saunders, J. T. (1961).
"The Invertebrata", 4th ed. (revised by G. A. Kerkut), pp. 578–651. Cambridge
University Press. [Illustrations of molluscan anatomy, including *Helix*.]
Brown, G. W., Jr. and Cohen, P. P. (1958). Comparative biochemistry of urea
synthesis. I. Methods for the quantitative assay of urea cycle enzymes in liver.
J. biol. Chem., **234**, 1769–1774. [Methods for arginase and OTC assay, as well
as other urea cycle enzymes, are discussed.]
Lang, C. A. (1958). Simple microdetermination of Kjeldahl nitrogen in biological
materials. *Analyt. Chem.*, **30**, 1692–1694. [Methods for ammonia determination.]
Linton, S. N. and Campbell, J. W. (1962). Studies on urea cycle enzymes in the
terrestrial snail, *Otala lactea. Arch. Biochem. Biophys.*, **97**, 360–369. [Describes
the methods used as modified for snail tissue as well as the results and significance of the enzyme studies in gastropods.]
Lowry, O. H., Roseborough, N. J., Farr, A. L. and Randall, R. J. (1951). Protein
measurement with Folin phenol reagent. *J. biol. Chem.*, **193**, 265–275. [Method
for protein determination.]
McLean, P., Novello, F. and Gurney, M. W. (1965). Some observations on the
colorimetric determination of citrulline and urea. *Biochem. J.*, **94**, 422–426.
[Method to correct citrulline determination in the presence of urea.]
Ratner, S. (1955). Enzymatic synthesis of arginine (condensing and splitting
enzymes). *In* "Methods in Enzymology" (S. P. Colowick and N. O. Kaplan,
eds.), Vol. 2, pp. 356–367. Academic Press, New York. [Methods for urea and
citrulline determination (modification of original Archibald method).]
Seligson, D. and Seligson, H. (1951). A microdiffusion method for the determination
of nitrogen liberated as ammonia. *J. Lab. clin. Med.*, **38**, 324–330. [Method for
ammonia determination.]

GENERAL

Bishop, S. H. and Campbell, J. W. (1965). Arginine and urea biosynthesis in the
earthworm *Lumbricus terrestris. Comp. Biochem. Physiol.*, **15**, 51–71. [Descrip-
tion of the "urea cycle" enzymes and their significance in the earthworm.
Methods are also presented for measuring the activities of these enzymes in
annelid tissue.]
Campbell, J. W. and Lee, T. W. (1963). Ornithine transcarbamylase and arginase
activity in flatworms. *Comp. Biochem. Physiol.*, **8**, 29–38. [Useful information
for comparison or extension of results.]

Cohen, P. P. and Brown, G. W., Jr. (1960). Ammonia metabolism and urea bio-synthesis. *In* "Comparative Biochemistry" (M. Florkin and H. S. Mason, eds.), Vol. 2, pp. 161–244. Academic Press, New York. [One of the most comprehensive reviews of urea metabolism in vertebrates available; comparative in approach.]

Heidermanns, C. and Kirchner-Kühn, I. (1952). Uber die Urease von *Helix pomatia. Z. vergl. Physiol.*, **34**, 166–178. [Description of the properties of urease from *Helix pomatia.*]

Simmons, J. E., Jr. (1961). Urease activity in trypanorhynch cestodes. *Biol. Bull. mar. Biol. Lab., Woods Hole*, **121**, 535–546. [In addition to the presentation of methods and results for urease in cestodes, the author presents considerable material for comparison among other invertebrates.]

2

A. **The Distribution and Pool Size of Free Amino Acids in Animal Tissue**

B. **The Detection and Estimation of α-L-Aminotransferase Activity in Animal Tissue**

C. **The Incorporation of Carbon from Radioactive Substrates into the Soluble Intermediates of Animal Tissues Using Two-dimensional Paper Autoradiography**

D. **Biochemical Changes During Muscle Contraction**

E. **Fermentation and Respiration in Yeast**

A. K. HUGGINS

Department of Biochemistry, University College London, England

A. **The Distribution and Pool Size of Free Amino Acids in Animal Tissue**

ANIMALS

A wide range of species can be selected according to local availability, the following being suitable examples: a mammal, rat; a mollusc, mussel (*Mytilus*); a crustacean, crab (*Carcinus*); an insect, *Locusta*.

APPARATUS

Two rectangular chromatography tanks for descending system with glass or stainless steel troughs to take sheets of paper 46 cm × 57 cm. The size of the tanks, which can be made of marine grade plywood with aluminium trays at the bottom, should be large enough to accommodate at least six and preferably twelve sheets simultaneously. Each tank should be pre-equilibrated with, and used for one solvent only and have close-fitting lids. A window in one end facilitates checking the position of the solvent front.

Homogenizer, electrically driven with cutting action, Measuring and

Scientific Equipment (MSE), London (Model 7700), fitted with micro blending assembly (77312) or hand operated, Griffiths type.

Hair dryer or compressed air source.

Balance, rapid weighing to two figures.

Centrifuge, preferably refrigerated, capable of $20\,000 \times g$. e.g. MSE High-Speed 18.

Colorimeter or spectrophotometer, e.g. Hilger & Watts Spekker or Unicam SP600.

Rotary shaker, sufficient agitation to mix 10 ml in 25 ml stoppered tube.

GLASSWARE

Centrifuge tubes, 15 ml (3–6).

Watch glasses for weighing tissue (3–6).

Micropipettes, Kirk type E-mil or RSCo. 50 μl, 100 μl, 250 μl and 2 ml hypodermic syringe to operate (Record fitting).

Pipettes graduated, 1 ml, 5 ml, 10 ml.

Glass stoppered tubes (6 in. $\times$ $\frac{3}{4}$ in.) (24).

Sintered filter crucibles or mercury filters (3).

SUNDRIES

Scissors, rough and dissecting.

Forceps, rough and dissecting.

Dip tray for chromatograms (Shandon Scientific).

Whatman No. 4 chromatography grade paper size 46 cm $\times$ 57 cm.

REAGENTS

Ethanol, methanol (Analar), n-butanol, n-propanol, isopropanol, 880 ammonia, propionic acid, acetic acid (glacial), isobutyric acid, acetone. Cadmium acetate (Analar), ninhydrin (indane trione hydrate).

Solvent I, Isobutyric acid mixture (Crowley *et al.*, 1963):

Ethylenediaminetetra-acetate (EDTA)	1·2 g
17 N Ammonia solution	100 ml
Water	950 ml
n-Propanol	350 ml
Isopropanol	75 ml
n-Butanol	75 ml
Isobutyric acid	2 500 ml

Leave to stand for 24 h before use.

Solvent II, Butanol–propionic acid. Make up in two parts, A and B, and mix equal volumes immediately prior to use:

    A. n-Butanol 919 ml + water 81 ml.
    B. Propionic acid 539 ml + water 461 ml.

Amino acid marker mixture, containing 2 mg/ml of alanine, aspartic acid, arginine, cystine, glutamic acid, glutamine, glycine, histidine, leucine, lysine, phenylalanine, proline, taurine and tyrosine.

Ninhydrin reagent may be used with or without cadmium added.

Ninhydrin (indane trione hydrate)	0·5 g
Acetone	100 ml
Cadmium acetate*	0·1 g
Acetic acid glacial*	2 ml
Water*	8 ml

* More convenient to add 10 ml of a stock solution containing these components.

PRINCIPLE OF EXPERIMENT

The free amino acid content of animal tissue varies greatly between phyla and the classes within them. Generally levels are higher in invertebrate groups than in vertebrates and in marine compared with related freshwater forms. The methods used familiarize the student with methods for the qualitative and quantitative estimation of amino acids.

EXPERIMENTAL PROCEDURE

EXTRACTION

Remove 1–2 g of the following tissues: rat liver and/or leg muscle, crab hepatopancreas and/or leg muscle (one to two animals required), locust thoracic muscle (three to four animals required). Blot gently on filter paper, weigh, and place in 2 vol of 80% ethanol in a test tube, bring to boil, then homogenize for 2–3 min in MSE homogenizer. Leave to extract for 30 min, then centrifuge for 30 min at 20 000 × *g*. Use the supernatants for chromatography, store in cold room in stoppered containers.

CHROMATOGRAPHY

The amino acids in the extract are analysed either qualitatively and/or quantitatively by two-dimensional descending paper chromatography using ninhydrin as the detection agent. The total ninhydrin-positive material may also be determined if desired. N.B. If only qualitative results are desired the separation can be made on thin layer plates using silica gel as the solid support instead of paper.

Take 50, 100 and 250 μl samples of rat extract and evaporate in air onto 46 cm × 57 cm sheet of Whatman No. 4 chromatography grade paper in as small an area as possible around a point 3 in. in from either edge at one corner, so that direction of milling (shown by arrow on box) is to the left along the long axis. Place papers in tanks and develop with solvent I to within 1½–2 in. of further edge of longer axis. (Running time about 12 h, i.e. overnight is convenient.) Dry in fume cupboard for 24 h. Then develop in solvent II along shorter axis. (Running time about 8 h, i.e. can be run during working day.) Dry for at least 3 h. To make the system as trouble free as possible add the following volumes of solvents: solvent I, 35 ml per chromatogram; solvent II, 40 ml per chromatogram. This saves the necessity of checking the progress of the solvent front since overrunning cannot occur.

Detection

Dip in ninhydrin and allow to dry, spots start to become visible in about 1 h at room temperature or heat at 120° for 5 min. For purposes of identification a marker mixture of amino acids is run under the same chromatographic conditions as tissue extracts (see p. 27 for composition). An illustration of separation achieved is shown in Fig. 1. The relative position of the ninhydrin reactive spots to one another is a more certain guide to their identity than

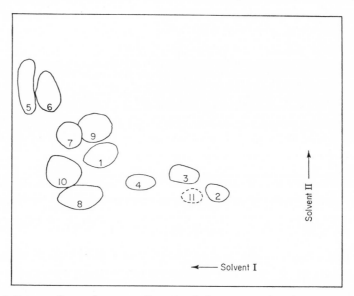

Fig. 1. Pattern of spots from two-dimensional chromatography of a marker solution containing (1) alanine, (2) aspartic acid, (3) glutamic acid, (4) glycine, (5) leucine, (6) valine, (7) proline, (8) lysine, (9) tyrosine, (10) arginine, and (11) taurine. Solvent I, isobutyric acid mixture; solvent II, butanol–propionic acid–water.

simply measuring their R_F values from the origin. If a measure of the relative distance moved in a solvent of a particular substance is required (R_F), then it is advisable to compute it as a ratio of the distance moved by a known spot (e.g. aspartic acid) with that moved by the desired compound.

The following points should also assist identification. Ninhydrin colours: glycine, orange; proline, yellow; aspartic acid, greyish-pink. Taurine is slow to develop, allow 48 h at room temperature.

QUANTITATIVE ESTIMATION

Select the quantity of rat extract which gives the best chromatographic separation, i.e. absence of streaking commensurate with density of colour sufficient for quantitative estimation to be carried out. Use similar volumes for crab and locust extracts. If quantitative estimations of the amino acids present are required then the following procedure should be applied.

The colour development is carried out in the usual way but it is advisable to increase the strength of the ninhydrin to 1%. The spots are cut out into thin strips to aid elution and the paper strips from each spot eluted in 10 ml of methanol by shaking mechanically for 30 min in glass stoppered test tubes (6 in. × $\frac{3}{4}$ in.). The eluates are filtered through sintered filters to remove particles of paper and optical density measured either in a colorimeter or a spectrophotometer (measure at 500 mμ for all amino acids, except glycine and proline which should be measured at 380 mμ). By comparison with optical densities of known amounts of each amino acid treated in the same way the amount of each amino acid may be determined. Results are usually expressed as mg or m-mole of amino acid per 100 g wet wt of tissue.

N.B. Proline is difficult to estimate quantitatively due to change in colour of the spot during development from pale lemon yellow to brownish-yellow, and if glycine and glutamine do not separate well the reading at 500 mμ will give an approximate indication of the combined quantity present.

SAMPLE RESULTS

Figure 1 illustrates the pattern of spots from two-dimensional chromatography, and Table I shows the quantitative distribution of the major amino acid components in the various tissues.

CONCLUSIONS

The overall level of amino acids is greater in invertebrates than in vertebrates. The most prominent amino acids in muscle are alanine, arginine, glutamic acid, glycine, proline and taurine in the crab; aspartic acid, glycine and glutamic acid in the rat; and arginine, aspartic acid, glycine and proline

TABLE I

Quantitative distribution of major amino acid components in various tissues

| | (mg/100 g wet wt—approx. ranges found) | | |
	Carcinus muscle	Rat muscle	Locust muscle
Alanine	150–200	<10	<10
Arginine	500–700	<10	20–40
Aspartic acid	30–50	10–15	15–25
Glutamic acid	400–500	10–15	<10
Glutamine ⎫ Glycine ⎭	700–1000	30–40	150–250
Leucine	10–35	<10	<10
Lysine	10–30	<10	<10
Proline	500–750	<10	15–20
Taurine	400–500	<10	—
Tyrosine	<10	<10	<10
Valine	10–40	<10	<10

in the locust. Thus there is no rigid pattern of distribution in animals, considerable species and intraspecial variation occurring. Marked differences in tissues from one animal are also found.

FURTHER EXPERIMENTS

These may be extended to other animals, plants or micro-organisms. In addition, changes in environment, e.g. osmolarity of water in the case of aquatic forms, or of different stages of life cycle, e.g. in insects, may also be studied. Further experiments to study metabolism of individual amino acids may be carried out by combining this technique with radioautography experiments described on p. 36.

TIME REQUIRED

Depending on whether qualitative results alone or both qualitative and quantitative results are required, these experiments will take between two and six 3 h periods according to number of species or samples analysed. In addition short periods to process chromatograms will be necessary.

BIBLIOGRAPHY

Crowley, G. J., Moses, V. and Ullrich, J. (1963). A versatile solvent to replace phenol. *J. Chromatog.*, **12**, 219–228.
Holden, J. T. (Ed.) (1962). "Amino Acid Pools." Elsevier, Amsterdam.
Smith, I. (Ed.) (1960). "Chromatographic and Electrophoretic Techniques," Vol. 1. Heinemann, London.

B. The Detection and Estimation of α-L-Aminotransferase Activity in Animal Tissue

ANIMALS

The details given are for experiments on crustaceans but the technique described may be applied to any species, providing a minimum of 1–2 g of tissue can be obtained.

APPARATUS

Balance, rapid weighing to two figures.

Centrifuge, refrigerated, capable of 20 000 × g, e.g. MSE High-Speed 18.

Colorimeter or Spectrophotometer,* e.g. Hilger & Watts Spekker or Unicam SP600.

Rotary Shaker,* sufficient agitation to mix 10 ml in 25 ml stoppered tube.

Homogenizer, electrically driven with cutting action, e.g. MSE London (Model 7700) fitted with micro blending assembly (77312), or hand operated Griffiths type.

Hair dryer or compressed air source.

Chromatography tanks, for descending system with glass or stainless steel troughs. Those used for experiment on pool size of free amino acids (see p. 25) are suitable although smaller ones would suffice in most cases for aminotransferase experiment.

Shaking incubator,* e.g. Dubnoff type, Mickle Engineering, Gomshall, Surrey, England. Static water bath could also be used.

GLASSWARE

Watch glasses for weighing tissue (2–6).

3–5 litre container for dialysis.

Small filter funnel 2–2½ in.

Micropipettes, Kirk type E—mil or RSCo. 10 μl, 50 μl, 100 μl and 250 μl and 2 ml hypodermic syringe to operate (Record fitting).

Pipettes bulb 10 ml.

Pipettes graduated 0·1 ml, 1 ml, 5 ml.

Glass stoppered tubes (6 in. × 2¾ in.) (6–12).

Pasteur pipettes (2–3).

SUNDRIES

Scissors, rough.

Forceps, rough and dissecting.

Dip tray for chromatograms (Shandon Scientific). Whatman No. 4. Chromatography grade paper size 46 cm × 57 cm sheets or smaller.

Dialysis tubing ¼ in. or ½ in.

* N.B. These items are only necessary if quantitative estimation of aminotransferase activity is required.

REAGENTS

Methanol* (Analar), n-butanol, n-propanol, isopropanol, 880 ammonia, propionic acid, acetic acid (glacial), isobutyric acid, acetone, cadmium acetate (Analar), ninhydrin (indane trione hydrate), 0·5 M sodium pyruvate, (5·5 g/100 ml), α-oxoglutarate (7·3 g/100 ml), oxaloacetic acid (6·6 g/100 ml), range of amino acids (0·5 M), pyridoxal phosphate (1 mg/ml), 0·1 M phosphate buffer pH 7·4 (1·41 g K_2HPO_4 + 0·26 g KH_2PO_4/100 ml).

PRINCIPLE OF EXPERIMENT

Enzymes which catalyse the transfer of an amino group from one molecule to another without the intermediate formation of ammonia are known as transaminases or aminotransferases. Sometimes amino group transfer can occur non-enzymatically so that appropriate controls must always be incorporated into the design of experiments involving aminotransferases.

Practically all the naturally occurring amino acids have been shown to undergo transamination, and aminotransferases play an important role in amino acid metabolism. Usually the two enzymes catalysing the following interconversions predominate in terms of the quantity of enzymatic activity present and are easily detectable, the presence of other aminotransferase systems being more difficult to prove.

(1)

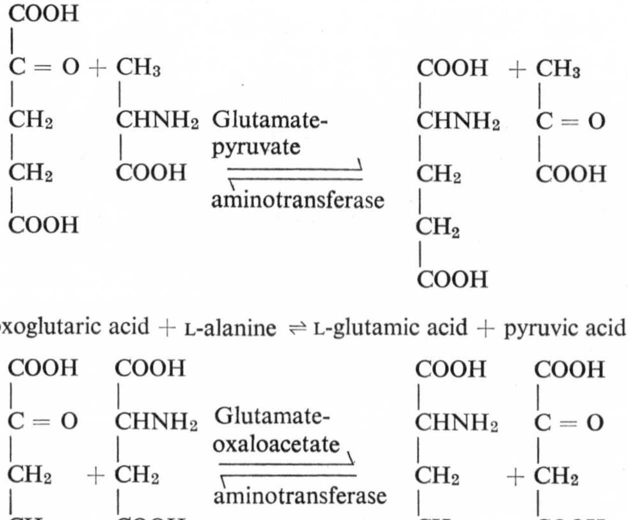

$$\text{α-oxoglutaric acid + L-alanine} \rightleftharpoons \text{L-glutamic acid + pyruvic acid}$$

(2)

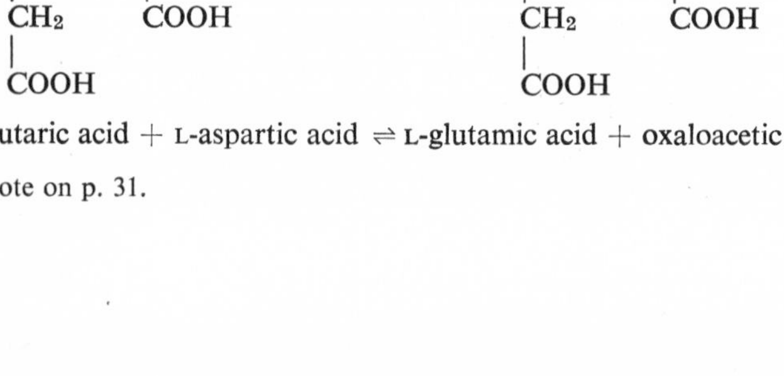

$$\text{α-oxoglutaric acid + L-aspartic acid} \rightleftharpoons \text{L-glutamic acid + oxaloacetic acid}$$

* See footnote on p. 31.

By incubating separately a range of different amino acids with a keto acid, e.g. pyruvic acid, and looking for the formation of its corresponding amino acid, i.e. alanine, the aminotransferase systems present which utilize pyruvic acid can be deduced. Similarly systems capable of utilizing α-oxoglutaric acid, oxaloacetic acid or other keto acids may be detected. Since all aminotransferase systems known require pyridoxal phosphate as a co-enzyme this substance is added to the incubation mixture. For further reading see Meister (1966) and Guirard and Snell (1964).

EXPERIMENTAL PROCEDURE

ENZYME PREPARATION

Four to five grams wet weight of muscle from the walking legs of approximately ten shore crabs (*Carcinus*) or one edible crab (*Cancer*) are thoroughly homogenized at 0°C in 20–25 ml of 0·1 M phosphate buffer pH 7·4 (1–2 min in the blender or ten to twelve strokes of the homogenizer). The homogenate is allowed to extract for 30 min at 0°C and is centrifuged at 20 000 g for 10 min to remove particulate material. The supernatant is carefully removed (Pasteur pipette) and placed in dialysis tubing (N.B. dialysis tubing should be thoroughly soaked in buffer prior to use, a knot tied in one end and the filter funnel stem inserted in the open end to assist filling), the funnel is removed and the tubing sealed by tying off. Place in 3–5 litres of phosphate buffer (at 0°C) and keep in a refrigerator until next day. Cut open tubing and store the solution at − 15°C until required for use. This enzyme preparation is stable for several weeks, providing it is not repeatedly thawed and frozen.

Dialysis of the homogenate is necessary to remove the interfering amino acids present.

Other tissues or animals can be treated in a similar manner.

ENZYME ASSAY

1. *Qualitative*

One millilitre of enzyme preparation is incubated aerobically for 1–3 h at 30°C in a shaking incubator with 0·5 m-mole (1·0 ml) of the amino acid, 0·5 m-mole (1·0 ml) of the α-keto acid and 0·1 ml pyridoxal phosphate. The appropriate controls must also be carried out simultaneously (see Table II, for suggested layout).

Ten microlitre samples of the incubation mixture were removed at the end of the incubation period and spotted directly onto sheets (46 cm × 57 cm) of Whatman No. 4 chromatography grade paper and chromatographed in one direction (long axis) with the isobutyric acid mixture or butanol–propionic acid (see p. 28).

C

TABLE II

	Substrate control	Enzyme control	Experimental
Amino acid in 0·1 M phosphate buffer pH 7·4	1·0	—	1·0
α-Keto acid in 0·1 M phosphate buffer pH 7·4	1·0	—	1·0
Enzyme preparation in 0·1 M phosphate buffer pH 7·4	—	1·0	1·0
Pyridoxal phosphate	0·1	0·1	0·1
0·1 M Phosphate buffer pH 7·4	1·0	2·0	—

The dried chromatograms are developed in the ninhydrin reagent as described on page 28. The appearance of the amino acid corresponding to the α-keto acid supplied as a substrate is taken to indicate the presence of the respective aminotransferase system. Separation of amino acids can also be carried out by TLC if only a qualitative picture is required.

2. *Quantitative*

The procedure is similar to that above except that 10 μl samples are withdrawn at intervals of 0, 2, 5, 10, 15, 20 and 30 min after the start of the incubation, and preliminary calibration experiments are required to determine a suitable dilution of the enzyme preparation so that the rate of the reaction can be conveniently estimated.

After development in ninhydrin the spots are cut out, immersed individually in 10 ml of redistilled methanol, shaken in stoppered tubes mechanically for 45 min and the optical density measured in a Spekker colorimeter using an L4 green filter etc. (see p. 29).

The amount of each amino acid present is determined by comparison with the values obtained for known amounts of the respective amino acid subjected to the same chromatographic conditions. The rates of formation of the amino acids between 2 and 5 min after starting the reaction are then calculated and used as a basis for computing the amount of the aminotransferase enzymes in each tissue. These are expressed as international units (μmoles of substrate utilized per min at 30°C) per g wet weight of tissue.

RESULTS

Table III shows the distribution of aminotransferases found in muscle of *Carcinus maenas* and is taken from Chaplin *et al.* (1967).

TABLE III

Amino Acid	Pyruvic acid	α-Oxaglutaric acid	Oxaloacetic acid	Glyoxylic acid
Alanine		+	+	+
Arginine	—	—	—	—
Aspartic acid	+	+		—
Glutamic acid	+		+	+
Glycine	—	—	—	
Leucine	+	+	—	—
Lysine	—	—	—	—
Ornithine	—	—	—	—
Phenylalanine	—	—	—	—
Tryptophan	—	—	—	—
Tyrosine	—	+	—	—
Valine	—	+	—	—

In *Carcinus* only glutamate-pyruvate (GPT) and glutamate-oxaloacetate (GOT) aminotransferases were present in sufficient activity for a quantitative estimation to be easily made. Results are shown below expressed as μ moles product per min per g wet wt at 30°C.

	Gill	Hepatopancreas	Muscle
GPT → Glutamate	3·7	6·8	21·6
GPT → Alanine	3·3	3·4	14·2
GOT → Glutamate	5·5	9·9	19·0
GOT → Aspartate	4·1	8·0	36·0

CONCLUSIONS

In *Carcinus* pyruvic acid will transaminate with aspartic acid, glutamic acid and leucine; α-oxoglutaric acid with alanine, aspartic acid, leucine, tyrosine and valine; oxaloacetic acid with alanine and glutamic acid; and glyoxylic acid with alanine and glutamic acid.

Alanine, aspartic acid and glutamic acid are most generally distributed amino group donors and the activity of these systems varies in different tissues.

FURTHER EXPERIMENTS

The effect of pyridoxal phosphate concentration, temperature, pH, on the reaction of a selected aminotransferase can be determined. GPT and GOT may also be estimated colorimetrically (see Bergmeyer, 1963).

TIME REQUIRED

For the qualitative section only three 2 h periods, which will leave some time in the first and third periods to carry out qualitative tests for amino acids, peptides, amines etc. if required. Time can be reduced to two 2 h periods if thin layer chromatography is used.

To include quantitative aspects three 3 h periods would be required plus time for servicing chromatograms, drying, ninhydrin development etc.

BIBLIOGRAPHY

Bergmeyer, H. U. (Ed.) (1963). "Methods of Enzymatic Analysis", pp. 842 and 851. Verlag Chemie and Academic Press, New York.

Chaplin, A. E., Huggins, A. K. and Munday, K. A. (1967). The distribution of L-α-aminotransferase in *Carcinus maenas. Comp. Biochem. Physiol.* **20**, 195–198.

Guirard, B. M. and Snell, E. E. (1964). *In* "Comprehensive Biochemistry" (M. Florkin and E. H. Stotz, eds.), Section III, Vol. 15. Group-Transfer Reactions. Elsevier, Amsterdam.

Meister, A. (1965). "The Biochemistry of Amino Acids", Vols. 1 and 2, 2nd ed. Academic Press, New York.

C. The Incorporation of Carbon from Radioactive Substrates into the Soluble Intermediates of Animal Tissues Using Two-dimensional Paper Autoradiography

ANIMALS

In principle any species may be used provided a minimum of 50–100 mg wet weight of tissue can be conveniently obtained. The experiments described here relate to the shore crab *Carcinus maenas*.

APPARATUS

Scaler preferably with automatic timing, if not a stop watch can be used.

Geiger-Müller tube either sealed or gas flow type with a mica end window of as large diameter as possible, e.g. Sealed, EW5A 20th Century Electronics, New Addington, Croydon, Surrey, England; gas flow (see Fuller (1956) for details of construction).

Shaking incubator, e.g. Dubnoff type, Mickle Laboratory Engineering, Gomshall, Surrey, England.

Torsion balance, 0–100 mg.

Two rectangular chromatography tanks and troughs for descending system, preferably to take sheets of paper 46 cm × 57 cm (see p. 25 for details of construction).

X-Ray developing assembly, e.g. Kodak No. 17, or dishes may be used but these are much less convenient.

Tension hangers to fit size of X-ray film used, i.e. 14 in. × 17 in. recommended (6–12), e.g. Kodak No. 17.

Safelight filter, Kodak 6B or equivalent.

Hair dryer or compressed air source.

Centrifuge bench model, e.g. MSE Minor.

GLASSWARE

Small test tubes 10 mm × 100 mm (12).

Beakers 50 ml (1), 250 ml (1).

Pipettes, autozero type preferable 10 μl; one for each different radioactive substrate used. 100 μl (2). Kirk type 500 μl or Pasteur type to fit polythene adaptor (see below).

Hypodermic syringe, record fitting 2 ml with polythene tubing to fit Kirk type syringe pipette.

Measuring cylinder 100 ml.

SUNDRIES

Scissors, rough and dissecting.

Forceps, rough and dissecting.

Filter paper Whatman No. 50 preferable 4·25–7·0 cm diam.

Chromatography paper Whatman No. 4 size 46 cm × 57 cm.

Chinagraph pencil.

Inking pad made radioactive with waste ^{14}C labelled material. Eccentric shaped design cut on rubber bung used as stamp (see p. 39).

Sheet of white card, hardboard for viewing autoradiograms.

X-ray film, Kodak Blue Brand or equivalent, size 14 in. × 17 in.

REAGENTS

Suitable incubation medium, e.g. sea water for marine animals, or appropriate Ringer solution (see Lockwood (1962) for details of composition)

Ethanol, n-butanol, n-propanol, isopropanol, 17 N ammonia, propionic acid, acetic acid (glacial), isobutyric acid.

Kodak FX 40 X-ray film fixer or equivalent.

Kodak DX 80 X-ray film developer or equivalent.

Radioactive substrates, e.g. [U-^{14}C]glucose, [2-^{14}C]sodium acetate, [1, 4-^{14}C]succinic acid.

Solvent I, isobutyric acid mixture (Crowley et al., 1963) (see p. 26 for composition). Leave to stand for 24 h before use.

C§

Solvent II, butanol–propionic acid. Make up in two parts A and B (as described on p. 27) and mix equal volumes immediately before use.

PRINCIPLE OF EXPERIMENT

The technique described enables the capacity of a tissue, animal, micro-organism etc., to metabolize a particular compound, to be readily determined with very small amounts of tissue compared with those required by other techniques. Further, the autoradiograms give a picture of the various routes taken by the carbon atoms derived from the radioactive substrate supplied and enable the simultaneous assessment of the different pathways present. The example described below compares the utilization of glucose, acetate and succinate by hepatopancreas from *Carcinus maenas*.

EXPERIMENTAL PROCEDURE

The technique is designed to carry out experiments conveniently on a microscale and is based on that described by Moses (1958) and Moses and Edwards (1958). A consideration of the experimental errors is given by Moses *et al.* (1962).

INCUBATION, EXTRACTION AND CHROMATOGRAPHY

Fifty milligrams wet weight of crab hepatopancreas is placed in small test tubes containing 0·1 ml sea water (if natural it should be boiled and filtered prior to use to kill contaminating micro-organisms) and incubated with shaking at 20°C for a minimum of 90 min (shorter time intervals may be used if more tissue or more substrate added).

Take care to damage tissue as little as possible during its removal. At the start of the incubation period the radioactive substrates, having been diluted with sea water, are added in 10 μl containing 1 μc. The incubation is terminated by the addition of 0·1 ml of absolute alcohol, to each tube, and placing tubes in a beaker of boiling water for 1–2 min. After allowing 30 min for extraction, the contents are centrifuged to remove precipitated protein (5 min at 3 000 g) and the supernatant evaporated onto 46 cm $\times$ 57 cm sheets of Whatman No. 4 paper in as small an area as possible around a point 3 in. in from either edge at one corner, so that direction of milling (shown by arrow on box) is to the left along the long axis. Place the papers in the tanks and develop with solvent I to within $1\frac{1}{2}$–2 in. of the edge (running time about 12 h, i.e. overnight is convenient). Dry in fume cupboard for 24 h. Then develop in solvent II along shorter axis (running time about 8 h, i.e. can be run during working day). Dry for at least 3 h. To make system as trouble free as possible add the following volumes of solvents: solvent I, 35 ml per chromatogram; solvent II, 40 ml per chromatogram.

AUTORADIOGRAPHY

It is advisable to check that the chromatographic separation is satisfactory before placing the chromatograms on film. This may be done by moving the Geiger-Müller tube slowly over the surface to detect the radioactive areas. The exact location of the labelled compounds is obtained by placing the chromatograms in close contact with sheets of X-ray film, and the procedure for this is described below and in Fig. 2.

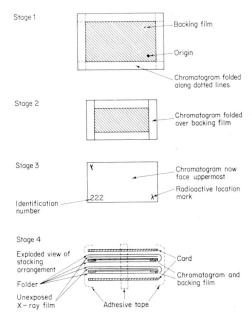

FIG. 2. Procedure for locating labelled compounds.

Stage 1. Place the chromatogram flat on a covered bench top and centre a piece of used X-ray film so that the origin is at one corner.

Stage 2. Fold over the edges of the chromatogram along the dotted lines.

Stage 3. Turn over so that main area of the chromatogram is uppermost. Stamp radioactive location marks at the corners and write on the identification number in large figures. Stack in numerical order.

Stage 4. *In dark room only*. Fit 6B filter to the safelight. Open a box of X-ray film, remove the sheets of film which are in individual folders. Write in pencil the corresponding chromatogram identification number in one corner away from the location marks on each sheet of X-ray film. Insert chromatogram (folded around backing film) so that the surface of the chromatogram is next to the unexposed X-ray film. Stack between pieces of card and tape up to prevent the films moving about relative to the chromatograms. N.B. Do not compress film stack unduly or roughly handle X-ray film otherwise pressure marks will appear when the films are developed.

Place the taped stack in a light-proof box (an old X-ray film box is ideal) and leave away from ionizing radiation for 1–2 weeks.

Develop, following instructions for the brand of developer and fixer used. A rough guide is 3–4 min in developer, wash 1–2 min, fix 6–8 min, final wash 30 min, at *ca* 20°C.

INTERPRETATION OF AUTORADIOGRAMS

When the films are dry, place them on a light surface or X-ray viewing box if available, so that the pattern of spots present which correspond to the radioactive areas may be examined. From the relative position of the spots try to identify the labelled intermediates and relate them to their respective metabolic pathways (see Figs. 3–5). For other preparations and different radioactive substrates it is necessary to compare chromatographic properties, colour reactions etc. of spots with known marker compounds and reference should be made to Smith (1958) and Crowley et al. (1963) for more details. The R_F values with respect to aspartic acid of some of the more commonly met compounds are given in Table IV.

ESTIMATION OF RADIOACTIVITY

The quantitative distribution of radiocarbon between the soluble intermediates as well as the qualitative pattern can also be a useful indicator of enzymatic activity in a tissue. In this experiment an end-window Geiger-Müller tube is used to count directly the radioactivity present in each spot. Outline the spots on the film with wax pencil, then centering the film and chromatogram carefully (image of the ink location marks on the film should match exactly with ink marks on the paper) trace outlines onto the chromatogram in pencil. Count each spot separately for 100 sec. Note the count after substracting background count. If the spot is too large to fit within the aperture of the Geiger-Müller tube, divide it into more than one part and count separately. N.B. The Geiger-Müller tube should be periodically compared with a standard sample and background checks should also be made. Tabulate results as shown in Table V.

RESULTS

QUALITATIVE

Typical patterns from experiments with hepatopancreas of *Carcinus* incubated with [U-^{14}C]glucose, [2-^{14}C]sodium acetate and [1, 4-^{14}C$_2$]succinic acid are shown in Figs. 3–5 taken from Huggins (1966).

TABLE IV

R_F aspartic acid values in isobutyric acid mixture and butanol–propionic acid

	Isobutyric acid mixture	Butanol–propionic acid
Amino acids		
Alanine	2·5	1·3
γ-Aminobutyric acid	3·5	2·0
Arginine	3·0	1·1
Aspartic acid	1·0	1·0
Glutamic acid	1·25	1·1
Glutamine	1·6	0·9
Glycine	1·8	1·0
Proline	3·1	1·65
Organic acids		
Citric acid	0·8	1·5
Fumaric acid	1·1	1·8
Lactic acid	2·5	2·2
Malic acid	1·1	1·6
α-Oxoglutaric acid	1·1	1·5
Succinic acid	2·0	1·9
Carbohydrates		
Fructose	1·5	1·3
Glucose	1·2	1·05
Maltose	0·7	0·7
Ribose	1·8	1·4
Sugar phosphates	0·4–0·8	0·5–0·8

Points to note

1. When [U^{14}C]glucose is substrate, major products are lactic acid and alanine which are both formed from pyruvic acid, thus indicating the presence of glycolysis. N.B. Pyruvic acid is labile in the chromatographic system and is usually lost entirely. Only very small amounts of radioactivity in the phosphate region demonstrate the principle that under normal conditions intermediates do not tend to accumulate, but only end products.

2. The acetate and succinate chromatograms demonstrate the presence of the enzymes involved in the tricarboxylic cycle and the close relationship of the amino acids alanine, glutamic acid and aspartic acid formed by transamination from pyruvic, α-oxoglutaric and oxaloacetic acids respectively, and of glutamine to the final oxidative pathway.

QUANTITATIVE

The quantitative relationships between the intermediates can be expressed in a number of ways, e.g. (a) as counts per min, (b) as percentage of total

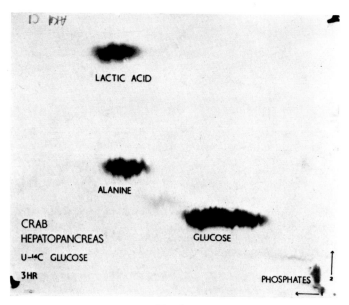

Fig. 3.

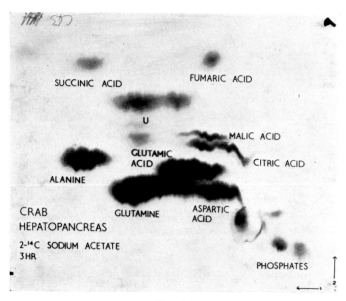

Fig. 4.

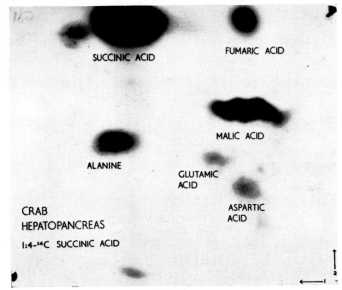

FIG. 5.

FIGS. 3–5. Typical patterns from experiments using hepatopancreas of *Carcinus*.

counts in soluble fraction *excluding* any remaining substrate, and (c) as a percentage of substrate metabolized.

Table V is calculated by method (b) since results are not markedly affected by differences in sample size etc., providing plenty of substrate remains unconverted at the end of the experiment.

CONCLUSIONS

Crab hepatopancreas will metabolize glucose, acetate and succinate into compounds demonstrating the existence of glycolysis, the tricarboxylic cycle and transamination. Carbon from acetate and succinate more readily oxidized completely than that of glucose which accumulates predominantly as alanine and lactic acid.

FURTHER EXPERIMENTS

Try the effect on the patterns of various metabolic inhibitors, e.g. iodo-acetate, 2,4-dinitrophenol and malonate. Homogenize a tissue and separate the subcellular components so that their metabolism may be separately characterized.

TIME REQUIRED

For incubation and spotting allowing two samples per student (3 h). Examination and counting etc. (3–4 h) plus short periods for chromatography, putting on film etc. Integrates well with other experiments because of its discontinuous time requirement except for counting. By suitably distributing samples among the class of students quite complex experiments can be carried out.

TABLE V

The percentage distribution of radiocarbon in the soluble fraction of carb hepato-pancreas incubated for 180 min with [U-14C] glucose, [2-14C] sodium acetate and [1,4-14C] succinic acid

	[U–14C]glucose	[2-14C]acetate	[1,4-14C]succinate
Alanine	54	11	20
Aspartic acid	—	8	5
Glutamic acid	—	43	3
Glutamine	—	19	—
Citric acid	0·1	2	0·5
Fumaric acid	0·1	1	9
Lactic acid	12	—	—
Malic acid	0·2	3	59
α-Oxoglutaric acid	—	1	—
Succinic acid	—	1	3
Sugar phosphates	34	4	—
Unknowns	—	7	—

BIBLIOGRAPHY

Crowley, G. J., Moses, V. and Ullrich, J. (1963). A versatile solvent to replace phenol. *J. Chromatog.*, **12**, 219–228.

Fuller, R. C. (1956). Modified end-window counting tube for paper chromatograms. *Science, N.Y.*, **124**, 1253.

Huggins, A. K. (1966).Intermediary metabolism in *Carcinus maenas*. *Comp. Biochem. Physiol.*, **18**, 283–290.

Lockwood, A. P. M. (1962). "Ringer" solutions and some notes on the physiological basis of their ionic composition. *Comp. Biochem. Physiol.*, **2**, 241–289.

Moses, V. (1958). Chromatography of labelled cell extracts. *In* "Chromatographic and Electrophoretic Techniques" (I. Smith, ed.), Vol. 1, pp. 507–533 Heinemann, London.

Moses, V. and Edwards, R. W. H. (1958). Chromatography of radioactive substances *In* "Chromatographic and Electrophoretic Techniques" (I. Smith, ed.), Vol. 1, p. 484–506. Heinemann, London.

Moses, V., Huggins, A. K. and Smith, M. J. H. (1962). Experimental and tissue variation in tracer studies of intermediary metabolism of isolated rat liver. *Anal. Biochem.*, **3**, 321–329.

Smith, I. (Ed.) (1958). "Chromatographic and Electrophoretic Techniques". Heinemann, London.

D. Biochemical Changes During Muscle Contraction

ANIMALS

A range of species of suitable size can be selected according to their availability, e.g. frogs, crabs, crayfish.

APPARATUS

Pulse stimulator to give shocks of controlled strength and duration at predetermined time intervals. Can be battery or mains operated.

Perspex tray to hold crushed ice and preparation.

Balance, rapid weighing to two figures.

Boiling water bath, to hold twelve test tubes.

Centrifuge, bench model to take 6 ml × 15 ml tubes.

Colorimeter, e.g. Hilger & Watts Spekker or E.E.L.

Rotary evaporator, Rinco or Stahlprodukter type.

Silver or platinum wire electrodes in swivel mounting (Palmer).

GLASSWARE

Centrifuge tubes 15 ml (6).

Graduated centrifuge tubes 1–10 ml (6).

Watch glasses for weighing tissue (6).

Pestle and mortar 2–3 in. diam.

Glass stoppered round-bottomed flasks (B24) 50 ml (4).

Steam distillation apparatus, all glass joints with three-necked pear-shaped distillation flask or 50 ml B 24 flask + 3 way adapter instead.

25 ml cylindrical separating funnel to fit three-necked flask or alternative arrangement.

Pipettes graduated 0·1, 1·0, 5·0, 10·0 ml; bulb 1, 5, 10 ml.

Boiling tubes 150 mm × 25 mm (6).

Beaker 50 ml (3).

Test tubes 150 mm × 16 mm (24).

Sintered glass filters porosity 1 (3).

Glass bubbles (6).

Beaker (1 litre) or crystallizing dish (1).

SUNDRIES

Scissors, rough and dissecting.

Forceps, rough and dissecting.

REAGENTS

1. LACTIC ACID ESTIMATION

1. Perchloric acid 15% w/v (mix 1 vol conc. $HClO_4$ with 3 vol H_2O).
2. 20% w/v copper sulphate (20 g $CuSO_4.5H_2O$/100 ml).
3. 5 N potassium hydroxide (28 g KOH/100 ml).
4. Calcium hydroxide (solid).
5. Ethanol.
6. 10 N sulphuric acid (30 ml conc. H_2SO_4 in 100 ml H_2O). Take care to add acid *to* H_2O slowly while mixing.
7. 0·5% w/v sodium bisulphite (0·5 g $NaHSO_3$/100 ml).
8. 0·05 N cerium sulphate in N H_2SO_4 (prepared by diluting 1 vol stock 0·5 N $Ce(SO_4)_2$ in N H_2SO_4 with 9 vol H_2O as sold by British Drug Houses, Poole, Dorset, England).
9. 0·1% soluble starch solution (0·1 g soluble starch/100 ml).
10. Approx. 0·1 N iodine in potassium iodide (12·7 g iodine + 18 g KI/litre).
11. Standard 0·005 N iodine in potassium iodide (dilute approx 0·1 N solution 1 part in 15; titrate against 0·005 N sodium thiosulphate; dilute to give 0·005 N solution).
12. Crushed ice.
13. Standard lithium lactate (288 mg lithium lactate/100 ml) assuming = $CH_3CHOHCOOLi$.

2. GLYCOGEN ESTIMATION

1. Ethanol.
2. 40% w/v potassium hydroxide (40 g KOH/100 ml).
3. 1 N sulphuric acid (3 ml H_4SO_4/100 ml).
4. 1 N potassium hydroxide (5·6 g KOH/100 ml).
5. Dianisidine-peroxidase reagent (125 mg glucose oxidase; BDH; 1·0 mg peroxidase Boehringer or BDH; 10 mg *o*-dianisidine/100 ml 0·5 M NaH_2PO_4 $2H_2O$ at pH 7·0). N. B. Must be kept refrigerated until required, stability improved to 3–4 days by keeping peroxidase/glucose oxidase separately in 20 ml buffer from dianisidine in 80 ml buffer and mixing just before use.
6. Standard glucose solution (10 mg glucose/100 ml).

PRINCIPLE OF EXPERIMENT

When muscle fibres contract energy is required which is supplied initially by the breakdown of ATP → ADP. To regenerate the ATP broken down, oxidizable substrates must be available and, in the case of muscle, glycogen is a major source of carbohydrate which can be rapidly oxidized by glycolysis to give lactic acid.

In skeletal muscle most of the lactic acid is transported to the liver or its equivalent for further oxidation rather than oxidized *in situ*. Hence by separating a suitable muscle from the circulation it is possible to demonstrate the accumulation of lactic acid and depletion of glycogen during muscular activity.

EXPERIMENTAL PROCEDURE

A pithed frog or other suitable animal is taken, the hind limbs skinned and severed by cutting the pelvic girdle. The preparation is placed on glass in contact with crushed ice to prevent undue drying out. One limb is stimulated directly or via the sciatic nerve by means of a pulse stimulator or induction coil until it will no longer contract, i.e. until it is in a state of rigor (3–5 shocks/sec at 10 V for 10 min is usually sufficient); it is important that the time taken to induce rigor is not prolonged, i.e. longer than 15 min, otherwise changes due to contraction will be masked by those caused by the anaerobic state of the muscle. The other limb is not stimulated.

Remove the muscle rapidly from each leg with a minimum amount of cutting. Weigh samples of 1–1·5 g for lactic acid and 0·2–0·5 g for glycogen estimations respectively.

1. LACTIC ACID ESTIMATION

Drop weighed sample of muscle into a cooled mortar containing a little sand and about 10 ml ice cold absolute ethanol. Crush and grind, allow to stand in refrigerator for 30 min (empty into a beaker for this period so that other samples may be processed). Filter through a sintered glass filter and retain the filtrate; grind the residue with 5 ml 80% ethanol, refilter and combine filtrates.

The combined ethanolic extracts are carefully evaporated to dryness using a 50 ml round-bottomed flask and a rotary evaporator and a water or vacuum pump. N.B. Evaporation of extracts is greatly assisted by allowing the flask to rotate in a dish or beaker of warm water (50–60°C) after vacuum conditions have been established. The residue in the flask is extracted with 2 ml of 15% perchloric acid and the extract poured into a graduated centrifuge tube. Wash the flask with a further 2 ml of perchloric acid and centrifuge the combined extracts, noting their volume.

It is necessary to remove carbohydrates, which interfere with the estimation. To each ml of extract add 0·1 ml 20% $CuSO_4$ and neutralize with 5 N KOH until a slight precipitate of cupric hydroxide forms, then a spatula full of solid $Ca(OH)_2$ (*ca* 1 g). Mix and centrifuge noting volume. Remove the supernatant with a Pasteur pipette and take 2·0 ml for lactic acid estimation by the method of Elsden and Gibson (1954).

Principle

The lactic acid is oxidized to acetaldehyde by ceric sulphate in N H_2SO_4 solution. The reaction conditions are controlled to avoid over-oxidation. The acetaldehyde is trapped as the bisulphite compound which, after removal of the excess of bisulphite, is decomposed by the addition of sodium bicarbonate. The bisulphite compound liberated is titrated with standard iodine solution.

Steam distillation apparatus

This consists of a wide-necked flask, heated by a micro burner, fitted with a narrow cylindrical dropping funnel (of about 25 ml capacity), a steam inlet tube which passes to within a few millimetres of the bottom tip of the flask, and a splash head leading by an upward-sloping tube to a vertical condenser of good capacity. The delivery tube from the condenser is of narrow bore (4 mm internal diam.) and long enough to reach almost to the bottom of a boiling tube, which will collect the distillate and in which the subsequent titration may be carried out.

METHOD

Measure accurately into the reaction flask not more than 5 ml of the test solution (which should contain up to about 30 μmoles lactic acid) and enough 10 N H_2SO_4 to make the final H_2SO_4 concentration N. Attach the flask to the apparatus. The receiving tube should contain 2 ml of the 0·5% sodium bisulphite and should be fixed so that the condenser dips below the surface. The condenser water must be running moderately fast. The flask is heated by the micro burner, which is adjusted so that the liquid just boils. The steam is then turned on and the steam flow adjusted so that 15–20 ml/min of distillate is collected (this rapid rate is essential and necessitates the use of an efficient condenser). The ceric sulphate (0·05 N) is then run dropwise into the reaction flask at such a rate that each drop is decolorized before the next drop goes in. When a permanent yellow colour is obtained, indicating an excess of $Ce(SO_4)_2$, further $Ce(SO_4)_2$ to make a total of 5 ml is added rapidly. When 15 ml of distillate has been collected the receiver is lowered and distillation is continued until 20 ml has been collected. The steam is discontinued, the micro burner removed and the receiver placed in an ice-water bath to cool. Immediately disconnect the reaction flask and thoroughly wash it and the still head with distilled water to remove all traces of $Ce(SO_4)_2$

which if left could effect premature oxidation of part of the lactic acid of the next sample to be analysed.

The titration is carried out when the distillate is at a temperature of 4–5° C. Add 5 drops starch solution and titrate with 0.1 N I_2 until a blue colour persists. Add one more drop of 1% NaHSO$_3$ to decolorize the solution and *titrate carefully this time* with 0.005 N I_2 until the first faint blue colour is reached.

(N.B. At this point all excess NaHSO$_3$ has been oxidized by the iodine and it remains to hydrolyse the acetaldehyde-bisulphite compound and to titrate accurately the bisulphite, equivalent to the acetaldehyde, so produced.)

Add 0.5 g solid NaHCO$_3$, the blue colour will then be discharged. Leave the tube to stand for 2 min and then titrate with 0.005 N I_2 until a faint blue colour, persisting for at least 1 min, is achieved.

$$[\text{NaHSO}_3 + \text{I}_2 + \text{H}_2\text{O} \rightarrow \text{NaHSO}_4 + 2\,\text{HI}]$$

A blank determination using 5 ml distilled water in place of the sample and suitable standard amounts (10, 20, 30, 40, 50 μmoles) of lithium lactate should always be run first to check the accuracy of the method. Results should be expressed as μmoles of lactic acid formed per g wet wt muscle per unit time.

2. GLYCOGEN ESTIMATION

Place the weighed sample in 1 ml 40% KOH in a centrifuge tube. Heat in a boiling water bath for 15 min to dissolve tissue. Add 2–5 ml absolute ethanol, allow to cool, centrifuge for 10 min ($2\,000$–$3\,000 \times g$), discard the supernatant. Hydrolyse precipitated glycogen with 1 ml 1 N H_2SO_4 in a boiling water bath for 90 min. Neutralize with 1 N KOH, dilute 1 in 10 and use 1.0 ml samples for glucose estimation according to the method of Huggett and Nixon (1957).

Principle

Glucose is oxidized to gluconic acid and hydrogen peroxide by action of the enzyme glucose oxidase. Hydrogen peroxide is broken down by peroxidase and the oxygen released combines with *o*-dianisidine to form an orange-brown complex. Intensity of the coloured complex formed is proportional to the amount of glucose present. The method is specific for glucose and hence the glycogen level may be expressed in terms of mg or m-mole glucose per g wet wt muscle.

Method

A sample containing glucose is incubated with 2.0 ml dianisidine-peroxidase reagent for 30 min at 37°C. The volume is made up to 10 ml with distilled water and the colour intensity measured in colorimeter using appropriate

D

filter (green). Colour is stable for approx. 60 min. A blank determination using water instead of glucose and a suitable series of glucose standards (25, 50, 75, 100, 125 and 150 μg glucose) must be run at the same time.

RESULTS

Figures given are for frog muscle and indicate magnitude of changes observed. Actual levels will vary considerably between individual animals. Lactic acid content mg/g wet wt muscle:

		Non-stimulated	Stimulated
Animal	(1)	1·50	2·30
	(2)	1·42	2·50
		1·46	2·40

Glycogen content mg/g wet wt muscle:

		Non-stimulated	Stimulated
Animal	(1)	1·52	0·70
	(2)	1·63	0·73
		1·57	0·71

CONCLUSIONS

When muscle is stimulated into rigor a greater breakdown of glycogen and accumulation of lactic acid occurs than in resting muscle. This reflects the increased glycolytic activity necessary to energize the rephosphorylation of ADP → ATP.

FURTHER EXPERIMENTS

Different types of muscle as well as different animals may be compared to determine whether lactic acid accumulation is as great, for example, in cardiac and smooth muscle compared with skeletal.

The time course of these biochemical changes may be determined by stimulating for different times instead of waiting until the muscle is in rigor.

The capacity of muscle to oxidize lactic acid etc. can be tested by allowing a period of recovery following stimulation.

TIME REQUIRED

For the basic experiments outlined three × 3 h periods would be necessary, but this could be reduced to two if pairs of students worked together.

REFERENCES

Elsden, S. R. and Gibson, Q. H. (1954). The estimation of lactic acid using ceric sulphate. *Biochem. J.*, **58**, 154–158.

Huggett, A. St. G. and Nixon, D. A. (1957). Use of glucose oxidase, peroxidase and o-dianisidine in the determination of blood and urinary glucose. *Lancet*, ii, 368–370.

E. Fermentation and Respiration in Yeast

ANIMALS

Fresh baker's yeast can be stored in refrigerator wrapped in aluminium foil for 7–14 days. Other micro-organisms, small animals, tissues etc. may also be used in similar experiments.

APPARATUS

Warburg manometer bath at 25°C.
Calibrated manometers.
Calibrated manometer flasks with one sidearm.

GLASSWARE

Pipettes, graduated 1 ml, 5 ml.
Pipettes, bulb 1 ml, 2 ml.
Beaker, 50 ml.
Dropping pipette.

SUNDRIES

Filter paper strips approx. 1 cm $\times$ 2 cm.
Rubber bands/springs for manometer flasks.
Forceps.
Absorbent tissue paper.

REAGENTS

4% w/v yeast suspension in pH 7·0 buffer (4 g yeast/100 ml).
3% w/v Glucose (3 g D-glucose/100 ml).
10% w/v Sodium hydroxide (10 g NaOH/100 ml).
0·1 M Potassium phosphate buffer pH 7·0. (1·06 g K_2HPO_4 + 0·53 g KH_2PO_4/100 ml).
Manometric fluid: Brodie; NaCl 46 g, sodium choleate 10 g, Evans blue 0·3 g/litre.
2 N sulphuric acid (6 ml H_2SO_4/100 ml).
0·01 N potassium cyanide (0·66 g KCN/100 ml).
Acetone.

PRINCIPLE OF EXPERIMENT

The majority of living organisms can respire, that is in the presence of oxygen they can break down carbohydrate, fat or protein etc. to carbon dioxide and water, the energy of the reactions involved serving to drive biosynthetic processes and maintain the supply of ATP. In addition plants and some micro-organisms possess the ability in the presence of light to synthesize carbohydrate and hence other substances from CO_2 and H_2O via the action of chlorophyll. Micro-organisms are often very versatile, having the capacity to adapt their metabolism to varying environmental conditions of food and oxygen supply, while other groups are very restricted in their growth requirements. The example chosen, ordinary baker's yeast, can respire under aerobic conditions and carry out fermentation under both aerobic and anaerobic conditions. Fermentation processes are characterized by the incomplete degradation of the substrate resulting in the accumulation of specific end products, in this case ethanol (see Fruton and Simmonds (1958) or Greenberg (1960) for fuller treatment).

Under aerobic conditions the catabolism of glucose by yeast cells can be represented as:

$$\underset{\text{Glucose}}{C_6H_{12}O_6} + O_2 \xrightarrow{\text{Glycolysis}} \underset{\text{Pyruvic acid}}{2CH_3CO\,COOH} + 2H_2O \qquad (1)$$

$$2CH_3COCOOH + 5O_2 \xrightarrow[\text{acid cycle}]{\text{Tricarboxylic}} 6\,CO_2 + 4\,H_2O \qquad (2)$$

Sum

$$C_6H_{12}O_6 + 6O_2 \longrightarrow 6\,CO_2 + 6\,H_2O \qquad (3)$$

N.B.   Complete degradation to CO_2 and H_2O.

Under anaerobic conditions the end product is ethanol.

$$\underset{\text{Glucose}}{C_6H_{12}O_6} + \xrightarrow{\text{Glycolysis}} \underset{\text{Pyruvic acid}}{2CH_3\,CO\,COOH} + 2H_2O \qquad (4)$$

$$2\,CH_3CO\,COOH \xrightarrow{\text{Carboxylase}} 2\,CO_2 + \underset{\text{Acetaldehyde}}{2\,CH_3CHO} \qquad (5)$$

$$2\,CH_3CHO + 2NADH + 2H^+ \xrightarrow[\text{dehydrogenase}]{\text{Alcohol}} \underset{\text{Ethanol}}{2\,CH_3\,CH_2\,OH} + 2NAD \quad (6)$$

Sum

$$C_6H_{12}O_6 + O_2 + 2H_2 \longrightarrow 2\,CH_3CH_2OH + 2CO_2 + 2H_2O \qquad (7)$$

This experiment is carried out in three stages: (1) measurement of respiration rate; (2) measurement of respiration plus aerobic fermentation; (3) measurement of anaerobic fermentation.

Initially in stage 1 the rate of oxygen consumption is measured; this equals the rate of carbon dioxide production if the respiratory quotient is assumed to be unity.

In stage 2 the rate of carbon dioxide production under aerobic conditions is measured, and the amount by which this value exceeds the estimated rate of respiratory carbon dioxide production is a measure of the fermentive processes.

In stage 3 the rate of anaerobic fermentation is measured by blocking respiration with cyanide to prevent oxygen utilization.

The results are expressed as the following metabolic quotients.

(1) Respiration, Q_{O_2} in air = rate of oxygen consumption, μl O_2/h/mg wet wt of yeast.

(2) Aerobic fermention, Q_{CO_2} in air = rate of carbon dioxide production due to aerobic fermentation, μl CO_2/hr/mg wet wt yeast.

(3) Anaerobic fermentation, Q_{CO_2} in presence of CN, μl CO_2/h/mg wet wt yeast.

These values should indicate the effect of oxygen on the rate of fermentation.

EXPERIMENTAL PROCEDURE

Basic knowledge of the Warburg manometric technique will be assumed in the following instructions with regard to the use of the apparatus, the derivation and application of flask and manometer constants and the use of the thermobarometer etc. Full details are given by Umbreit et al. (1964). For convenience the basic equation, absorption coefficients etc. are given below.

The total volume of gas absorbed or given out x is calculated from the following equation.

$$x = h \left[\frac{V_G 273/T + V_F \alpha}{P_0} \right]$$

or x is hK if for a given gas and apparatus the liquid volume and temperature remain constant.

N.B. V_G is volume of the gas space in the flask (including the manometer capillary down to the calibration mark) in mm³; V_F is the volume of liquid in the flask in mm³ (μl); T is the temperature of the bath in degrees absolute, and α is the absorption coefficient of the gas formed or absorbed (volume of gas at NTP absorbed by 1 vol of liquid at a specified temperature when partial pressure of the gas is 760 mm Hg or 10 000 mm³ manometer fluid).

Temperature	25°C	38°C
α O_2	0·03	0·024
α CO_2	0·76	0·55

P_0 is the normal pressure in mm of manometer fluid, i.e. 10 000 mm, and h is the change in pressure of manometer fluid in mm during experiment.

EXPERIMENT 1. RESPIRATION

In this experiment the carbon dioxide given out is absorbed so that the pressure change caused by the uptake of oxygen can be measured.

1. Set up a series of manometer flasks as indicated in Table VI.

TABLE VI

Flask		E1	E2	C1	C2	T
Yeast suspension 4% w/v in pH 7·0 buffer	M	2·0	2·0	2·0	2·0	—
Glucose 6% w/v	S	1·0	1·0	—	—	—
Water	M	—	—	1·0	1·0	3·2
NaOH 10% w/v	W	0·2	0·2	0·2	0·2	—

E, Experimental; C, control; T, thermobarometer; M, main compartment of flask; S, sidearm; W, centre well.

2. Place a small cylinder or concertina of filter paper in the centre well to increase effective absorbing surface of the alkali.

3. Insert stoppers and mount flasks on manometers checking that the greasing on the joint is evenly distributed, bores of taps are not blocked, etc.

4. Place in bath, equilibrate for 5–10 min, check for leaks. *Close taps.*

5. Adjust manometer fluid for gas *uptake*, i.e. fluid level in open (left hand) arm should be higher than in reference (right hand) arm. *Note readings.*

6. Tip substrate to start reaction and take readings at intervals of 5 min for 25–30 min. N.B. A minimum of five readings are necessary to establish a reasonable plot so that the rate of oxygen consumption may be calculated.

7. *Open taps.* Remove manometers from bath and proceed to expt 2.

EXPERIMENT 2. AEROBIC FERMENTATION

In this experiment the net pressure change resulting from simultaneous respiration and fermentation is measured.

1. Disconnect the flasks from expt 1—except the thermobarometer. Remove grease with tissue. *Carefully* remove filter paper from centre wells, *avoid spillage* of alkali into yeast suspension in main compartment. Dry out centre wells with fresh filter paper. Add, *carefully*, 0·2 ml 2 N H_2SO_4 to neutralize traces of alkali in the centre well.

2. Regrease and reassemble manometers etc.

3. Equilibrate, check for leaks etc. *Close taps.*

4. Adjust manometer fluid for gas *output*, i.e. fluid level in the open (left hand) arm should be lower than in reference (right hand) arm. *Note readings.*

5. Take a set of readings after intervals of 5 min for 25–30 min. Plot rate of carbon dioxide output.

6. *Open taps.* Remove manometers from bath and proceed to expt 3.

EXPERIMENT 3. ANAEROBIC FERMENTATION

In this part of the experiment the uptake of oxygen is prevented by blocking respiration with cyanide. The carbon dioxide produced by anaerobic fermentation may be then measured.

Care must be exercised when handling cyanide solutions. Never pipette by mouth, use rubber teats or hypodermic syringes to actuate pipettes.

1. Disconnect flasks from expt 2 except the thermobarometer. Remove grease. Add one drop 0·01 N KCN by means of a dropping pipette to the yeast suspension in each flask.

2. Regrease and re-assemble manometers etc.

3. Equilibrate, check for leaks etc. *Close taps.*

4. Adjust manometer fluid for gas *output*. *Note readings.*

5. Take a set of readings after intervals of 5 min for 25–30 min. Plot rate of carbon dioxide output.

6. *Open taps.* Remove manometers from bath, disconnect flasks, remove grease with tissue soaked in acetone. Wash out thoroughly in tap water (ten changes) followed by distilled water (five changes).

CALCULATION OF RESULTS

From plot of gas uptake or output the change in pressure h in mm/h is determined (see Fig. 6) for each section of experiment, i.e. h_1, h_2, h_3.

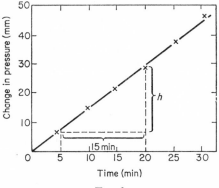

FIG. 6.

$$h/h = h \times \tfrac{60}{15} = ha, hb, hc$$

Wt of yeast present in 2·0 ml of 4% w/v suspension, i.e.

$$\frac{4 \times 1\,000}{100} \times 2 = 80 \text{ mg}$$

Thus h/h is divided by 80 to get h change/h/mg wet wt yeast, i.e. ch_1, ch_2, ch_3.

It is then necessary to convert these pressure changes into volume changes, by use of flask and manometer constants so that metabolic quotients may be calculated.

For expt 1, Respiration RQ_{O_2}

$$RQ_{O_2} = ch_1 \times KO_2 \; \mu l/mg/h$$

For expt 2, Aerobic fermentation AFQ_{CO_2}

Three processes contribute to the total observed pressure changes: (1) O_2 uptake due to respiration; (2) CO_2 output due to respiration; (3) CO_2 output due to fermentation. When glucose is the substrate, volume of CO_2 formed during respiration is equal to the volume of CO_2 consumed, i.e. RQ_{CO_2}. Hence total change of pressure in expt 2

$$ch_2 = \frac{(RQ_{CO_2} + AFQ_{CO_2})}{KCO_2} - \frac{(RQ_{O_2})}{KO_2}$$

$$AFQ_{CO_2} = KCO_2 \frac{(chb + RQ_{O_2})}{KO_2} - RQ_{CO_2}$$

RQ_{O_2} and RQ_{CO_2} are known from expt 1, ch_2 $\mu l/mg/h$ is calculated from data from expt 2. AFQ_{CO_2} may then be calculated.

For expt 3, Anaerobic fermentation FQ_{CO_2}

$$FQ_{CO_2} = ch_3 \times KCO_2 \; \mu l/mg/h$$

Typical values of quotients are as follows:

RQ_{O_2}	10–20 $\mu l/mg/h$
AFQ_{CO_2}	5–10 $\mu l/mg/h$
FQ_{CO_2}	50–60 $\mu l/mg/h$

CONCLUSIONS

Yeast can ferment glucose under anaerobic conditions. Under aerobic conditions both respiration and fermentation occur but the fermentation rate is greatly depressed. The inhibition of fermentation by respiration is known as the Pasteur effect.

TIME

One period of 3 h if basic manometric technique has been taught.

BIBLIOGRAPHY

Fruton, J. S. and Simmonds, S. (1958). "General Biochemistry", 2nd ed. Wiley, New York.
Greenberg, D. M. (1960). "Metabolic Pathways", Vol. 1. Academic Press, New York.
Umbreit, W. W., Burris, R. H. and Stauffer, J. F. (1964). "Manometric Techniques", 4th ed. Burgess Publishing Co., Minneapolis.

3 | The Relation Between the Amount of Oxygen Available to Tissues and the Type of Enzyme Present

School of Biological Sciences, University of Sydney, N.S.W., Australia

ANIMALS

Bees, blowfly larvae, *Tenebrio molitor* (meal-worm) larvae, muscle from mice.

APPARATUS

Pestle and mortar.
Test tubes.
Dissecting scissors and forceps.
Pipettes.
Stop clock or watches with second hands.
Distilled water.

CHEMICALS

0·1 M Tris (hydroxymethyl) aminomethane buffer pH 7·4. Dissolve 2·42 g tris in 100 ml H_2O. Add 82·2 ml 0·2 N HCl (2 ml conc. HCl made up to 100 ml with H_2O). Check that the pH is 7·4. Make up to 200 ml with H_2O.

0·05 M KCN (*poison—use extreme caution*). Dissolve 325 mg KCN in H_2O and make to 100 ml dichlorphenol indophenol. Make up two batches, one 0·025% (approx. 10^{-3} M) and the other 0·005%. Dissolve 25 mg (and 5 mg) dichlorphenol indophenol in water and make to 100 ml.

Nicotinamide adenine dinucleotide (NAD). Dissolve 0·2 mg NAD per ml H_2O; about 4 ml per student should be ample.

0·2 M Lactate. Dissolve 1·9 g lithium lactate in H_2O and make up to 100 ml.

0·2 M α-Glycerophosphate. Dissolve 3·9 g pure sodium α-glycerophosphate in H_2O and make to 100 ml. Suitable allowance should be made if the α-glycerophosphate used is not pure.

PRINCIPLE OF THE EXPERIMENT

During the breakdown of glucose to pyruvate (glycolysis) NAD is reduced (to NADH). There are two possible ways by which this NADH can be re-oxidized using substrates produced by the glycolytic pathway. The two reactions are

$$\text{Pyruvate} + \text{NADH} + \text{H}^+ \xrightarrow{\text{lactic dehydrogenase}} \text{lactate} + \text{NAD} \qquad (1)$$

$$\text{Dihydroxyacetone phosphate} + \text{NADH} + \text{H}^+ \xrightarrow{\text{α-glycerophosphate dehydrogenase}} \text{α-glycerophosphate} + \text{NAD} \qquad (2)$$

By re-oxidizing NADH both these reactions prevent the accumulation of quantities of NADH which would eventually stop the breakdown of glucose. Both these enzymes are found in the cytoplasm.

The amount of oxygen available to enzymes in animal tissues varies. In some animals the requirement for oxygen is greater than the supply. In others there is plenty of oxygen available, either because the supply is comparatively great or because the requirement is comparatively low.

In animals in which the supply of oxygen to the tissues can be limiting, for example in the muscles of mice (inadequate supply during exercise), or in blowfly larvae (anaerobic type of environment—rotting meat), lactic dehydrogenase is found in greater quantities than α-glycerophosphate dehydrogenase. In the mouse lactate accumulates during periods of exercise, but is re-oxidized during rest when the supply of oxygen is comparatively plentiful. The animal is said to go into "oxygen debt" during exercise.

In animals in which the supply of oxygen to the tissues is adequate (either because of an efficient supplying system, e.g. the tracheole system supplying the flight muscle of bees, or because of a relatively low requirement, e.g. *T. molitor* larvae) more α-glycerophosphate dehydrogenase than lactic dehydrogenase is found. The α-glycerophosphate formed under these circumstances is re-oxidized by a flavoprotein α-glycerophosphate oxidase found in the mitochondria (or sarcosomes):

$$\text{α-glycerophosphate} + \tfrac{1}{2}O_2 \xrightarrow[\substack{\text{flavoprotein} \\ \text{oxidase}}]{\text{mitochondrial}} \text{dihydroxyacetone phosphate} + H_2O$$

The purpose of this experiment is to estimate the relative amounts of lactic and α-glycerophosphate dehydrogenases in the tissues of different animals, and thus form a judgement about the conditions of oxygen supply in these tissues.

EXPERIMENTAL DETAILS

PREPARATION OF ENZYME

Bees. Put the bees in a refrigerator until they are inactive. Remove the head, wings, and abdomen from about ten bees and put the thoraces into a pestle and mortar with a pinch of sand and 3 ml tris buffer. Grind the preparation well and then wash the mince out of the mortar with 2 ml buffer.

Blowfly larvae. Remove the heads and tails from about ten blowfly larvae and grind up the eviscerated animals as above.

T. molitor. This animal contains a fat-body, an organ roughly equivalent to a liver. To obtain the fat-body, remove the head and tail of the larvae, pull out the gut, and then squeeze gently up from the posterior end of the body. The fat-body should emerge like toothpaste from a tube. Grind about fifteen fat-bodies in a mortar without the addition of sand (but with buffer).

Mice. Kill the mouse by breaking its neck and quickly remove about 1 g of back muscle. Cut the muscle up as finely as possible and grind in a pestle and mortar with sand and buffer as above.

ASSAY METHOD

Place the following reagents in a series of test tubes:

	ml
Substrate (α-glycerophosphate or lactate) 0·2 M	0·3
Tris buffer pH 7·4	1·0
KCN 0·05 M	0·5
Dichlorphenolindophenol	0·5
NAD (0·2 mg/ml)	0·2

Add 0·5 ml enzyme to the tubes noting the *exact* time of addition to each tube. Record the time taken for the decolorization of the dye. Include a blank with boiled enzyme. A blank containing water in place of substrate may also be included.

THE FUNCTION OF THE COMPONENTS OF THE SYSTEM

Dichlorphenolindophenol is a dye which is blue when oxidized and colourless when reduced. It will accept electrons from flavoprotein. The cyanide blocks the cytochrome oxidase component of the electron transport system so that the electrons pass to dichlorphenolindophenol rather than through the system. NAD is added to ensure that there is enough present to allow full activity of the lactic and α-glycerophosphate dehydrogenases.

Sample Results

Table I

Time of decolorization in minutes and seconds

	Bee	Blowfly	*T. molitor*	Mouse
Lactic dehydrogenase	2 min 15 sec	2 min 45 sec	6 min 10 sec	1 min 45 sec
α-Glycerophosphate dehydrogenase	1 min 20 sec	5 min 45 sec	4 min 30 sec	2 min 45 sec

Trouble-shooting

If the dye is not decolorized by any of the enzyme preparations: (a) check the pH of the tubes, and of the enzyme preparation itself, and make sure that it is close to pH 7·4; (b) repeat the experiment reducing the amount of the dye to one-fifth of the original amount; (c) if the dye is decolorized too fast to allow accurate timing, reduce the amount of enzyme added to the incubation medium.

Further Experiments

The protein content of the enzyme preparations may be estimated so that the activity of each enzyme may be compared *between* animals. The experiment may be repeated using a buffer of different pH, e.g. pH 8·0 or 6·5, to see whether pH has an equal effect on the activity of the enzymes in different animals.

Bibliography

Schimassek, H., Kadenbach, B., Rüssman, W., and Bücher, T. (1963). The oxidation of α-glycerophosphate: a possible example of metabolic control by enzyme induction. *In* "Advances in Enzyme Regulation" (G. Weber, ed.), Vol. 1, p. 103. Pergamon Press, Oxford. [Discusses methods of control of these enzymes.]

Zebe, E. C. and McShan, W. H. (1957). Lactic and α-glycerophosphate dehydrogenase in insect flight muscle. *J. gen. Physiol.*, **40**, 799. [Deals mainly with the activity of the enzymes in insects.]

4

A. Biological Oxidation
B. Digestion by Mammalian Gut Tissues
C. The Measurement of Enzyme Activity in Digestive Gland of Slug *Arion ater*

W. A. L. EVANS

*Department of Zoology, University of Wales,
Cardiff, Wales*

A. Biological Oxidation

GENERAL PRINCIPLES

Biological oxidations seldom proceed by the direct addition of oxygen to a particular substrate. Oxidation is usually effected by the transfer of hydrogen atoms or electrons from the substrate to a suitable hydrogen acceptor which, of course, is thereby reduced. Such oxidizing reactions are catalysed intracellularly by enzymes which show varying degrees of specificity towards the substrates and also to the substances acting as hydrogen acceptors.

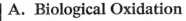

A is a substrate or hydrogen *donator* $\quad$ B is a hydrogen *acceptor*

Enzyme

An oxidase or dehydrogenase

Oxygen is usually involved in the oxidation process after the activity of one or more intermediary reactions each of which is controlled by an enzyme or enzyme system. The sequence of reactions can be represented:

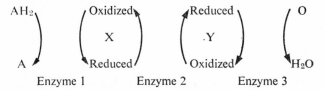

X and Y are intermediary substances (e.g. co-enzymes 1 and 11, and flavo-proteins) which accept hydrogen atoms or electrons and then donate them to a suitable acceptor. These intermediaries are continually being reduced and re-oxidized.

The ultimate reaction in which atmospheric oxygen takes part depends upon the presence of a very important cell constituent, cytochrome. This substance, which exists in a range of forms with different properties, is a conjugated protein with a haem prosthetic group. Most cytochromes, including the commonest, cytochrome c, require the enzyme cytochrome oxidase to re-oxidize the reduced form of the cytochrome. In the diagram above showing the sequence of reactions, enzyme 3 represents cytochrome oxidase. Some cytochromes such as cytochrome b_5, which occurs in some insects, are autoxidizable and so cytochrome oxidase is unnecessary for the re-oxidation of reduced cytochrome. This fact must be borne in mind when devising experiments to illustrate cytochrome oxidase activity. That a cytochrome is dependent upon enzyme activity for re-oxidation can be shown by adding cyanide which is a powerful inhibitor of cytochrome oxidase. The re-oxidation of autoxidizable cytochrome is not inhibited by cyanide.

The enzymes which catalyse the transfer of hydrogen atoms or electrons are generally called oxidases or dehydrogenases. The *oxygenases* are a small group of enzymes which catalyse the direct oxidation of a substrate by the addition of oxygen. They are particularly important in the oxidation of aromatic compounds, e.g. phenylalanine to tyrosine. Lactic acid decarboxylase is another example.

METHODS OF STUDY

1. Measurement of the chemical change when a substrate is oxidized, either by measuring a decrease in substrate concentration or an increase in acceptor concentration.

2. Manometric measurement of oxygen uptake during an oxidation reaction.

3. Using artificial dyes which can accept hydrogen from the substrate being oxidized and during which process a colour change takes place. In recent years there has been a considerable development of this technique, particularly for the histochemical and cytochemical location of dehydrogenases.

EXPERIMENT 1. TO DEMONSTRATE GLUCOSE OXIDASE ACTIVITY

MATERIALS

Glucose stock solution containing 100 μg/ml.

Glucose oxidase reagent (after M. R. J. Morgan). Dissolve 61 g tris in 425 ml N HCl. Add 400 ml glycerol and 100 ml water and adjust to pH 7·0. Dissolve in 125 mg glucose oxidase and 5 mg peroxidase. Add 5 ml o-dianisidine (10 mg per ml of the hydrochloride) and make up to 1 litre. Store in a refrigerator. Warm to room temperature before use.

Sulphuric acid 50% (v/v).

PRINCIPLE

Glucose oxidase specifically oxidizes β-D-glucopyranose. Although α-D-glucopyranose is oxidized 150 times as slowly at room temperature, preparations of the enzyme can be used to oxidize glucose solutions which will generally contain much more of the α-isomer. This results from the presence of a mutarotase which is present even in very highly purified preparations of glucose oxidase. Mutarotase converts the α-isomer into the β-isomer rapidly enough for all the glucose to assume the β-isomeric form

$$\beta\text{-D-Glucose} + H_2O + O_2 \rightarrow \text{D-gluconic acid} + H_2O_2$$

The hydrogen peroxide formed can be used to form a coloured compound from a suitable chromogen in the presence of a peroxidase

$$\underset{\substack{\text{Chromogen} \\ \text{a hydrogen donor}}}{DH_2} + H_2O_2 \xrightarrow{\quad\text{Peroxidase}\quad} 2H_2O + \underset{\substack{\text{Coloured} \\ \text{compound}}}{D}$$

o-Dianisidine is a suitable chromogen which can be incorporated into a glucose oxidase reagent (GOR) which is stable in the dark at 0°C. The coloured compound obtained is reasonably stable at room temperature; the addition of sulphuric acid results in a red-violet colour which is stable. These reactions can be used very effectively to estimate glucose colorimetrically. They also form the basis of the "Clinistix" paper strip method for detecting glucose (see the section on digestive enzymes).

PROCEDURE

Prepare a series of five glucose solutions, 1 ml containing 5, 10, 20, 50, 100 μg of glucose by suitable dilution of the stock solution provided. To each 2 ml glucose solution (and 2 ml water as a reagent blank) add 2 ml GOR and incubate for 1 h at approx. 37°C. Then add 2 ml 50% (v/v) sulphuric acid. Note the range of coloured solutions produced—the colour intensity increases with the glucose concentration.

FURTHER EXPERIMENTS

The glucose oxidase reaction can be used for the accurate quantitative estimation of glucose. The reagent prepared and used as above with glucose solutions of varying concentrations, ranging from 10 to 100 μg, gives a series of coloured solutions the intensity of which corresponds directly to the glucose concentration. A calibration curve can be readily obtained by plotting absorptiometer extinction values against glucose concentration using a light filter of 520 mμ.

The glucose content of biological fluids can be determined by using a calibration curve provided proteins are precipitated first.

EXPERIMENT 2. TO DEMONSTRATE CYTOCHROME OXIDASE ACTIVITY

MATERIALS

0·1% Dimethyl phenylene diamine sulphate.

0·1% α-Naphthol (prepared by dissolving 0·1 g α-naphthol in 5·0 ml ethyl alcohol and diluting to 100 ml with water).

0·1 M Phosphate buffer at pH 7·2.

Insect saline.

0·1 M Potassium cyanide in a teat pipette.

Blowfly larvae; 3–4 days old if kept at 25°C.

PRINCIPLE

The cytochromes constitute a very important group of intracellular substances concerned with biological oxidation-reduction reactions. They are conjugated proteins with an iron containing prosthetic group (haem, which is very similar to the haem of haemoglobin). The iron atom in the haem molecule can alternate between an oxidized (ferric, Fe^{+++}) or reduced (ferrous, Fe^{++}) form and thus allow chemical oxidations and reductions to proceed in a chain reaction in which a substrate is originally oxidized by the removal of the hydrogen, and oxygen is finally reduced by the addition of hydrogen.

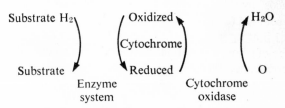

There are several kinds of cytochrome of which cytochrome c is the most common. Reduced cytochrome c is re-oxidized in the presence of atmospheric oxygen and an enzyme, cytochrome oxidase. Other cytochromes, a and members of the b group, are re-oxidized in a similar manner, but one member of the b group, b_5, is slowly autoxidizable even in the absence of cytochrome oxidase.

Insects are a convenient source of tissues which can be used to demonstrate cytochrome oxidase activity. Table I shows the variation in the cytochrome complement in insect tissues.

TABLE I

The cytochrome complement of different insect tissues

| Tissue | Cytochrome | | | |
	a	b	b_5	c
Muscles of all stages	Present	Present	Very low or absent	Abundant
Non-muscular tissue of larvae and adult	Present	Low concn	Present, variable concn	Present, variable concn
Non-muscular tissue of pupae	Small	Very low or absent	Small quantity	Very low or absent

The intracellular location of the insect cytochromes is similar to that of their mammalian counterparts; cytochromes a, b, c and cytochrome b_5 are found in the mitochondria.

In the presence of oxidized cytochrome and atmospheric oxygen indophenol blue is produced by the condensation of dimethyl *p*-phenylenediamine with α-naphthol both of which are only faintly coloured in dilute solution. These two compounds form what is known as the "Nadi" reagent.

Since there is only a limited supply of oxidized cytochrome in cells, this reaction depnds upon the re-oxidization of reduced cytochrome in order to produce sufficient indophenol blue to be visible. The presence of cytochrome oxidase maintains an adequate concentration of oxidized cytochrome.

$$
\text{``Nadi''} + 2H_2 \Bigg) \quad \Bigg(\begin{array}{c} \text{Oxidized} \\ \text{Cytochrome} \\ \text{Reduced} \end{array} \Bigg) \quad \Bigg(\begin{array}{c} 2H_2O \\ \\ O_2 \end{array}
$$

Indophenol
blue

Non-enzymatic   Cytochrome
                          oxidase

PROCEDURE

Prepare 2 ml of Nadi reagent immediately before use by mixing 1 ml 0·1% dimethyl phenylene diamine sulphate and 1 ml 0·1% α-naphthol. This reagent slowly oxidizes to indophenol blue in the presence of atmospheric oxygen and so it must be freshly prepared.

Obtain the following tissues from a blowfly larva (any size conveniently large will do) by cutting off the "head" and "tail" and gently squeezing out the contents: salivary glands, some fat body cells, Malpighian tubes and a portion of body wall. This operation is best carried out under insect saline.

In a watch glass place a piece of blowfly tissue, add 0·5 ml M/10 phosphate buffer at pH 7·2 and 0·5 ml *freshly* prepared Nadi reagent. Carry out a control test using the same buffer and Nadi solutions but with tissue which has been placed in water at 95°C for 5 min. Compare the colour change of the cytoplasm in test and control reactions every 5 min for 30 min. Tabulate your results after using the various larvae tissues.

Find the effect of adding 5 drops (0·5 ml approx.) of M/10 potassium cyanide to the tissues *before* the addition of the Nadi reagent. N.B. *Potassium cyanide* is a deadly poison and it *must not* be sucked into an ordinary pipette. Use the teat-pipette provided.

EXPERIMENT 3. TO DEMONSTRATE SUCCINIC DEHYDROGENASE ACTIVITY USING METHYLENE BLUE AS A HYDROGEN ACCEPTOR

MATERIALS

0·1 M Sodium succinate.
0·1 M Phosphate buffer at pH 7·2.
0·02% Methylene blue.
Strong test tubes which can be evacuated.
Insect saline.
Adult cockroaches or locusts.

Anaerobic dehydrogenases catalyse the removal of hydrogen from a substrate to a particular acceptor which is not molecular oxygen. Succinic dehydrogenase, which catalyses the oxidation of succinic acid to fumaric acid, can utilize oxidized cytochrome as hydrogen acceptor.

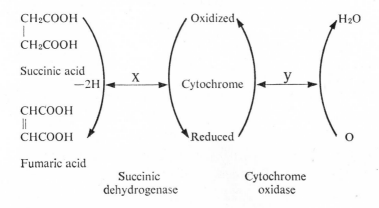

In vitro methylene blue, which will act as hydrogen acceptor for succinic dehydrogenase, becomes reduced to the colourless leuco-methylene blue. Since this substance is autoxidizable in the presence of atmospheric oxygen the reaction must be carried out in vacuo.

Remove the thoracic muscles from several cockroaches or locust and make a suspension in 3 ml phosphate buffer in a small graduated tube. Into labelled tubes place:

Tube A. 0·5 ml Buffer + 0·5 ml succinate + 0·5 ml tissue suspension

Tube B. 0·5 ml Buffer + 0·5 ml succinate + 0·5 ml denatured suspension

Tube C. 0·5 ml Buffer + 0·5 ml water + 0·5 ml tissue suspension

Into each tube place a small glass tube making sure that none of the tube contents gets into it. Add 0·5 ml methylene blue to the small tube. Evacuate the tubes at a filter pump and adjust the screw-clip on the pressure tubing connecting the reaction tubes to the pump very tighly before dismantling. Place in a water bath at 37°C and when the contents of the tubes have acquired the temperature of the bath, tilt and allow the methylene blue to mix with the other solutions. Observe and record the colour change, if any, in the various tubes after a few hours incubation.

Explain fully your observations.

EXPERIMENT 4. TO DEMONSTRATE DEHYDROGENASE ACTIVITY USING A TETRAZOLIUM SALT AS HYDROGEN ACCEPTOR

MATERIALS

0·1 M Phosphate buffer at pH 7·2.

Insect saline.

0·1 M Sodium succinate.

0·1% Tetrazolium chloride (or neonitrotetrazolium for precise cytological work).

PRINCIPLE

Tetrazolium salts are readily reduced under certain conditions to give highly coloured formazan compounds which are insoluble in aqueous solutions.

$$\underset{\text{Colourless triphenyltetrazolium chloride (TPTCl)}}{C_6H_5-C\begin{array}{c} N-N-C_6H_5 \\ | \\ \overset{+}{N}=N-C_6H_5 \\ Cl^- \end{array}} \xrightarrow[]{2H^+-2e^-} \underset{\text{Red triphenylformazan}}{C_6H_5-C\begin{array}{c} N-NH-C_6H_5 \\ \\ N=N-C_6H_5 \end{array}}$$

Use can be made of this reaction to demonstrate dehydrogenase activity histochemically and cytochemically. Tissues incubated in a suitable reaction mixture containing tetrazolium salt become colorized with the formazan compound if dehydrogenase activity is present. TPTCl does not yield good formazan crystals. The red coloration is often due to the solubility of formazan in the lipid rich components of the cells. With some tetrazolium salts, e.g. neonitrotetrazolium, intracellular location of the sites (viz. mitochondria) of dehydrogenase activity is often possible.

PROCEDURE

Carefully remove as much of the alimentary tract of a blowfly larva as possible in a small glass dish containing insect saline. To do this decapitate the larva about 1 mm from the anterior end and then cut off the terminal millimetre. Squeeze the animal from posterior to anterior whereupon the alimentary tract and other contents should be extruded. Unravel the gut carefully and study the anatomical relations of the various parts. Set up the following reaction mixtures in solid watch glasses:

(A) 1 ml Phosphate buffer + 0·5 ml tetrazolium salt + 0·5 ml sodium succinate.
(B) Similar to A.
(C) 1 ml Phosphate buffer + 0·5 ml tetrazolium salt + 0·5 ml water.
(D) 1 ml Phosphate buffer + 0·5 ml water + 0·5 ml sodium succinate.

Place freshly dissected and unravelled guts into solutions A, C and D and into B place a gut which has been placed in water at 95°C for 5 min. Note the colour pattern in the guts in the various solutions after 30 min and 60 min incubation at 25°C (or room temperature). Reaction B is a control; the gut remains colourless because the dehydrogenases are inactivated by denaturation. The gut in reaction vessel D also remains colourless because there is no tetrazolium salt present. The reaction in C is much weaker than in A. It shows the presence of endogenous substrate which might be succinate.

FURTHER EXPERIMENTS

For a more detailed study of the cellular location of enzyme activity blowfly salivary glands and Malpighian tubes should be used with neonitrotetrazolium as the hydrogen acceptor. After a suitable incubation period (determined by trial and microscope examination) fix the tissue in formolcalcium for 10 min and mount in glycerol-jelly. Detailed high power microscope study is then possible.

BIBLIOGRAPHY

Gilmour, D. (1960). "Biochemistry of Insects." Academic Press, New York.

B. Digestion by Mammalian Gut Tissues

MATERIALS

1. A recently killed small mammal, e.g. laboratory rat.
2. A small glass pestle and mortar.
3. Powdered glass or fine acid washed sand.
4. The substrates, buffers and reagents required are indicated in relation to the appropriate enzymes.

GENERAL PRINCIPLES

The principle underlying these experiments is simple: an enzyme extract is added to a food substance and the product or products of activity tested for after a period of incubation at a suitable temperature. To ensure that chemical changes taking place are due to the presence of enzymes *a control reaction is always employed*. The control reaction is set up in a similar manner to the test reaction except that the enzyme solution is denatured by prior heating to approx. 95°C for 20 min. It is assumed that denaturation, and hence inactivation of the enzyme protein, is the only relevant chemical difference between the test and control reaction mixture. Hence any chemical changes occurring in the test reaction, but not in the control reaction, must be due to enzyme activity alone. In both test and control reactions bacterial activity is prevented by the addition of a few drops of toluene. Because enzymes are generally more active at a particular pH, suitable and similar buffer solutions are introduced into the reaction mixtures of both test and control reactions.

The simple qualitative tests given below only indicate the presence or absence of extractable enzymes in the gut tissues. Similar experiments can be carried out on the gut contents, and by comparing the results from tissue extract and gut contents experiments a preliminary picture of the digestive capability of the animal can be obtained.

INITIAL PROCEDURE

Dissect the mammal to expose the alimentary canal and pancreas. Prepare aqueous extracts of regions of the gut, after thoroughly washing away the lumen contents, by grinding with sand or powdered glass. Add a minimum of distilled water for the grinding process (approx. 1·0–2·0 ml) and then make up to the volume required (see Table II). Stir well and decant the gut suspension leaving as much of the sand as possible in the mortar.

TABLE II

Preparation of gut tissue extracts

Region of gut	Vol of water (ml)
Stomach (pyloric half only)	3
Pancreas	5
2 in. small intestine (note precisely the region used; on either side of the opening of the pancreatic duct is preferable)	5
1 in. large intestine (colon)	5

Denature one half of each of the enzyme extracts by placing in a water bath at approx. 95°C for 20 min.

CARBOHYDRASES

MATERIALS

0·1 M Phosphate buffer at pH 7·0.
Toluene.
4% Solutions of the following substrates: starch, sucrose, maltose and lactose.
Benedict's or Fehling's solution.
"Clinistix", obtained from Ames Co., Slough, Bucks, England.

PRINCIPLES

Carbohydrate foods are digested by a variety of enzymes. Generally the product or products of hydrolyses are monosaccharides or disaccharides with reducing properties. If the substrate (or food substance) in the reaction mixture is itself non-reducing, then the detection of hydrolysis is easy; a reducing sugar test (e.g. Benedict's) is carried out on the test and control reaction. A positive result in the test reaction compared to a negative in the control indicates enzyme activity.

To detect the hydrolysis of food carbohydrates with reducing or non-reducing properties glucose, which is always one product, can be detected by the activity of the highly specific enzyme glucose oxidase. The "Clinistix" paper strip test for glucose in urine is based on glucose oxidase activity and can be readily adapted for carbohydrase detection.

Both the reducing sugar test and the glucose oxidase method used here are, of course, qualitative in nature. In some circumstances it is essential to carry out quantitative experiments to establish the presence or absence of enzyme activity. It is important to remember that the basis of these tests is a comparison between test and control reactions. Sometimes controls give weak positive reactions owing to the pressure of contaminants, especially glucose, in the extract and/or substrate. However, by comparing test with control reactions there should be little doubt as to the presence of a particular carbohydrase in the extract.

N.B. Whatever method (quantitative or qualitative) is used the detection of activity is limited by the sensitivity of the method for detecting the product(s) of hydrolysis. A negative result should, strictly speaking, be interpreted as no hydrolysis above a certain value. This value is set by the sensitivity of the analytical procedure; e.g. if 10 μg glucose is necessary for detection and the reaction mixture samples contained 1 mg maltose initially, then any hydrolysis below 1% would not be detected.

Set up test and control (with denatured enzyme extract) reaction mixtures as follows.

Substrate (4%)	0·5 ml
0·1 M Phosphate buffer (pH 7·0)	1 ml
Enzyme extract	0·5 ml
Toluene	2 drops

Incubate and test for reducing sugar and/or glucose after 1 h incubation. Use part of the reaction mixture only for the test, so that repeat examinations can be made after further incubation.

1. For non-reducing substrates take 0·5 ml test solution and add 0·5 ml Benedict's solution; if a brown precipitate appears after heating this shows a positive reaction.

2. For the glucose production test dip the "Clinistix" strip into the control and test reactions and compare the coloration after 30–60 sec only. A much stronger blue colour in the test indicates a greater concentration of glucose and hence hydrolysis of the substrate.

Use the following substrates for the different tissue extracts: stomach—starch, sucrose; small intestine—starch, sucrose, maltose, lactose; pancreas—starch, sucrose, maltose, lactose; large intestine—starch, sucrose, maltose, lactose; saliva (human, 50% v/v with H_2O)—starch, maltose, sucrose.

FURTHER EXPERIMENTS

The digestive enzymes in the alimentary tract of any animal of a convenient size can be investigated by the methods given above. For small animals several guts, or gut regions, can be pooled; or "semi-micro" tests using small volumes of reaction mixture and pieces of gut tissue can be set up on welled microscope slides. The latter must be incubated in a saturated atmosphere to prevent evaporation of the reaction mixture.

The range of carbohydrate substrates should be extended for animals like cockroaches, locusts, blowfly larvae, slugs or snails. In particular β-linked substrates like cellobiose, "cellofas B", and cellulose would be well worth using.

BIBLIOGRAPHY

Evans, W. A. L. (1956). Studies on the Digestive Enzymes of the Blowfly *Calliphora erythrociphala*. 1. The Carbohydrasis. *Expl Parasit.*, **5**, 191–206.
Evans, W. A. L. and Payne, D. W. (1964). Carbohydrases of the Alimentary Tract of the Desert Locust, *Schistocerca gregaria*. *J. Insect Physiol.*, **10**, 657–674.

C. The Measurement of Enzyme Activity in Digestive Gland of Slug *Arion ater*

GENERAL PRINCIPLES

Enzymes play an essential role in the metabolism of organisms. Cell activity and replacement depends upon the integrated action of enzymes controlling energy production and transfer along with those enzymes involved in synthetic processes. The necessary raw materials are of course found in the food which usually has to be digested by hydrolytic enzymes into utilizable products.

The glycosidase group of enzymes hydrolyse disaccharides and oligosaccharides into their constituent monosaccharides. These enzymes exhibit a group specificity which is determined by the nature of the glycosidic bond present in the substrate. Thus most α-glucosides, which include such sugars as maltose and sucrose, are hydrolysed by ageneral α-glucosidase, β-galactosidases hydrolyse β-galactosides such as lactose, and β-glucosidases hydrolyse a range of β-glucosides.

The β-glucoside, salicin, is a very convenient substrate for the measurement of enzyme activity because one of the products of hydrolysis, saligenin, can be estimated by a rapid absorptiometric or colorimetric procedure.

Salicin   β-Glucose   Saligenin

The digestive gland of the slug *Arion ater* is a rich source of β-glucosidase which can be obtained in solution by filtration or centrifugation after homogenization and aqueous extraction. Freeze-dried preparations of such extracts remain active for several years.

The principle of the absorptiometric methods depends on the two fundamental laws relating to light absorption which are:

1. Lambert's law: the proportion of light absorbed by a substance is independent of the intensity of the incident light.

2. Beer's law: the proportion of light absorbed depends on the total number of absorbing molecules through which it passes.

From these laws the following relationship can be derived for light passing through a solution of an absorbing substance in a non-absorbing solvent.

$$\log \frac{I_0}{I} = ECL$$

where I_0 is the intensity of incident light, I is the intensity of emergent light, C is the concentration of the absorbing substance, L is the depth of absorbing layer and E is a constant. Clearly if L is kept constant $\log(I_0/I)$ gives a direct measure of the concentration of solute. The value of $\log(I_0/I)$ can be read directly on most absorptiometers on a log scale and it is called the optical density, d, or more usually nowadays the extinction, E. In some absorptiometers a transmission scale is provided. This measures the ratio of the intensity of the transmitted light to that of the incident light, $T = I/I_0$.

For enzyme work it is not necessary to measure absolutely the concentration of one of the products of a reaction, although this can be easily done by constructing a calibration curve for the substance being estimated. Values for measuring the relative velocities of enzyme activity can be obtained directly merely by reading the extinction values on the absorptiometer for the various suitably treated reaction mixtures. Another point to remember in enzyme work is that it is usual to prepare a reagent blank so that extraneous colour can be accounted for. In practice this usually means measuring the colour in a treated reaction mixture sample after zero time incubation of the enzyme reaction and subtracting this value from the extinction value obtained after t min incubation.

The following experiments are designed to illustrate how various factors can influence enzyme activity.

Experiment 1. The Effect of pH on β-Glucosidase Activity

MATERIALS

Buffer stock solutions, 0·1 N acetic acid and 0·1 M sodium acetate (see Table III).

Table III

Proportion of acetic acid and sodium acetate for acetate buffer solutions
(Sodium acetate is prepared by mixing equal vol of
0·1 N acetic acid and 0·1 N sodium hydroxide)

pH	Sodium acetate 0·1 M	Acetic acid 0·1 N	pH	Sodium acetate 0·1 M	Acetic acid 0·1 N
3·8	1·2	8·8	4·8	6·0	4·0
4·0	1·8	8·2	5·0	7·0	3·0
4·2	2·65	7·35	5·2	7·85	2·15
4·4	3·7	6·3	5·4	8·5	1·5
4·6	4·8	5·2	5·6	9·05	0·95

0·05 M Salicin (1·43 g in 100 ml water).

Enzyme solution, 2 mg per ml of a freeze-dried preparation of slug digestive gland, or the diluted supernatant of a centrifuged extract (the dilution to be determined after a trial incubation at pH 4·8).

0·2% Potassium ferricyanide.

4-Amino antipyrine (4-aminophenazone) solution prepared by dissolving 0·1 g antipyrine in 10 ml 50% (v/v) aqueous ethanol, adding 25 ml 2 N ammonium hydroxide and diluting to 250 ml. Store in a cool dark place.

PRINCIPLE

It has been known since the early years of the century that enzyme activity is markedly influenced by the hydrogen ion concentration or pH. The similarity of the characteristic bell-shaped pH–enzyme activity curve (see Fig. 1)

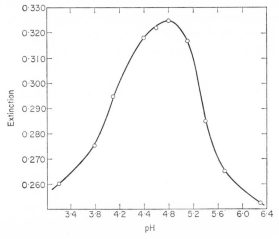

FIG. 1. pH–activity curve for salicin hydrolysis by slug (*Arion ater*) digestive gland extract. A universal buffer was used and the incubation time was 200 min at 25°C.

to the dissociation curves for proteins under different pH conditions helped to confirm the protein nature of enzymes and to establish the fact that activity depends upon the ionic state of the enzyme. More recently pH–activity studies using different concentrations of substrate has led to the identification of the nature of ionizing or dissociating groups within the enzyme molecule.

PROCEDURE

Prepare a series of buffer–substrate solutions containing 1 ml salicin and 2 ml buffer at different pH values over the pH range 3·8–5·6. Duplicate the solution at pH 5·0. Place the solutions, in 4 in. clearly labelled test tubes with a bulb blown out at the end, in a water bath at 25°C. Separately place 15 ml enzyme solution in the same bath and allow sufficient time for all the solutions to attain the bath temperature. Label sufficient test tubes, or standard absorptiometer tubes, and add 2 ml antipyrine to each tube. At a convenient time, which must be noted, and subsequently at 2-min intervals, add 1 ml enzyme solution to each of the buffer–substrate solutions and shake well. Immediately withdraw a 1 ml reaction mixture sample and add it to the amino antipyrine solution.

After 50 min incubation remove a second sample from one of the reaction tubes at pH 5·0 and add it to the amino antipyrine solution. Then add 1 ml potassium ferricyanide and examine carefully the colour intensity of the solution so that a satisfactory incubation period can be determined. Ideally the colour intensity of the test reaction should give a reading on the absorptiometer of approx. 0·5 on the log scale whether the solution is placed in absorptiometer cells (usually 1 cm deep) or in a standard absorptiometer tube. The most suitable wavelength of light for this colour measurement is 515 mμ. If the preliminary test reveals low enzyme activity, i.e. absorptiometer extinction values less than 0·4, then the incubation period should be increased appropriately but it should not exceed 200 min. Also if the extinction value in the test reaction were above 0·8 then the colour intensity of treated samples could be reduced by dilution with water. If the test sample produces an extinction value of the right order, i.e. between 0·4 and 0·7, then withdraw second samples from each tube after 60 min incubation and add them directly to the amino antipyrine solution. At this point the solution can be stored, before the addition of potassium ferricyanide, because the high alkalinity prevents further glucosidase activity. After all the samples have been taken, add the potassium ferricyanide to each of the sample tubes and allow approx. 15 min for the full development of colour. Although the colour is reasonably stable in the dark for several hours, it is preferable to measure the colour intensities as soon as possible. The pH of the reaction mixtures can be checked during and at the end of the incubation period by means of a pH meter.

Plot the pH–activity curve using the difference between the extinction values at zero time and after t min incubation as a measure of enzyme activity.

EXPERIMENT 2. THE EFFECT OF SUBSTRATE CONCENTRATION ON ENZYME ACTIVITY

MATERIALS

0·2 M Acetate buffer at pH 4·8, prepared by mixing 0·2 M sodium acetate and 0·2 N acetic acid in the ratio 6 : 4; 0·05 M salicin; enzyme solution;

2 mg per ml of a freeze-dried preparation of digestive gland; 0·2% potassium ferricyanide; 4 amino antipyrine solution (for preparation, see p. 77).

(for preparation, see p. 77)

PRINCIPLE

At low substrate concentrations enzyme activity increases with increasing substrate concentration but the relationship is not a linear one. Substrate concentrations above a certain limit generally result in little or no increased

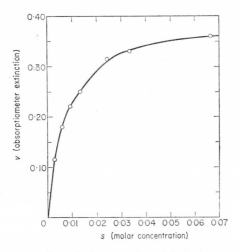

FIG. 2. Substrate concentration–velocity curve for salicin hydrolysis by slug (*Arion ater*) digestive gland extract. The pH was 4·8 and the incubation period 120 min at 25°C.

activity. Indeed in some cases very high substrate concentrations may be inhibitory. Figure 2 shows the form of a typical substrate concentration/velocity curve which graphically represents the Michaelis–Menten equation:

$$v = \frac{Vs}{K_m + s}$$

where v is the velocity of reaction, s is the substrate concentration, V is the maximum velocity, and K_m is the Michaelis constant. Maximum velocity values are often required for kinetic studies and they can be determined from substrate concentration studies even though the maximum velocity is not attained practically. The Michaelis constant K_m is another useful constant for kinetic work and for categorizing an enzyme. The substrate concentration/activity (or s/v) plot is not very satisfactory for the calculation of V and K_m values. However, several other plots, which are based on the transposition of the Michaelis–Menten equation, can be used satisfactorily (see Table IV).

TABLE IV

Transformations of the Michaelis–Menten equation and corresponding plots for the determination of the Michaelis constant, K_m, and maximum velocity V

Equation	Plot	Determination of K_m and V values
$v = \dfrac{Vs}{K_m + s}$ Michaelis–Menten equation	v against s	An approximate value for V can be obtained by extrapolating from the horizontal part of curve. K_m corresponds to the substrate concentration at half maximum velocity (see Fig. 2)
$\dfrac{1}{v} = \dfrac{1}{s}\dfrac{K_m}{V} + \dfrac{1}{V}$	$\dfrac{1}{v}$ against $\dfrac{1}{s}$	This gives a straight line of slope $\dfrac{K_m}{V}$. $\dfrac{1}{V}$ is obtained by extrapolation to the $\dfrac{1}{v}$ axis. If one line is continued to the abscissa a value for $-\dfrac{1}{K_m}$ corresponding to $-\dfrac{1}{s}$ is obtained
$\dfrac{s}{v} = \dfrac{1}{v}s + \dfrac{K_m}{V}$	$\dfrac{s}{v}$ against s	This gives a straight line of slope $\dfrac{1}{v}$. After extrapolation the ordinate intercept gives a value for $\dfrac{K_m}{V}$ whilst the abscissa intercept gives a value for K_m
$v = V - \dfrac{v}{s}K_m$	v against $\dfrac{v}{s}$	K_m corresponds to the slope, which is negative, and V is obtained by extrapolation to the ordinate

Because of the relative low solubility of salicin in water (36 g/l at 15°C) it is advisable to prepare buffer–substrate solutions by dissolving salicin directly in the buffer solution. In this way reaction mixtures with a sufficiently high substrate concentration can be obtained.

PROCEDURE

Prepare a stock solution of buffer–substrate (substrate $= 0.1$ M) by dissolving 0·572 g salicin in 20 ml 0·2 M acetate buffer at pH 4·8. By suitable dilution with the acetate buffer, obtain a series of solutions at least 5 ml in volume and of the following substrate concentrations: 0·75 M, 0·05 M, 0·025 M, 0·01 M, 0·0075 M, 0·005 M, 0·0025 M, and 0·001 M. Place 4 ml of each of the buffer–substrate solutions in a series of labelled reaction tubes, to equilibrate in a constant temperature bath at 25°C. Duplicate the tube with buffer-solution at 0·01 M concentration. After allowing the enzyme solution to acquire the bath temperature, add 1 ml to each of the reaction vessels leaving a 2-min interval between each addition. Immediately withdraw a 1 ml reaction mixture sample and add it to 2 ml amino antipyrine solution and leave for colour production and measurement as described in the previous experiment. It is very useful to have some idea of the reaction rate before deciding the period of incubation. For this remove a test sample from one of the duplicate reactions, with the initial buffer-substrate concentration of 0·01 M, after 50 min. If the absorptiometer extinction value is in the order of 0·2–0·3, then the incubation period should extend for 60 min. If the value is much lower, then the incubation time must be increased.

Check the pH of the reaction mixtures during the course of the reaction.

Using the difference between the extinction values at zero time and after t min incubation as a measure of enzyme activity, plot the various curves indicated in Table IV and obtain values for K_m and V. Note the variation in the values for K_m and V and consider carefully which method gives the most reliable values.

FURTHER INVESTIGATIONS

For critical kinetic studies the maximum velocity, V, values are generally required. More precise pH–activity curves and temperature-velocity curves can be determined by obtaining values for V at each pH or temperature respectively. This requires measuring the effect of pH, or temperature, when using a series of reactions at different substrate concentration. Such investigations will, of course, require the use of about sixty reaction vessels.

EXPERIMENT 3. THE EFFECT OF TEMPERATURE ON ENZYME ACTIVITY

MATERIALS

0·1 M Acetate buffer at pH 4·8.

0·05 M Salicin (1·43 g in 100 ml water).

Enzyme solution: 2 mg per ml of a freeze-dried preparation of slug digestive gland.

0·2% Potassium ferricyanide.

4-Amino antipyrine solution (for preparation, see p. 77).

PRINCIPLE

Like other chemical reactions the velocity of enzyme controlled reactions is influenced by temperature. In the simplest terms a rise in temperature

E

increases the energy for promoting a chemical reaction and so the reaction rate increases with temperature. However, unlike most non-enzyme chemical reactions, enzyme controlled reactions increase with temperature over a very limited temperature range only. This range, sometimes referred to as the "biokinetic range", extends approximately from 0 to 45°C. Above 40°C, and lower for many enzymes found in poikilotherms, enzyme reactions come under the influence of another factor, that of protein denaturation, a process which inactivates enzymes. Heat denaturation is not a sudden phenomenon acting at a particular temperature. Its effect is gradual and is a function of both temperature and time. For example, an enzyme kept at 60°C for a few minutes might be inactivated as much as if it were kept at 45°C for several hours. Consequently when designing temperature effect experiments it is very desirable to limit the period of incubation as much as possible.

The effect of temperature can be expressed in terms of the temperature coefficient Q_{10} which can readily be calculated from a temperature/log activity plot, Q_{10} = antilog (slope × 10). The apparent activation energy constant, E_A, a useful constant in kinetic studies, can also be obtained from temperature experiments. The Arrhenius equation states that

$$\frac{\mathrm{d}\ln v}{\mathrm{d}T} = \frac{E_A}{RT^2}$$

where v is the reaction velocity (measured as extinction values), T is the temperature in °K, R is the gas constant 1·98 cal/mole, and E_A is the activation energy. On integration the equation becomes:

$$\ln v = \frac{E_A}{RT} + C$$

or

$$\log v = -\frac{1}{T}\frac{E_A}{2\cdot303R} + C$$

The plot of log v against $1/T$°K yields a straight line of negative slope from which E_A can be easily calculated.

$$E_A = -\text{slope} \times (2\cdot303R)$$
$$= -\text{slope} \times 4\cdot566.$$

PROCEDURE

Set up the following reaction mixtures in constant temperature baths at 10°, 15°, 20°, 25°, 30°, 40°, 50° and 60°C after allowing the solutions to attain the same temperature as the bath before mixing.

	ml
0·1 M Acetate buffer at pH 4·8	2
0·05 M Salicin	1
Enzyme solution	1

Remove 1 ml samples immediately after mixing and add to 2 ml antipyrine solution. Remove a second sample after a suitable incubation period, e.g. 45 min. Check the rate of the reaction by carrying out a duplicate run at 30°C and noting the colour intensity of a treated sample after 30 min incubation (see expt 1).

Use the difference between the extinction values at zero time and after t min incubation as a measure of enzyme activity. Plot a log v/temperature curve to determine Q_{10} and a log v versus $1/T°K$ curve to find E_A, the apparent activation energy constant. Table V shows a record of the results from a typical experiment and in Fig. 3 the plots for Q_{10} and E_A estimation are drawn.

TABLE V

Data from a typical experiment for measuring the effect of temperature on enzyme activity

Temperature °C	$1/T°K$	pH at 30 min	Absorptiometer extinction values (a) Zero time	Absorptiometer extinction values (b) 50 min	Reaction velocity (b–a)	Log reaction velocity
10	$3·55 \times 10^{-3}$	4·75	0·031	0·068	0·037	$\bar{2}·5682$
15	$3·47 \times 10^{-3}$	4·75	0·030	0·089	0·059	$\bar{2}·7709$
21	$3·41 \times 10^{-3}$	4·75	0·034	0·142	0·108	$\bar{1}·0334$
25	$3·36 \times 10^{-3}$	4·75	0·029	0·186	0·157	$\bar{1}·1959$
31	$3·29 \times 10^{-3}$	4·75	0·029	0·287	0·258	$\bar{1}·4116$
40	$3·20 \times 10^{-3}$	4·75	0·032	0·496	0·464	$\bar{1}·6665$
50	$3·10 \times 10^{-3}$	4·75	0·031	0·103	0·072	$\bar{2}·8373$

		ml
Reaction mixture	0·1 M Phosphate buffer at pH 4·8	2
	0·1 M Salicin	1
	Enzyme extract 2 mg/ml *Arion* digestive gland freeze-dried preparation	1

Calculation of the temperature coefficient Q_{10} and E_A is as follows. From the log velocity versus temperature plot in Fig. 3 the slope was found to be 0·040,

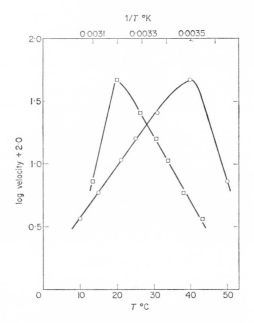

Fig. 3. Log velocity versus temperature plot (○) and log velocity versus $1/T°K$ plot (□) for salicin hydrolysis by slug (*Arion ater*) digestive gland extract. The pH was 4·8 and the period of incubation 50 min. Note the method of plotting the ordinate values to eliminate negative logarithm values. This does not, of course, alter the values obtained for the slopes.

and so the Q_{10} = antilog (slope × 10) was 2·51. From the log velocity versus $1/T°K$ plot the slope was found to be $-3·3 \times 10^3$ and since $E_A = -$slope × 4·566, its value was 15,000 cal/mole.

BIBLIOGRAPHY

Dixon, M. and Webb, E. C. (1964). "Enzymes," 2nd ed. Longmans, Green, London.
Gutfreund, H. (1965). "An Introduction to the Study of Enzymes." Blackwells, Oxford.

5 | A. Snake Venom Peptidase Activities
B. Hydrolyses of Arginine Esters by Snake Venoms

ANTHONY T. TU*

Department of Chemistry and Interdepartmental Curriculum in Toxicology, Utah State University, Logan, Utah, U.S.A.

A. Snake Venom Peptidase Activities

MATERIALS AND APPARATUS

SNAKE VENOMS

A wide variety of snake venoms are commercially available and their selection for this experiment can be decided by the instructor after consulting the sample results in Table I. The names and addresses of companies and available venoms are listed here.

Miami Serpentarium Laboratories, Miami, Florida, 33156, U.S.A.

Boulengerina annulata	*Bitis gabonica*	*Agkistrodon piscivorus*
Bungarus caeruleus	*rhinoceros*	*piscivorus*
Bungarus fasciatus	*Bitis nasicornis*	*Agkistrodon piscivorus*
Bungarus multicinctus	*Causus rhombeatus*	*leukostoma*
Dendraspis angusticeps	*Cerastes cerastes*	*Bothrops atrox*
Dendraspis jamesonii	*(cornutus)*	*Crotalus adamanteus*
Dendraspis polylepis	*Cerastes vipera*	*Crotalus atrox*
Dendraspis viridis	*(cerastes)*	*Crotalus basiliscus*
Hemachatus haemacha-	*Echis carinatus,*	*Crotalus durissus terrificus*
tus	*Vipera ammodytes*	*Crotalus durissus*
Micrurus fulvius	*Vipera aspis*	*totonacus*
Naja haje	*Vipera russellii*	*Crotalus horridus*
Naja melanoleuca	*Dispholidus typus*	*Crotalus horridus*
Naja naja	*Agkistrodon acutus*	*atricaudatus*
Naja naja atra	*Agkistrodon bilineatus*	*Crotalus viridis viridis*
Naja nigricollis	*Agkistrodon contortrix*	*Crotalus viridis oreganus*
Naja nivea (flava)	*contortrix*	*Sistrurus miliarius*
Naja hannah	*Agkistrodon contortrix*	*barbouri*
Pseudechis collettii	*mokasen*	*Trimeresurus flavoviridis*
Bitis arietans	*Agkistrodon halys*	*Trimeresurus okinavensis*
Bitis gabonica	*blomhoffii*	*Trimeresurus popeorum*

* Present address: Department of Biochemistry, Colorado State University, Fort Collins, Colorado, U.S.A.

Ross Allen's Reptile Institute, Inc., Silver Springs, Florida, 32688, U.S.A.

Agkistrodon acutus
Agkistrodon contortrix
Agkistrodon halys
Agkistrodon piscivorus
   piscivorus
Bothrops alternata
Bothrops atrox
Bothrops jararaca
Bungarus caeruleus
Crotalus adamateus
Crotalus atrox

Crotalus basiliscus
Crotalus durissus
   durissus
Crotalus durissus
   terrificus
Crotalus durissus
   totonacus
Crotalus horridus
   atricaudatus
Crotalus viridis viridis
Echis carinatus

Naja naja
Naja naja atra
Naja nivea
Trimeresurus elegans
Trimeresurus flavoviridis
Naja hannah
Vipera ammodytes
Vipera russellii
Sistrurus miliarius
   barbouri

Sigma Chemical Company, 3500 Dekalb Street, St. Louis, Mo., 63118, U.S.A.

Acanthophis antarcticus
Agkistrodon contortrix
   contortrix
Agkistrodon contortrix
   laticinctux
Agkistrodon contortrix
   mokasen
Agkistrodon halys
Agkistrodon piscivorus
   piscivorus
Austrelaps superba
Bothrops jararaca
Crotalus adamanteus
Crotalus atrox

Crotalus terrificus
   terrificus
Dendroaspis angusti-
   ceps
Dendroaspis polylepis
Naja naja
Notechis ater
   humphreysi
Notechis ater niger
Notechis ater serventyi
Notechis scutatus
Naja hannah
Oxyuranus scutellatus
   canni

Oxyuranus scutellatus
   scutellatus
Pseudechis australlis
Pseudechis colletti
   guttatus
Pseudechis papuanus
Pseudechis porphyriacus
Pseudonaja textillis
   textillis
Trimeresurus flavoviridis
Trimeresurus okinavenisis
Tropidechis carinatus
Vipera ammodytes
Vipera russelli

APPARATUS

Water bath maintaining temperature at 37°C.
Small test tubes, 1 cm $\times$ 7$\frac{1}{2}$ cm.
Capillary tubes or micropipette.
Paper chromatographic equipment, descending method preferred.
Filter paper, Whatman No. 1.
Sprayer.
Peptides.
n-Butyl alcohol.
Glacial acetic acid.
Ninhydrin.
Acetone.
Phenol.

n-Butyl alcohol-acetic acid-water (4:1:5 v/v). The solution is prepared by mixing 400 ml of n-butyl alcohol (n-butanol), 100 ml of glacial acetic acid and 500 ml of distilled water. The solution is mixed thoroughly by shaking. Stand the solution in a separatory funnel until two clear layers are formed. Separate the two layers, the lower layer is the aqueous solution and the upper layer is the butanol solution.

Phenol-water (4:1 v/v). Liquefy phenol by placing jar of phenol crystals in warm water and mix with 100 ml of water.

Ninhydrin solution. Weigh 200 mg ninhydrin and dissolve in 100 ml of acetone to make 0·2% solution.

PRINCIPLE

Poisonous snakes occur in many parts of the world. The venom is not a single substance common to all poisonous snakes but a complex mixture in which the proportions of the different compounds and their nature varies from species to species. The symptoms observed after a snake bite are caused by the combined action of all the toxic principles contained in the venom. It has been reported that antivenom for Formosan cobra is ineffective for Thailand cobra. Another example is that the antisera prepared from northern Brazilian rattlesnake venom is ineffective for southern Brazilian snakes. This is striking evidence that venom properties are different from species to species. Recent investigations by a number of workers indicate that chemical properties of venoms have a correlation to the taxonomy and phylogenesis of poisonous snakes. It is important to know the position of venomous snakes in the taxonomic classification of reptiles before proceeding with chemical investigation.

The "class" Reptilia is divided into four "orders": (1) Rhynchocephalia, with a single representative, the Tuatera of New Zealand, which is the sole remnant of an order long extinct; (2) Loricata, composed of the crocodiles, caimans, alligators, and gavials; (3) Chelonia, consisting of turtles, terrapins and tortoises, and (4) Squamata, including the lizards and snakes. An "order" is in turn divided into "families". There are four different families among the poisonous snakes, namely Elapidae, Viperidae, Crotalidae and Hydrophiidae. The families are composed of "genera". The respective genera contain the "species", and "subspecies" denote the variations occurring among the species. An example is *Agkistrodon contortrix mokasen*, the taxonomic name of the copperhead snake: *Agkistrodon* is the generic name, *contortrix* denotes the species, and *mokasen* the subspecies.

It is known that various snake venoms contain a number of peptidases. Using the paper chromatographic technique, it is possible to identify peptides from their constituent amino acids by selecting suitable solvents. Therefore, actions and specificities of snake venom peptidases can be detected by this method. Recently Tu *et al.* (1965, 1967) reported that specificities of snake venom peptidases have a correlation to the genetic identity of poisonous snakes.

EXPERIMENTAL

For each experiment, 5 mg of peptide is mixed with 2 mg of venom in 0·5 ml of water. If peptide is not soluble in water, add a minimum amount of HCl until it is dissolved. The mixture is incubated at 37°C for 24 h. Aliquots are removed with a capillary tube and spotted on filter paper, Whatman No. 1. Suitable standard amino acids and peptides are also spotted on the same paper for comparison; for instance, for the study of glycylleucyltyrosine, such controls as glycylleucine, leucyltyrosine, glycine, leucine, tyrosine, and the original peptide without venom should be spotted on the same paper. Do not make the spot larger than 7 mm in diameter. The aqueous solution in beaker is placed at the bottom of the jar. The spotted paper is placed in the chromatographic chamber and equilibrated with the vapor of the aqueous solution for at least half an hour. Butanol solution is poured gently into the trough and the jar is covered. In order to assure tight sealing, the cover is greased. After the solvent moves about 40 cm, the solvent front is marked with pencil and dried. For the experiments of lysylglycine, serylglycine, glycylglycine, tripeptides and tetraglycine, phenol-water will be used for chromatography. The chromatogram is sprayed with ninhydrin uniformly and heated in the oven for 1 min at 80°C.

RESULTS

Peptidase activities of snake venoms are illustrated in Fig. 1 as an example using a dipeptide, ala-val, and *Notechis ater niger* (Peninsula tiger) venom of Australian origin. The snake venom itself does not show any spot after spraying with ninhydrin. Ala-val shows only one spot. However, after incubating with the peptide and venom of *Notechis ater niger*, two new spots appear on the chromatogram. The R_F values of these spots exactly correspond to those of alanine and valine. Apparently, the venom splits alanylvaline linkage of ala-val and produces the free amino acids. The spot corresponding to ala-val is the unreacted original peptide. In contrast to *Notechis ater niger* venom, *Naja hannah* (King cobra) venom of Indian origin does not split this linkage. The spot produced on the chromatogram is identical to the original peptide ala-val. Published results of snake venom peptidase activies (Tu *et al.*, 1965) are used as an example and shown in Tables I–III.

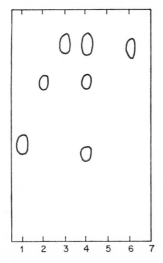

FIG. 1. Hydrolysis of ala-val by snake venoms. (1) Valine, (2) alanine, (3) ala-val, (4) ala-val *N. a. niger* venom, (5) *N. a. niger* venom only, (6) ala-val *N. hannah* venom, (7) *N. hannah* venom only.

TROUBLE-SHOOTING

Ninhydrin reaction is more sensitive for amino acids than peptides and it may require more sample of peptides for coloration. It is advisable to duplicate or triplicate the chromatograms and spot different amounts of samples on each paper. Do not write anything on filter paper other than with lead pencil. The developing solvent will smear colored pencil, ink, or ball pen markings. Do not touch chromatograms with fingers as fingerprints will show up on spraying with ninhydrin.

CONCLUSIONS

Peptidases present in snake venoms are very specific. For instance, many snake venoms split leucylglycine linkage of leu-gly but most of them do not hydrolyze the leucylglycine linkage of leu-gly-phe. Snake venoms do not contain aminopeptidase and carboxypeptidase as amino- and carboxyl terminal amino acids of tripeptides are not always hydrolyzed.

It may be seen from Tables I–III that the closer the species, the greater are the similarities in the patterns of peptidase activities. For instance, peptidase specificities of *Naja naja samarensis*, *N. haje* and *N. melanoleuca* venoms are exactly identical. *Oxyuranus scutellatus scutellatus* and *O. s. canni* venoms also have the same specificities. The venoms of snakes of North American origin such as *Agkistrodon contortrix mokasen*, *A. c. contortrix*, *A. c. laticinctus* and

TABLE I

Peptidase activity of Elapidae venoms

Peptides	Naja naja atra	Naja naja samerensis	Naja haje	Naja melanoleuca	Oxyuranus scutellatus scutellatus	Oxyuranus scutellatus canni	Dendraspis angusticeps
Lys-gly	−	−	−	−	−	−	−
Phe-gly	−	+	+	+	+	+	+
Tyr-gly	−	−	−	−	−	−	−
Leu-gly	−	+	+	+	+	+	+
Leu↓gly-phe	−	−	−	−	−	−	−
Leu↓gly↓gly	−	+1	+1	+1	+1, +2	+1, +2	+1, +2
Gly-pro	−	−	−	−	−	−	−
Gly-gly	−	−	−	−	−	−	−
Gly-leu	−	+	+	+	+	+	+
Gly-tyr	−	+	+	+	−	−	−
Gly↓leu↓tyr	+1	−	−	−	+1, +2	+1, +2	+1, +2
Gly-gly-gly-gly	−	−	−	−	−	−	−
Ser-gly	−	−	−	−	+	+	+
Ala-phe	−	−	−	−	+	+	+
Ala↓gly↓gly	+1	+1	+1	+1	+1, +2	+1, +2	+1

↓ Peptide linkage split; + positive reaction; − no reaction.

TABLE II

Peptidase activity of Viperidae venoms

Peptides	Vipera russellii formosensis	Vipera ammodytes	Bitis arietans
Lys-gly	−	−	−
Phe-gly	+	+	+
Tyr-gly	−	−	+
Leu-gly	+	+	+
Leu-gly-phe	−	−	−
Leu-gly-gly	−	−	−
Gly-pro	−	−	−
Gly-gly	−	−	−
Gly-leu	−	+	+
Gly-tyr	−	−	+
Gly↓leu↓tyr	−	−	+
Gly-gly-gly-gly	−	−	−
Ser-gly	−	−	−
Ala-phe	−	−	−
Ala↓gly-gly	−	+	+

↓ Peptide linkage split; + positive reaction; − no reaction.

A. c. piscivorus are very similar and differ only in one or two peptides. Venoms of North American rattlesnakes such as *Crotalus adamanteus, C. atrox,* and *C. viridis oreganus* are similar to each other but more different from the *Agkistrodon* series.

FURTHER IDEAS

Modern biochemistry indicates that genetic information is coded into the base sequence in DNA, and DNA transfers the information to messenger RNA. Messenger RNA directs the sequence of the amino acids in protein. Since all enzymes are protein, enzymes are also synthesized by the directive action of DNA. Therefore, enzyme distribution patterns are also the manifestation of genetic identity. It is therefore reasonable that the closer the genetic identity, the more similar are the enzyme distribution patterns.

In order to detect the relationship of peptidase to venomous snake classification, a large number of peptides and snake venoms must be used. Examples from published results are reproduced in Tables I–III, where it can be seen that the closer the species of snakes, the more similar are the specificities of the peptidase activities of the venoms.

There are twenty common amino acids constituting peptides and proteins. Therefore, there are large numbers of di- and tripeptides which can be formed

TABLE III

Peptidase activity of Crotalidae venoms

Peptides	*Agkistrodon acutus*	*Agkistrodon contortrix mokasen*	*Agkistrodon contortrix contortrix*	*Agkistrodon contortrix laticinctus*	*Agkistrodon piscivorus piscivorus*	*Crotalus adamanteus*	*Crotalus atrox*	*Crotalus viridis oreganus*	*Trimeresurus mucrosquamatus*	*Trimeresurus okinavensis*	*Bothrops jararaca*
Lys-gly	−	−	−	−	−	−	−	−	−	−	−
Phe-gly	−	+	+	+	+	+	+	+	+	+	+
Tyr-gly	−	+	+	+	+	+	+	−	−	+	+
Leu-gly	−	+	+	+	+	−	+	+	+	+	+
Leu-gly-phe	−	−	+	−	−	−	−	−	−	−	−
Leu-↓gly-gly	−	+	−	−	−	−	−	+	+	−	−
Gly-pro	−	−	−	−	−	−	−	−	−	−	−
Gly-gly	−	+	+	+	+	−	−	−	−	−	−
Gly-leu	−	+	+	+	+	−	−	−	−	−	−
Gly-tyr	−	−	−	−	−	−	−	+	+	−	+
Gly-↓leu-↓tyr	+1, +2	+1, +2	+1, +2	+1	+1, +2	+1, +2	+1	−	−	+1	+2
Gly-gly-gly-gly	+1, +2	+1, +2	+1, +2	−	+1, +2	+1, +2	−	−	−	−	−
Ser-gly	−	−	−	−	−	−	−	−	−	−	−
Ala-phe	−	−	−	−	−	−	−	−	−	−	+
Ala-↓gly-gly	−	+	+	+	+	+	−	+	+	−	−

↓ Peptide linkage split; + positive reaction; − no reaction.

by combination of these amino acids. However, due to the difficulty in the syntheses of certain peptides, the number of commercially available peptides is relatively limited. As yet, the specificity of snake venom peptidases has been studied very little.

CLEANING UP

Do not contact venoms with skin or fingers having abrasions or cuts. These venoms are extremely poisonous in the blood-stream. In case of skin contact with venoms wash off thoroughly with running water; since venoms are quite soluble in water, they will be washed out easily.

If the same venom solution is to be used for future experiments, it should be kept frozen. Frozen venoms retain toxicity and enzyme activity for a considerable length of time.

All glassware should be washed first with detergent and then with water.

BIBLIOGRAPHY

Buckley, E. E. and Porges, N. (1956). Venoms. *Publs Am. Ass. Advmt. Sci.*, No. 44. [Chemical, physiological, and toxicological studies of snake venoms are discussed by a number of experts.]

Ditmars, R. L. (1951). "Snakes of the World." Macmillan Co., New York. [This is a good general reference book on snakes. The book describes habits, distribution, classification, harmless snakes, and poisonous snakes. No description on chemical properties of venom is made in this book.]

Keegan, H. L. and Macfarlane, W. V. (1963). "Venomous and Poisonous Animals and Noxious Plants of the Pacific Region." Macmillan Co., New York. [Venomous snakes of the Pacific area are well described and the properties of venoms are also discussed by several investigators.]

Russell, F. E. and Scharffenberg, R. S. (1964). "Bibliography of Snake Venoms and Venomous Snakes." Pergamon Press, Oxford. [A list of 9173 publications on snake venoms is collected in this book. It is a useful book in which to find specific information on snake venoms.]

Tu, A. T., Chua, A. and James, G. P. (1965). Peptidase activities of snake venoms. *Comp. Biochem. Physiol.*, 523, **15**. [Peptidase activities of twenty-one snake venoms were investigated using fifteen different dipeptides, tripeptides, and tetrapeptides.]

Tu, A. T., Toom, P. M. and Murdock, D. S. (1967). Chemical differences in the venoms of genetically different snakes. "Animal Toxins", Pergamon Press, Oxford, [Peptidases and proteolytic enzyme activities of 49 snake venoms are described.]

B.   Hydrolyses of Arginine Esters by Snake Venoms

MATERIALS AND APPARATUS

SNAKE VENOMS

See the list of commercially available snake venoms and the addresses of the companies supplying them on pp. 85–86. For this experiment, it is advisable to choose one each from venoms of Crotalidae, Viperidae and Elapidae.

MATERIALS

Sodium phosphate monosodium and disodium salts.
Hydrochloric acid.
Ultraviolet spectrophotometer.
Wax paper.
N-Benzoyl-L-arginine ethyl ester (BAEE).
p-Toluenesulfonyl-L-arginine methyl ester (TAME).

Preweighed tubes of TAME and BAEE are commercially available and can be purchased from Worthington Biochemical Corporation, Freehold, New Jersey, U.S.A. By dissolving in a specified amount of water, the tubes will give the desired concentrations of substrates and buffer. The commercial name for preweighed TAME is Determatube TAME and BAEE is Determatube TRY.

REAGENTS

Phosphate buffer, pH 8, 0·05 M. Weigh 6·248 g sodium phosphate dibasic anhydrous (Na_2HPO_4) and 0·828 g sodium phosphate monobasic ($NaH_2PO_4.H_2O$), dissolve in water and dilute to 1 liter.

TAME, 0·87 mM. Weigh 32·9 mg TAME and dissolve with 0·05 M phosphate buffer at pH 8 to 100 ml using volumetric flask.

HCl, 0·001 M. Take 8·3 ml of conc. HCl (37–38%) and dilute to 100 ml. Dilute 1 ml of this solution to 1 liter.

Venom solution. Make 1 mg/ml using 0·001 M HCl for the experiment of TAME. It is advisable to weigh 3 mg in order to make an accurate weighing. For the experiment of BAEE, 1 mg/ml venom solution is made using distilled water.

BAEE, 0·25 mM. Dissolve 42·9 mg BAEE hydrochloride in 0·067 M phosphate buffer at pH 7·0 and make volume to 500 ml using volumetric flask.

Phosphate buffer, 0·067 M. Dissolve 5·244 g $NaH_2PO_4.H_2O$ and 4·118 g Na_2HPO_4 and make volume to 1 liter.

IDEA AND PRINCIPLE

Recently, comparative studies of the chemical structure in different living materials have become important.

Herpetologists classify poisonous snakes into four families, namely Crotalidae, Viperidae, Elapidae and Hydrophiidae. The classification is based on morphology of snakes. Recently, a number of workers found that certain enzymes in snake venoms are related to the taxonomy of snakes. Since enzyme activity is relatively easier to determine than the chemical structures, it is a useful general approach in comparative studies of genetically different materials.

It is known that TAME is a specific substrate for thrombin and trypsin. This substrate is not hydrolyzed by chymotrypsin. BAEE is also considered as a specific substrate for trypsin. It is of interest that the hydrolyses of these two substrates by venoms are quite "family" specific.

EXPERIMENTAL

TAME

An aliquot of 2·9 ml is transferred to a test cuvette and 3 ml to a control cuvette. At zero time, 0·1 ml of venom solution in 0·001 HCl is introduced and mixed by inverting with wax paper over the cuvette top. The absorbance increase at 247 mμ is recorded at 30 sec intervals. A plot of absorbance versus time is made and absorbance change per minute is obtained from the straight line portion of the slope. The venom enzyme activity is calculated from the equation

$$\text{units/mg} = \frac{(\text{absorbance change/min}) \times 1\,000}{\text{mg venom used}}$$

One unit of enzyme activity causes an absorbance increase of 0·001 per min.

If Determatube TAME is used, dissolve the content in 6·0 ml of distilled water. An aliquot of 2·9 ml is transferred to a test cuvette and the remainder to a control cuvette. The same procedure can be followed as described above.

BAEE

An aliquot of 2·9 ml of BAEE solution is transferred to a test cuvette and 3·0 ml to a control cuvette. At zero time, 0·1 ml of venom solution is introduced and mixed by inverting. The absorbance increase is recorded at 30 sec intervals for 5 min at 254 mμ. Absorbance is plotted against time. Absorbance change per minute is calculated from the straight part of the line. A unit of enzyme activity causes an absorbance increase of 0·001 per min. Therefore, the same equation given for TAME is used for calculation of venom enzyme activity.

RESULTS

Figure 2 shows that TAME and BAEE are hydrolyzed by the venom of *Crotalus admanteus* (Eastern diamondback). To calculate the venom enzyme activity, the absorbance change per minute must be found first from the

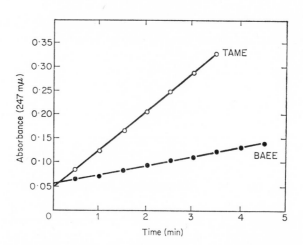

Fig. 2. Hydrolysis of TAME and BAEE by venom of *Crotalus admanteus*.

straight portion of the curve. At 3·5 min, the absorbance is 0·330 units and 0·088 at 0·5 min for TAME.

Therefore, the absorbance difference within 3 min interval is 0·330–0·088 = 0·242 units. The absorbance change per minute is therefore 0·242/3 = 0·0806. The amount of venom used for this experiment is 0·1 mg. By substituting these numbers in the equation given before:

$$\text{units/mg} = \frac{0·0806 \times 1\,000}{0·1} = 806$$

The calculation can be made in the same way for BAEE. From the curve, absorbance change per minute is 0·0393 and the amount of venom is also 0·1 mg; therefore, the activity of venom proteolytic enzyme using BAEE is

$$\text{units/mg} = \frac{0·0393 \times 1\,000}{0·1} = 393$$

The distribution of proteolytic enzyme activity in various snake venoms using TAME and BAEE is quoted from published results and given in Table IV as an example.

TROUBLE-SHOOTING

In case the hydrolyses are too fast or too slow, the concentrations of venom solution should be adjusted so that a straight line relationship for absorbance increase against time can be obtained for at least 3 min. The experiment should be performed at 25°C or in the vicinity of this temperature. Substrate solutions should be prepared daily.

TABLE IV

Distribution of proteolytic enzyme activity in snake venoms using
TAME and BAEE as substrates

| | Enzyme activity | |
Snake venoms	TAME	BAEE
Crotalidae		
Agkistrodon acutus	292	104
halys	100	148
contortrix contortrix	700	1 730
laticinctus	433	872
mokasen	457	1 060
piscivorus leukostoma	208	475
Bothrops jararaca	187	107
Crotalus atrox (U.S.A.)	280	481
adamanteus	806	393
terificus terificus	288	270
viridis oreganus	557	709
Trimeresurus mucrosquamatus	2 000	729
okinavenisis	725	1 110
Viperidae		
Bitis arietans	80	280
Vipera russellii formosensis	87	161
ammodytes	71	242
Elapidae		
Acanthophis antarcticus	0	0
Bungarus multicinctus	0	0
Dendroaspis angusticeps	0	0
Denisonia superba	0	0
Naja naja	0	0
naja atra	0	0
samarensis	0	0
suamensis	0	0
flava	0	0
haje	0	0
melanoleuca	0	0
nigricollis	0	0
Notechis ater niger	0	0
serventyi	0	0
scutellatus scutellatus	0	0
Oxyuranus scutellatus canni	0	0
scutellatus	0	0
Hydrophiidae		
Laticauda colubrina	0	0

Enzyme activity was calculated using the equation:

$$\text{units/mg} = \frac{(\text{absorbance change/min}) \times 1\ 000}{\text{mg venom used}}$$

Conclusions

It has been considered that TAME and BAEE are specific substrates for trypsin with the exception that thrombin also hydrolyzes TAME. Apparently, snake venoms contain a non-trypsin enzyme which is also able to hydrolyze these substrates.

None of the Elapidae and Hydrophiidae venoms hydrolyzed these two substrates, and their inability to do so seems to be characteristic. It is of interest to note that, regardless of geographical origin, this rule is observed. For instance, *Agkistrodon acutus* and *Trimeresurus mucrosquamatus* originate from Formosa, *T. okinavenisis* from Okinawa, *Bothrops jararaca*, *Crotalus terificus terificus* and *Bothrops atrox* from South America, *Agkistrodon halys* from Japan and Central Asia, while *Crotalus viridis oreganus*, *C. atrox*, *C. adamanteus*, *Agkistrodon contortrix mokasen*, *A. c. laticinctus* and *A. piscivorus leukostoma* come from North America, but they all hydrolyzed TAME and BAEE.

Of the Viperidae venoms, *Vipera russellii formosensis* of Formosan origin, *Vipera ammodytes* of European origin and *Bitis arietans* of African origin showed enzyme activity. Elapidae venoms such as *Naja naja atra* from Formosa, *N. n. samarensis* from the Philippines, *N. haje* from North Africa, *N. melanoleuca* from East Africa, *Bungarus multicinctus* from Formosa, *Dendraospis angusticeps* from Africa, *Oxyuranus scutellatus scutellatus* from Northern Australia, *O. s. canni* from southern New Guinea, *Naja naja* from India, *Acanthophis antarcticus*, *Denisonia superba*, *Notechis ater niger*, *N. a. serventyi*, and *N. scutatus scutatus* of Australian origin did not hydrolyze these substrates.

Further Ideas

All Crotalidae and Viperidae venoms hydrolyze TAME and BAEE. In this respect, they are similar to pancreatic trypsin. However, proteolytic activities of venoms are not inhibited by ovomucoid and soybean trypsin inhibitors. When pancreatic trypsin is used in the presence of ovomucoid or soybean trypsin inhibitors, the hydrolyses of TAME and BAEE are inhibited completely. This suggests that the proteolytic enzyme present in Crotalidae and Viperidae is similar to trypsin but not identical. Other evidence is that none of the venoms hydrolyze the peptides containing lysine.

Although thrombin, a blood coagulation enzyme, hydrolyzes TAME, Crotalidae and Viperidae venoms do not contain this enzyme. The venoms also hydrolyze BAEE which is specific substrate for trypsin but not for thrombin. Moreover, many Crotalidae and Viperidae venoms do not convert fibrinogen to fibrin.

Cleaning Up

See p. 93.

BIBLIOGRAPHY

Hummel, B. C. W. (1959). A modified spectrophotometric determination of chymo-trypsin, trypsin, and thrombin. *Can. J. Biochem. Physiol.*, **37**, 1393. [Principles involved in the determination of trypsin using TAME are described.]

Jimenez-Porras, J. M. (1965). Venom proteins of the fer-de-lance, *Bothrops atrox*, from Costa Rica. *Toxicon* **2**, 155. Intraspecific variations in composition of venom of the Jumping viper, *Bothrops nummifera*. *Toxicon*, **2**, 187. [Starch gel electrophoresis was used to detect the difference in venom proteins among different subspecies of Central American snakes.]

Schwert, G. W. and Takenaka, Y. A. (1955). A spectrophotometric determination of trypsin and chymotrypsin. *Biochim. biophys. Acta*, **26**, 570. [Principle involved in the determination of trypsin using BAEE is described.]

Tu, A. T., James, G. P. and Chua, A. (1965). Some biochemical evidence in support of the classification of venomous snakes. *Toxicon*, **3**, 5. [Hydrolyses of arginine esters by Crotalidae and Viperidae venoms are described.]

Tu, A. T., Chua, A and James, G. P. (1966). Proteolytic enzyme activities in a variety of snake venoms. *Toxicol. appl. Pharmac.*, **8**, 218. [Trypsin-like proper-ties of Crotalidae and Viperidae venoms are described.]

Tu, A. T Toom, P. M.. and Ganthavorm, S. (1967). Hemorrhagic and proteolytic activities of Thailand snake venoms. *Biochem. Pharmacol.*, **16**, 2125. [Proteolytic enzyme activities of six common Thailand snake venoms were investigated using TAME and BAEE.]

6 | A. Estimation of the Esterase Activity of Serum
| B. Starch-gel Electrophoresis of Mouse Serum

E. M. PANTELOURIS

Department of Biology, University of Strathclyde, Glasgow, Scotland

A. Estimation of the Esterase Activity of Serum

The procedure described below is based on a method developed by Ravin *et al.* (1951). These authors synthesized specific substrates for cholinesterases and measured colorimetrically the rate of hydrolysis of the substrates by enzymes in the serum. We are following the modified technique described by Bamford and Harris (1964), but we are extending it to other substrates and using Fast Garnet instead of Fast Red as the coupling dye.

Starch electrophoresis (see page 104) resolves the serum esterases into fractions. It is possible by suitable scanners to obtain from the starch gel a measure of the relative amounts of different fractions. Where, however, an estimate of the overall esterase activity in the serum is required, the spectrophotometric technique is preferable, and is also simpler.

PREPARATIONS REQUIRED

SUBSTRATE UNBUFFERED SOLUTION

Dissolve one of the substrates in the amounts listed below, in 25 ml of the solvent specified, and make up to 100 ml. The wavelengths in $m\mu$ given in parentheses are those at which optical density measurements will be made.

1-Naphthyl acetate	4 mg (ethanol)	($560\ m\mu$)
Naphthol-AS-acetate	6 mg (ethanol with trace of acetone)	($540\ m\mu$)
β-Naphthyl laurate or stearate	8 mg (ethanol with trace of acetone)	($530\ m\mu$)
6-Bromo-carbonaphthoxy choline iodide	16 mg (ethanol with trace of acetone)	($520\ m\mu$)
1-Naphthyl phosphate, sodium salt	8 mg (water)	($560\ m\mu$)

If it is found that the reaction proceeds too quickly, the substrate solution can, of course, be diluted further.

BUFFERS

(a) *Tris-citrate pH 7·4*

0·76 M (92·07 g/l) Tris (hydroxymethylaminomethane)	187 ml
0·05 M (10·5 g/l) Citric acid	820 ml

Mix, check pH and adjust it if necessary. Before use dilute so as to reduce the concentration of tris to 0·1 M.

(b) *Veronal acetate stock solution*

Sodium acetate (anhydrous)	10·20 g
Sodium diethylbarbiturate	29·42 g

Make up to 1 000 ml.

(c) *Veronal acetate—HCl pH 8·8*

Veronal acetate stock solution	100 ml
1 N HCl	1 ml

Make up to 500 ml

(d) *Veronal acetate—HCl pH 4·5–5·0*

Veronal acetate stock solution	100 ml
1 N HCl	22 ml

Make up to 500 ml.

SUBSTRATE BUFFERED SOLUTION

Substrate unbuffered solution	20 ml
Buffer (a) for esterases, or	
(b) for alkaline phosphatases, or	40 ml
(d) for acid phosphatases	

Make up to 100 ml with distilled water.
To the solution of phosphatases add traces of Mg^{++} and Mn^{++}.

COUPLING DYE

Dissolve 200 mg of Fast Garnet GBC (Gurr's) in 100 ml of distilled water. Filter before use.

TCA

80% Trichloracetic acid.

DILUTED SAMPLE

For esterases, dilute 0·1 ml of serum with 16 ml of the tris-citrate buffer pH 7·4 diluted to 0·05 M tris.

For phosphatases, dilute 0·1 ml of serum with 5 ml of distilled water.

MEASUREMENTS

Prepare the necessary test tubes. To avoid transfer of contents choose preferably tubes that will take about 20 ml and yet will fit in the centrifuges available. This volume is necessary when 6 ml cuvettes are going to be used for the spectrophotometric measurements. If microcuvettes are available, quantities (and size of test tubes) can be reduced accordingly.

1. Measure from a burette 5 ml of the buffered substrate solution into each tube.

2. Add 1 ml of the diluted sample. In control tubes add 1 ml of buffer without serum.

3. Incubate at 37°C for a constant period. The period to be preferred will be determined by test so as to give satisfactory readings in the spectrophotometer. With mouse serum, periods in the range 30–60 min should be adequate.

4. Remove tubes from incubator and add to each 1 ml of the coupling dye solution. Shake for 4 min.

5. Stop the reaction by adding 1 ml of TCA.

6. Extract the coupled dye; add 5 ml of ethyl acetate and centrifuge. The top layer is the ethyl acetate with the coupled dye.

7. Measure the optical density of an aliquot of the ethyl acetate layer. The wavelengths for each substrate are given above in parentheses.

NOTES

The control tubes provide a correction for any hydrolysis occurring irrespective of the presence of enzymes.

Organize your series of measurements so as to obtain an answer to specific questions—to compare individual sera, to study changes with age, to plot activity versus time, and so on.

Make sure that the number of samples you include in each experiment are not more than you can handle without affecting the accuracy of timing.

In experiments aiming at measuring the effect of inhibitors on enzymatic activity, study first the hazards involved and the precautions that are necessary. Dissolve the inhibitor in the water used for the buffered substrate solution. Calculate the amount of inhibitor so as to give, in the incubation mixture, the inhibitor concentration required, for example 10^{-3} M or 10^{-4} M, etc.

REFERENCES

Bamford, K. F. and Harris, H. (1964). *Ann. hum. Genet.*, **27**, 417–425.
Ravin, H. A., Tsou, Kwan-Chung and Seligman, A. M. (1951). *J. biol. Chem.*, **191**, 843–851.

B.   Starch-gel Electrophoresis of Mouse Serum

APPARATUS

The components of the apparatus for horizontal starch gel electrophoresis are shown in Fig. 1 and briefly described in the legend. The run must be made in a cool place.

MATERIALS AND SOLUTIONS REQUIRED

STARCH

The gel is prepared from the hydrolysed starch for electrophoresis commercially available from Connaught Medical Laboratories (Toronto). (BDH also supply starch for electrophoresis.) This can also be produced in the laboratory by controlled hydrolysis of pure potato starch, with varying degrees of success and consistency from batch to batch.

BUFFERS

(a) *Borate buffer for the vessels*

Boric acid	18·6 g
Sodium hydroxide	2·0 g

Make up to 1 000 ml with distilled water.

(b) *Tris-citrate pH 7·6 buffer for the gel*

0·05 M Citric acid (10·51 g/l)		812·5 ml
0·76 M Tris	(92·07 g/l)	187·5 ml

Mix. Check the pH and if necessary adjust to 7·6.
Before use dilute 1 : 10.

(c) *Reaction buffer (phosphate pH 6·0)*

0·5 M KH_2PO_4	289 ml
0·5 M Na_2HPO_4	0·26 ml

Make up to 1 000 ml and check pH.

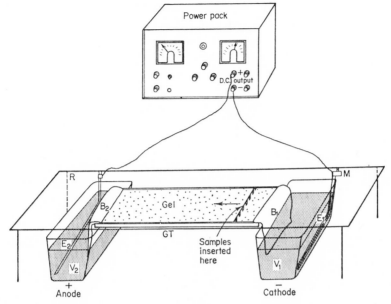

FIG. 1.

P, Power pack. Constant voltage preferred to constant current for reasons of safety. To yield up to 300 V and V 150 mA.

V_1, V_2, Two plastic vessels. Must be somewhat wider than the tray and a few inches deep. They are filled with the vessel buffer to exactly the same level (to avoid siphoning effects).

E_1, E_2, Electrodes. E_1, the cathode may be platinum or steel or silver. The electrodes are supported by a Perspex rod like the string on the bow of a violin, and are positioned horizontally in the vessels. E_2, is the anode, made of platinum.

B_1, B_2, "Bridges". These are pieces of lint (folded double) linking the buffer in the vessels to the gel (*G*). The bridges should not be near the electrodes, in fact a perforated Perspex partition may be interposed between the two, to avoid products of electrolysis finding their way into the starch.

GT, Gel tray. Made of thick Perspex with accurately measured 50 mm high rims all round. (The base could be of plate glass.) The gel (*G*) fills the tray.

R, "Roof". Because of the need for cooling, the apparatus cannot be completely enclosed, but a roofing heavy glass plate extending much beyond the apparatus is a useful safety precaution.

M, Safety microswitch. Closed when the roofing plate (*R*) presses on it. Interrupts the circuit when the roof is lifted.

CHEMICALS

Non-specific ester *substrate*: 1-naphthyl acetate.

Coupling dye: Fast Garnet GBC (Gurr's).

Reaction solution (for 1 000 ml). This is made fresh before use. In 300 ml of the phosphate buffer (pH 6·0) dissolve 500–1 000 mg of Fast Garnet or sufficient to produce a red-wine coloured solution. Make up to 1 000 ml

with water. Just before use, dissolve 50–100 mg of the substrate in a few ml
of absolute ethanol or methanol, and add it to the Fast Garnet solution.

OTHER ITEMS

"Sample holders". Cut No. 1 filter paper into pieces 50 × 100 mm (or
some other convenient size). Keep these clean and covered. You can use
No. 3 filter paper when a larger sample is required, for example where
esterase content is low.

Fuse wire, finest wire, used for cutting through the gel.

Staining trays of dimensions larger than the gel trays. Plastic, enamel,
glass, even aluminium trays or dishes are all satisfactory. After repeated use,
however, all of these get stained unless thoroughly cleaned each time.

PRINCIPLE OF THE EXPERIMENT

This experiment will enable you to discover whether the serum contains
esterases (i.e. enzymes hydrolysing esters) and at the same time will separate
any distinct molecular species of these enzymes. To sum up, insert a small piece
of filter paper soaked in serum in the starch gel. This gel is moulded in the
form of a flat thin plate and forms part of an electric circuit. The sample is
inserted near the cathode end of the plate, but, once the circuit is switched
on, the charged molecules (including esterases) will move from their original
position and will travel in a direction and at a speed depending on their
charges and on the amount of current passing and also on their size in relation
to the "pores" of the gel. When the electrophoretic run is ended, these
molecules will find themselves separated and stopped at different distances
from the origin. It remains to make them visible, and the reaction used will,
of course, depend on the types of substances looked for.

One plate can take a whole number of samples, so that differences in the
esterase complement of many sera may be detected under identical electrophoretic conditions. Differences may be due to species, age or genotype,
and a wide range of comparisons may be made by this technique.

PREPARATION OF STARCH GEL

Have a clean Perspex tray ready on a flat bench, smear it thinly with liquid
paraffin and have ready a glass plate for covering. Smear the under side of
this plate also.

Assuming that the dimensions of your tray are approx. 20 × 12 × 0·5 cm,
you will need about 24 g of starch in 200 ml of buffer. For the exact amount
of starch follow instructions on the label of the starch container.

Put 200 ml of your gel buffer in a 1 litre Pyrex side-arm flask (strongest
glass), add the 24 g of starch and stir until dissolved. (Any starch left undis-

solved will cause the formation of lumps or flakes which may make the gel useless.)

Now heat the flask slowly on an asbestos sheet over a Bunsen burner. The solution must be stirred continuously, for example by shaking the flask whilst heating it. To do this, wear asbestos gloves. The solution gradually becomes viscous and opaque, but at about 74°C there is a further change and it becomes again more fluid and clear. Very soon after this point has been reached the flask should be removed from the heat.

Stopper the flask with a rubber bung and connect its side arm by rubber tubing to a water flow vacuum pump attached to a running water tap. The moderate vacuum formed will cause the release of air bubbles from the solution. Once the rate of bubbling slows down disconnect the flask from the pump, remove the stopper and promptly pour the gel into the gel tray. See that the gel fills the tray in a continuous mass and reaches above the rims. Let stand for a few minutes and then gently cover the whole tray with the glass plate. Make sure no air is trapped in the tray. This is easy to achieve if the glass plate is first held against one rim of the tray at an angle and is then lowered carefully over the whole tray. If the glass plate is not heavy enough, a small weight may be put on it to help a complete seal.

The plate will need 2–3 h to "set" and it may even be preferable to leave it overnight before use.

APPLICATION OF SAMPLES AND ELECTROPHORETIC "RUN"

When ready to apply samples, lift the glass cover from the starch plate and blot any condensation off the surface of the gel. Divide the plate with a ruler and scalpel by two parallel slits (50 mm from each other) at a distance of say 4 cm from the near side end of the plate. Remove the ribbon of starch between the two slits leaving an empty trench. The walls of this trench must be smooth, vertical and straight.

With fine forceps take one piece of filter paper (No. 1) of dimensions 5 × 10 mm and dip it in the serum sample. For better resolution blot this "sample-holder" lightly, and place it against the face of one vertical wall of the trench. Continue placing the rest of your samples in the same way, leaving 5 mm or more between them.

Now push the small portion of the starch gel to meet the other, eliminating the trench and forming a continuous plate with the samples "inserted" in it. To keep the portions of gel united in this way, put between gel and tray rim a rod of Perspex 1 cm in width (and as long as the tray is wide). This "compressor" not only fills the space left by the ribbon of starch removed, but also tightens the gel somewhat, ensuring that no "gaping" develops at the slit.

The plate is now ready to be put in position bridging the two buffer vessels of the apparatus. Place it, with the samples nearer the cathode, and apply the "bridges". These are rectangular pieces of lint (wetted in the vessel buffers). The one end of the bridge forms a straight line near and parallel to the slit with the samples. The other end reaches into the vessel buffer. The other piece of lint bridges in the same way the gap between starch plate and the other vessel. No more than 3–4 cm of the starch plate need be covered by the lint pieces on either side.

The heat produced by the current would cause evaporation from the upper surface of the plate. Even if this were not sufficient to dry the plate, it would in any case cause distortion of the pattern. For this reason cover the surface of the starch with a piece of "Handi-wrap", a very thin film which clings to the gel surface. There must be no wrinkles and no hollows under this cover.

Everything is now ready for the "run", but safety precautions must be taken before the current is switched on. Place the glass plate "roof" over the apparatus to prevent anyone inadvertently touching the circuit. (There should be a microswitch to interrupt the circuit if the plate is lifted.) Switch on the current and regulate the voltage to about 10 V per cm length of the gel. Make a note of the corresponding amperage (about 5 mA per cm width of the gel is desirable). Readjust after half an hour or so, if the readings have changed. Switch on a fan to keep the surface of the gel as cool as possible. (Higher voltage will speed the run, but may cause overheating of the gels.)

TERMINATION OF THE RUN

The buffer system used in this experiment has the advantage that a brown line moves in the starch at the front of the vessel buffer advancing in the starch. By watching this line you know how far the fastest molecules have travelled. It is suggested that you end the run when this front has advanced 7–9 cm from the sample holders.

Switch off the apparatus, lift the glass "roof", then the gel tray. Pull the starch portion behind the samples and remove sample holders with forceps. Lift the starch plate carefully and put it onto a flat clean glass surface. The plate must now be sliced horizontally and stained on the cut surfaces. (The original upper and lower surfaces of the gel do not give a good electrophoretic pattern because of some unavoidable spread of water in the interphase of starch and Perspex, etc.)

To slice the plate, put a glass plate approximately half the thickness of the starch gel into the Perspex tray. On top of this put the trimmed starch plate; it now stands proud of the rims by about half its thickness. Take a piece of fine fuse wire and stretch it taut from side to side of the tray, keeping it firmly on the rims. If you now move the wire firmly and quickly through the gel you can slice it horizontally with smooth inside surfaces (in the way that cheese is cut by wire).

You can "stain" both slices by transferring them into a tray with the reaction solution. The cut surfaces must be uppermost and, of course, submerged. The gel slices are just firm enough for nimble hands to move them without breaking them.

STAINING OF THE GEL SLICES

The reaction solution for esterases is freshly made as described above (p. 105). The substrate incorporated in the solution is 1-naphthyl-acetate, an ester that is hydrolysed by most types of esterases. The enzymes release naphthol and this couples with the azo-dye present, Fast Garnet, to form a purple precipitate in the starch in the positions where various esterases have migrated during the run.

Within 10–20 min the bands or zones marking the location of esterases will begin to appear. Prolonged staining will bring up the weaker fractions, but may result in the coalescing of neighbouring strong fractions. The answer is either to photograph the plate at intervals, or to "understain" one slice of the plate and "overstain" the other.

To stop the reaction, replace the solution with water. The plates can be kept for a long time under water in a cold room; at room temperature they soon become "fluffy" (bacterial attack?).

FLEXIBILITY OF THE TECHNIQUE

Sample results with mouse serum are described and illustrated by Pantelouris and Arnason (1966a, b). Starch gel electrophoresis is being widely used, and references are now numerous. A bibliography, perhaps incomplete, is published by the University of Toronto Connaught Medical Research Laboratories.

It must be realized that the buffer system described for this experiment is one of several dozen systems and pH values recommended for specific enzymes.

The experiment can be expanded by the use of ester substrates other than 1-naphthyl acetate and of specific inhibitors (see Pantelouris and Arnason, 1966a, b) with the purpose of describing any specificity differences between esterase fractions.

BIBLIOGRAPHY

Pantelouris, E. M. and Arnason, A. (1966a). *Comp. Biochem. Physiol.*, **21**, 533–539.
Pantelouris, E. M. and Arnason, A. (1966b). *J. exp. Morph. Embryol.*, **16**, 55–64.

7 | A. Buffering Capacity of Snail Blood
    | B. To Determine the Choline Esterase Activity in Snail Blood

G. A. KERKUT

Department of Physiology and Biochemistry,
University of Southampton, England

A. Buffering Capacity of Snail Blood

APPARATUS

pH Meter and electrodes.
Magnetic stirrer and flea.
100 ml beakers (three).
Buffer tablets, pH 7, pH 4 and pH 9.
3 Burettes, 10 ml, 50 ml and 25 ml.
Pipette 10 ml.
Pipette 5 ml (continuously calibrated).
3 in. glass funnel. Test tubes. Test tube stand.
Burette stands and clamp.
Paper tissues.
Thermometer.

CHEMICALS

N/20 HCl (approx. 5·5 ml of concentrated acid to 1 litre).
N/100 HCl (1·5 ml of conc. acid to 1 litre).
Distilled water.
N/20 NaOH (2 g of NaOH per litre).
Buffer solution pH 7, pH 4, pH 9, or other convenient values. Make from tablets provided by suppliers.
Snail blood. Take twelve snails and place them in a beaker containing water at about 20°C. Leave them in this *covered* beaker for 15 min. The snails should by this time be extended and actively crawling up the sides of the beaker. Take a snail, wipe it with tissue to remove the excess water. Pierce the apex (point) of the shell with a knife or a pair of scissors. Place the snail in the glass funnel and have the funnel stand in a test tube. The blue blood will trickle out of the snail into the funnel and be collected in the test tube.

You can usually get about 1–1·5 ml of blood from each snail. For the experiment you require 15–20 ml of blood.

IDEA AND PRINCIPLE

A buffer solution will maintain the pH relatively constant when acids or bases are added to the solution. The measure of the buffer capacity is the extent to which this constancy is achieved. In this experiment one carries out a pH titration of acid against base and then repeats the experiments adding different amounts of snail blood. The difference between the curves will indicate the buffering capacity of the blood. The blood can then be compared experimentally with a known bicarbonate buffer solution.

PROCEDURE

The experiment is divided into three parts.

The first part is to get to know how to use the pH meter and calibrate it. The second part is a simple acid base titration. The third part is the effect of adding blood to the titration system.

1. PH METER

The procedure here will vary according to the exact type of pH meter that is being used. There are, however, several points that are common to most pH meters. If they are operated from the mains power supply it is necessary that they are switched on for some time before the experiment is carried out (at least 1 h). The pH meter is in general a comparative machine, it compares an unknown solution with a standard buffer solution of known pH. For accurate readings it is necessary to test the machine and to calibrate it with standard solutions near the pH of the unknown solution, i.e. if you are interested in measuring solutions at pH 2 then calibrate the meter with buffers at pH 2 and not at pH 10 or 7. The meters in general are true over the whole range but may be out 0·1 of a pH unit if calibrated by a buffer at the extreme other end of the scale.

Check the electrodes. Make sure that there is saturated KCl in the reference (calomel) electrode; you can usually see the KCl crystals. On the other hand, do not have a thick snowfall of crystals clogging up the porous plug. The glass electrode should be treated with care. The surface is delicate and should not be banged or scraped. Do not leave the electrode for more than 1 min in solutions that are very acid or very alkaline. These may disturb the glass surface and it will take some time before the electrode can settle down again. Solutions containing high concentrations of protein may form a film over the electrodes and cause faulty readings. In this case wipe the electrode surface *gently* with soft tissue paper.

Calibrating the pH meter

There may be special instructions with the meter. If so consult these. Make sure that the meter is switched on.

1. Take the three buffer solutions (pH 4, pH 7 and pH 9) and place these in the 100 ml beakers, marking each beaker with the pH of the buffer solution.

2. Have the electrode standing in a beaker containing distilled water.

3. Raise the electrodes from the beaker and replace by the beaker containing the buffer pH 4.

4. Switch the meter to "read". The indicator lever will now swing to indicate the pH value. If there is a mirror behind the lever adjust your position to get the reading without parallax. Wait about 15 sec. Take a reading.

5. If the reading differs from pH 4 adjust the meter with the calibration control until the meter reads 4.

6. Switch the meter to "stand by". Remove the electrodes from the buffer pH 4. Wash the electrodes in distilled water for about 20 sec.

7. Place the electrodes in the buffer pH 7 and now test by switching to "read". The meter should read about pH 7. It should not be more than 0·1 pH units away.

8. Repeat the process, i.e. wash the electrodes in distilled water and test with buffer 9. Often there may be a difference in the readings from 7 and 9 when the meter is adjusted for pH 4. If it is more than 0·2 pH units ask the demonstrator for advice.

9. For the present experiment it is necessary to calibrate the meter to buffer at pH 7.

Many meters will have a third electrode system for adjusting the temperature system since pH readings are very dependent upon pH. In most cases you will here be using solutions at the same temperature and so it is not necessary to use automatic temperature compensation though it can be left on for convenience. If the machine has not got automatic temperature compensation, then there will be a control which should be set to the temperature of the solutions that you are measuring.

2. PH TITRATION

1. Calibrate the pH meter at pH 7.

2. Place 30 ml of N/20 HCl in the 50 ml burette.

3. Place a 100 ml beaker containing 20 ml of N/20 NaOH and the magnetic flea on the stirrer and put the electrodes in the beaker. Adjust the stand so

that the electrodes are about half an inch away from the bottom of the beaker. Arrange the burette on the clamp stand so that the tip will easily pour into the beaker.

4. Read the pH of the N/20 NaOH. It will be about 12. Now switch on the magnetic stirrer. Have the flea move *slowly* otherwise you will set up a vortex around the electrodes and they will not record the pH of the solution. Make sure the flea does not bang the electrodes.

5. Add the N/20 HCl from the burette 2 ml at a time and note the pH of the solution. It is necessary to wait some 15 sec after adding the 2 ml in order to get a steady reading. Note that as the solutions approached pH 7 so the additions from the burette should be made in smaller quantities, i.e. 0·5 ml instead of 2 ml (see Table I). This experiment is plotted in Fig. 1.

6. You should get a table something like Table I.

TABLE I

ml of N/20 HCl added	pH	ml of N/20 HCl added	pH
0	12·5	19	9·0
2	12·4	19·5	7
4	12·4	20	4·2
6	12·4	20·5	3·7
8	12·4	21	3·5
10	12·4	22	3·2
12	12·2	23	3·0
14	12·1	24	2·9
16	11·7	26	2·7
18	11·0	28	2·7

3. TO DETERMINE THE TITRATION CURVE OF A BUFFER SOLUTION

1. Set up the apparatus with N/20 NaOH in the burette.
2. Put 15 ml of distilled water in the beaker.
3. Add the alkali from the burette at the rate of 0·5 ml at a time. Note the pH change and plot this on the graph as shown in Fig. 2.
4. Wash the electrodes in distilled water.
5. Place 15 ml of pH 7 buffer solution in the beaker and add the NaOH at 0·5 ml at a time. Record the pH changes and plot this on the curve. Note the difference to distilled water curve. In Fig. 2 it took only 2 ml of N/20 NaOH to get the distilled water to a pH of 11·5, whilst for the buffer solution it took 10 ml of NaOH.

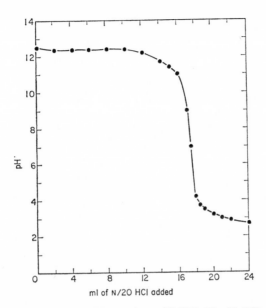

FIG. 1. Titration curve of N/20 NaOH against N/20 HCl. The NaOH was in the beaker and as the HCl was added so the pH of the solution changed. Note that the HCl was added in smaller volumes around the end point (pH 7) so as to get greater accuracy over the area where there was the greatest change in pH.

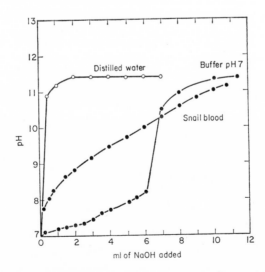

FIG. 2. Comparison of distilled water, buffer pH 7 and snail blood for their buffering capacity. The blood was better than the distilled water and also had a more even change of pH for addition of NaOH compared with the buffer solution.

6. Wash the electrodes. Place 15 ml of snail blood in the beaker. Titrate with the NaOH from the burette adding the NaOH 1 ml at a time. Wait 15 sec after each addition to allow the meter to reach a steady reading. Plot the result on the graph (Fig. 2).

4. BUFFERING CAPACITY OF SNAIL BLOOD

20 ml of snail blood.
N/100 HCl solution.
10 ml burette.
Distilled water.
25 ml burette containing distilled water.
Burette stand.
5 ml graduated pipette.

1. In this experiment put the N/100 HCl in the 10 ml burette and have the experimental solution in the beaker. In the beaker have different solutions containing an increasing volume of snail blood. First of all start with 15 ml of distilled water in the beaker. Note the pH change as you add the HCl 0·5 ml at a time (Fig. 3).

2. Repeat the experiment having this time 14 ml of distilled water in the beaker plus 1 ml of snail blood (Fig. 3).

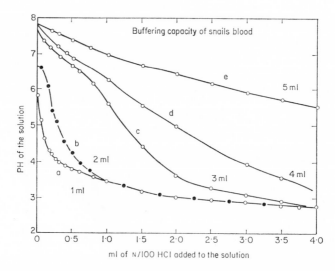

FIG. 3. The effect of increasing volumes of blood on the buffering capacity of the system. Greater volumes of blood increase the buffering capacity of the system.

3. Repeat with 13 ml of distilled water and 2 ml of snail blood in the beaker.

4. Repeat with 12 ml of distilled water and 3 ml of snail blood in the beaker.

5. Repeat with 11 ml of distilled water and 4 ml of snail blood in the beaker.

6. Repeat with 10 ml of distilled water and 5 ml of snail blood in the beaker.

7. Repeat with various volumes of a known buffer solution added to distilled water in order to get a similar series of curves to those obtained with snail blood.

CONCLUSIONS

Snail blood has a buffering capacity. This capacity is due to various substances (bicarbonate, phosphate, proteins) and it is easy for you to determine the amount of bicarbonate in snail blood and determine whether this accounts for the observed buffering capacity.

It is necessary that you read the theory of acid-base systems and be able to calculate the pH of a solution from the Henderson-Hasselbalch equation. The way to do this will be found in the references given below.

BIBLIOGRAPHY

The references given below are to help in understanding pH and acid base regulation.

Bittar, E. E. (1964). "Cell pH". Butterworths, London.
Eisenmann, G. (Ed.) (1966). "The Glass Electrode". Interscience, New York.
Robinson, J. R. (1961). "Fundamentals of Acid-Base Regulation". Blackwells, Oxford.

B. To Determine the Choline Esterase Activity in Snail Blood

This experiment should follow after the estimation of the buffer activity of snail blood. The present experiment will demonstrate two main points: (1) the design of a "pilot" experiment; (2) the estimation of an enzyme, choline esterase, by a titrometric method. Note that a colorimetric method has been described on p. 101 for the estimation of esterase colorimetrically, and for the separation of esterases on starch gel electrophoresis.

PILOT EXPERIMENT

In many biological experiments it is necessary to do a preliminary or "pilot" experiment to see how things go before you can do the full and exact experiment. In the present estimation of choline esterase in snail blood we cannot predict exactly what the enzyme concentration will be. It is therefore necessary to do a rough test to discover the necessary volume of blood to use and the necessary concentration of NaOH to titrate. Thus, if the NaOH is too strong, you will miss the reaction and if the enzyme is too weak you will wait all day before anything happens. In most enzyme experiments (you may have already estimated the strength of the amylase in your saliva and had to adjust the concentration of the starch solution to give a result in a reasonable time) it is necessary to carry out pilot experiments to determine the necessary concentrations. Pilot experiments are useful in biological investigations because they will quickly indicate whether you are going to get a result or not. You can then adjust the conditions and concentrations to give the experiment the best possible chance of working in a finite and convenient time.

PRINCIPLE

The enzyme choline esterase will split acetylcholine to give choline and acetic acid

Choline esterase

Acetylcholine ⟶ choline + acetic acid

This means that through the enzyme action the solution will become more acid due to the production of acetic acid. In this experiment we add the enzyme to a solution of acetylcholine and then every minute add a volume of NaOH sufficient to keep the pH constant at pH 8. The volume of NaOH added will indicate the speed of the reaction, and this is then plotted against time.

If the NaOH is too strong then only small volumes are added and this makes the system inaccurate. If the NaOH is too weak then large volumes are added and this can disturb the enzyme action. For this reason one does the pilot experiment first of all.

APPARATUS

pH Meter, magnetic stirrer, magnetic flea, glass electrode, reference electrode.
Three 100 ml beakers.
10 ml Burette.
5 ml Graduated pipette.
15 ml Pipette.
Buffer solution at pH 8 or thereabouts.
Clock with minute hand.
Snail blood (see p. 111). You will want 20 ml of blood.

CHEMICALS

Acetylcholine solution 10^{-3} g/ml (dissolve 0·2 g in 200 ml water).
Acetylcholine solution 10^{-4} g/ml. (Make up 100 ml from the 10^{-3} solution.)
NaOH solution (N/100; 0·4 g in 1 litre).

EXPERIMENT 1. (PILOT EXPERIMENT)

CONTROL

1. Put the N/100 NaOH in the 10 ml burette and arrange the apparatus as for a pH titration.
2. Put 15 ml of the 10^{-4} acetylcholine (ACh) solution into the beaker.
3. Watch the clock and add NaOH so as to bring the pH of the solution to pH 8. Have the stirrer going gently. Ignore this reading.
4. Every minute add more NaOH to bring the pH back to 8. Note the reading. If the reaction is too fast, then you will have to add a lot of NaOH (i.e. more than 1 ml per min). If the reaction is too slow, i.e. you add less than 0·1 ml of NaOH in 10 min, then the NaOH is too strong.

At this stage carry on with the experiment but note what has happened and compare with the control line on Fig. 4.

EXPERIMENT

1. Remove the beaker and wash it out. Replace with 15 ml of fresh 10^{-4} ACh and place electrode in beaker. Start stirrer. Top up the burette with NaOH.
2. Add 0·5 ml of snail blood to the beaker.
3. Add NaOH to bring the pH to 8. Ignore this reading.
4. Repeat every minute adding NaOH to bring the pH to 8. Note the amount added each minute. Plot it on a graph. You should get a result similar to that shown in Fig. 4 at 0·4 ml. If there is no difference from the control then your enzyme solution is weak and you will have to add more blood, i.e. repeat with 1 ml or 2 ml of blood. If the reaction is very fast then you will have to add less blood, say 0·1 ml.

If your NaOH was too strong (as shown by the control experiment) then dilute it and do another trial run, both the control and with a known volume of blood added. Repeat with different concentrations of NaOH and blood till you get a result similar to Fig. 4.

Once the conditions are right you are ready to do a simple quantitative experiment.

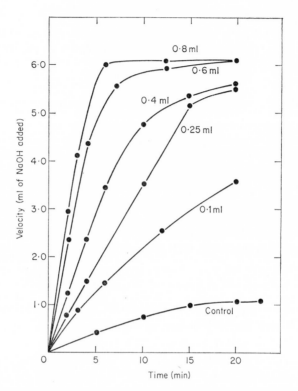

Fig. 4. The effect of increasing volumes of blood (enzyme) on the rate of breakdown of acetylcholine.

Experiment 2. The Effect of Enzyme Concentration on the Rate of the Reaction

1. Do a control run with 15 ml of substrate (10^{-4} ACh) in the beaker and no blood. Draw up a table as shown below (Table II) and plot this curve.

2. Now repeat the experiment with 0·1 ml of blood.

3. Repeat with 0·25 ml of blood.

4. Repeat with 0·4 ml of blood.

5. Repeat with 0·6 ml of blood.

6. Repeat with 0·8 ml of blood.

(If the blood has proved to be low in enzyme activity, then use the necessary range of concentrations to give a result similar to that shown in Fig. 4.)

TABLE II

Time	Vol of blood added					
	0 ml	0·1 ml	0·25 ml	0·4 ml	0·6 ml	0·8 ml
	Vol of NaOH added					
2	0·2	0·5	1·0	1·4	2·5	3·5
5	0·4	1·2	1·7	2·8	4·6	5·5
10	0·7	2·3	3·5	4·8	5·7	6·1
15	1·0	3·1	5·0	5·2	6·0	6·3
20	1·1	3·6	5·3	5·8	6·2	6·3

EXPERIMENT 3. EFFECT OF SUBSTRATE CONCENTRATION

In this experiment one chooses a concentration of enzyme (blood) that will give a good rate of breakdown of the substrate and then tests it with various dilutions of substrate.

1. Prepare a series of dilutions of ACh, say 10^{-5} g/ml; 5×10^{-5} g/ml; 10^{-4} g/ml; 5×10^{-4} g/ml; 10^{-3} g/ml. You will want at least 15 ml of each.

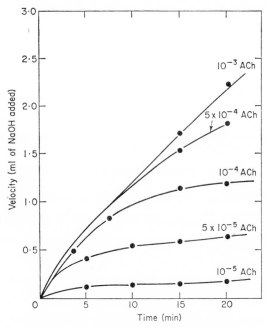

FIG. 5. The effect of substrate concentration (ACh) on the rate of activity of the enzyme choline esterase.

2. For each experiment take 15 ml of the ACh and add 0·5 ml of blood (or whatever gives a good rate.) Titrate this with NaOH (N/100 if this has proved to be the correct concentration).

3. You should be able to get a similar series of curves to those shown in Fig. 5.

You can calculate the velocity of the reaction by taking the volume of NaOH that you had to add in 5 min.

TABLE III

Substrate concn	Velocity (ml of NaOH)
10^{-5}	0·12
5×10^{-5}	0·48
10^{-4}	0·64
5×10^{-4}	0·75
10^{-3}	0·5

This can be plotted as in Fig. 6.

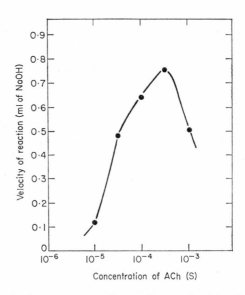

FIG. 6. The effect of substrate concentration on the rate of activity of the enzyme choline esterase. Note that at higher concentrations there is a decrease in the initial velocity of the reaction.

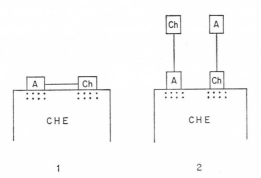

FIG. 7. Suggestion for explaining why choline esterase (CHE) activity falls off at higher substrate concentrations. Normally the ACh lies across the active sites of the enzyme (1), but at high concentrations (2) two molecules of ACh attach and the enzyme is then incapable of breaking the bond between the acetyl and the choline.

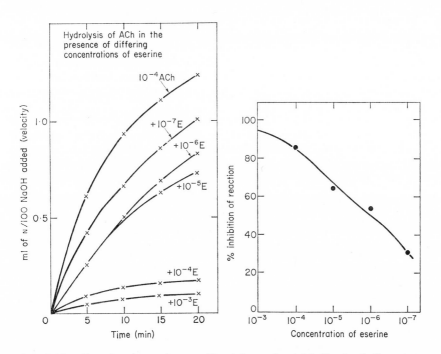

FIG. 8. The effect of eserine on the rate of breakdown of acetylcholine by choline esterase Eserine at high concentrations inhibits the action of choline esterase. This is shown by a direct plot, and also by a plot of the per cent inhibition against the concentration of eserine.

Acetylcholine at higher concentrations tends to inhibit the activity of choline esterase. If the enzyme is considered as having to get the ACh lying across the molecule to break it: at high concentrations one can consider two molecules of ACh attaching, one by the acetyl end and the other by the choline end, and the enzyme cannot then break the bond (see Fig. 7).

SUGGESTIONS FOR FURTHER EXPERIMENTS

BUTYRYLCHOLINE, PROPIONYL CHOLINE

It is possible to determine whether you have a true acetylcholine esterase or an aliesterase by seeing the rate at which it hydrolyses acetylcholine in relation to butyrylcholine and propionylcholine. Thus you have to repeat the experiments using butyrylcholine and propionyl choline as the substrates and compare the rates at equivalent molar concentrations with acetylcholine. True acetylcholine esterase will hydrolyse the acetylcholine solution at a faster rate than the equivalent concentration of BuCh or PrCh.

ESERINE

Eserine tends to inhibit the action of choline esterase. Determine the hydrolysis of acetylcholine by the enzyme in the presence of various concentrations of eserine (Fig. 8).

BIBLIOGRAPHY

Davies, D. R. and Green, A. C. (1958). The mechanism of hydrolysis by choline esterase and related enzymes. *Adv. Enzymol.*, **20**, 283–318.
Dixon, M. and Webb, E. C. (1964). "The Enzymes". Longmans, London.
Nachmansohn, D. and Wilson, I. B. (1951). The enzymic hydrolysis and synthesis of acetylcholine. *Adv. Enzymol.*, **12**, 259–339.
Wilkinson, J. H. (1965). "Isoenzymes". Spon, London.

8

A. The Role of the Contractile Vacuole

B. Ion Antagonism and Physiologically Balanced Salt Solutions

C. Some Effects of Radiation on Cells

D. Bioluminescence

E. Oxygen Equilibrium Curve of Hemocyanin

F. Active Transport Through Cell Membranes

G. Salinity and the Volume or Weight of Animals

H. Physiological Color Changes of Vertebrates

W. S. HOAR

Department of Zoology, University of British Columbia, Vancouver, Canada

A. The Role of the Contractile Vacuole

ANIMALS

Rich cultures of *Paramecium* or other protozoan with conspicuous contractile vacuoles are required. The animals must be sufficiently numerous so that each drop of culture fluid contains several individuals, otherwise the students will spend all their time searching for animals. Methods for culturing paramecia are given in Needham (1959).

APPARATUS

Microscope of good quality provided with ocular micrometer (calibration slide available).

Microscope slides, cover glasses.

Lens paper or cotton wool.

Medicine droppers or pipettes.

Time clock with electric bell or buzzer to ring at 30 sec intervals.

CHEMICAL SOLUTIONS

10% methyl cellulose (10 g/100 ml distilled water). Prepare a small amount and store in Barnes dropping bottles for class. Different lots of methyl cellulose vary in their viscosity; the amount of water can be varied to produce a solution with the consistency of molasses or corn syrup.

Neutral Red (10 mg/100 ml water). Prepare small amounts and store in Barnes bottles for class.

Sea water. Natural, of salinity 25–30‰, or any artificial sea water (see Hale, 1958).

M/500 KCN (130 mg/100 ml). Prepare small amounts and store in Barnes dropping bottles for class. Label *Caution Poison*.

Indian ink.

PRINCIPLE OF THE EXPERIMENT

This demonstrates one of the problems encountered by animals which live in a hypo-osmotic environment. In such an environment the animal is constantly flooded with water due to the relatively high osmotic content of its body fluids; there are other problems such as those which involve electrolytes but these are not being examined in this experiment. Thus *Paramecium* is continually taking in water because of this osmotic difference; this water is eliminated by the contractile vacuoles. In this experiment it is shown (a) that as the osmotic difference is reduced by raising the osmotic content of the environment, the activity of the contractile vacuole decreases; the amount of work performed by the vacuole depends on the osmotic gradient, and (b) that active metabolic processes are involved since cyanide eliminates the action of the vacuole. Cyanide blocks oxidative phosphorylation by its action on the cytochrome system, and consequently the animal's supply of ATP is soon exhausted.

EXPERIMENTAL DETAILS

Study the contractile vacuoles of *Paramecium* or other protozoa available. To slow down activity of the animals the microslide may be *thinly smeared* with 10% methyl cellulose before applying the drop of culture fluid. Alternatively, a tangle of lens paper or cotton wool is helpful.

Are these vacuoles temporary or permanent structures? Do the anterior and posterior vacuoles contract at the same time, or at the same rate? Do the vacuoles pulsate while the animal moves? Can you see that the contents of the vacuoles are actually extruded from the animal? To do this satisfactorily it may be necessary to place the animal in a thick suspension of indian ink. Are the contents of the vacuoles acid or alkaline? Use Neutral

Red (1 : 10 000) as indicator. The dye is red when acid and yellow when alkaline.

Determine the rate of pulsation in the following solutions. With the ocular micrometer determine the average size of the vacuole in the different solutions. To obtain a solution of approximately the correct concentration mix one drop of culture fluid containing paramecia with one drop of solution *twice* the final concentration desired. Show the results graphically.

(a) Culture fluid.
(b) Distilled water.
(c) Sea water 2·5%, 5%, 7·5%, and 10%.
(d) Culture fluid plus KCN.

RESULTS

The normal rate of pulsation varies somewhat with the conditions; you may expect a rate of six to ten pulsations per minute in the culture fluid with somewhat higher values in distilled water and progressively lower values in sea water (Fig. 1).

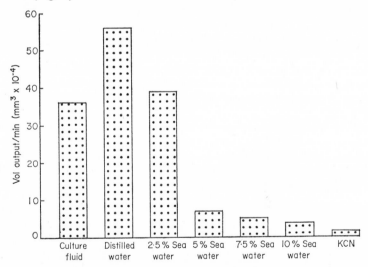

FIG. 1. The estimated vol per min put out by the contractile vacuole of *Paramecium* in cultures of different tonicity and in KCN. Data obtained in the comparative physiology laboratory.

Prepare a graph to show the relation between salinity and vacuolar activity. What evidence does the experiment provide for the function of the contractile vacuole? Discuss.

Make a diagram of the structure of the contractile vacuole as revealed by the electron microscope (Schneider, 1960; Hoar, 1966).

TROUBLE-SHOOTING

The only problems associated with this experiment are the optical ones of identifying the vacuole; this is largely a matter of proper illumination. If *Paramecium caudatum* is used counts can readily be made at magnifications provided by 10 × objective and 10 × ocular, once the vacuoles and their pulsations have been observed. During the early part of the class, the instructor should check each student's preparation to see that vacuoles have been identified and are being properly observed.

BIBLIOGRAPHY

Davson, H. (1964). "A Textbook of General Physiology", 3rd ed. Churchill, London. [Brief discussion of contractile vacuoles.]

Hale, L. J. (1958). "Biological Laboratory Data." Methuen, London. [Formula for artificial sea water.]

Hoar, W. S. (1966). "General and Comparative Physiology." Prentice-Hall, Englewood Cliffs, New Jersey. [Discussion of osmotic and ionic regulation with diagram of contractile vacuole.]

Kitching, J. A. (1954). Osmoregulation and ionic regulation in animals without kidneys. *Symp. Soc. exp. Biol.* **8**, 63–75. [Review of earlier work on contractile vacuoles.]

Needham, J. G. (Ed.) (1959). "Culture Methods for Invertebrate Animals." Dover, New York.

Potts, W. T. N. and Parry, G. (1964). "Osmotic and Ionic Regulation in Animals." Pergamon Press, Oxford. [General monograph on this topic.]

Schneider, L. (1960). Elektronmikroskopische Untersuchungen über das Nephridialsystem von *Paramecium. J. Protozol.* **7**, 75–90. [Electron microscope study of contractile vacuole.]

B.   Ion Antagonism and Physiologically Balanced Salt Solutions

ANIMALS

Ciliated epithelial cells may be obtained from many different sources. These directions are written for the sea mussel *Mytilus* but other marine or freshwater bivalves are just as satisfactory; alternatively but less satisfactorily, one may obtain ciliated cells by scraping the roof of the mouth and pharynx of a frog.

APPARATUS

Microscopes. It is well to put a glass plate on the stage of the microscope to protect it from the occasional spilling of solutions.

Twenty-one Syracuse dishes. If less than 10 ml solution is placed in the dish, observations can be made directly at a suitable magnification without transferring cilia to glass slides while avoiding contact of microscope lens and solution.

Tray, on which to place the twenty-one dishes.

CHEMICAL SOLUTIONS

The amounts given below (for M/2 solutions) are for the marine bivalves. The control solution is the sea water in which the animals are living. If freshwater clams are used all solutions are appropriately diluted to M/16 (1 : 8); if frog epithelial cells are used, all solutions are diluted to M/8 (1 : 4). The control solution for frog is Ringer's solution*; the control for the freshwater mussel is Ringer's solution in half concentration.

Group 1. *Single salt solutions* (M/2 concn, g/litre)

⌐ NaCl	29·2		NaI	75·0
⌐ KCl	37·3		NaBr	51·5
MgCl₂	47·6		NaNO₃	42·5
⌐ CaCl₂	55·5		NaCNS	40·5
Na₂SO₄	71·0		Control	

Group 2. *Solutions with only two salts* (prepared from the above)

- 25 vol NaCl and 1 vol KCl
- 25 vol NaCl and 1 vol CaCl₂
- 25 vol NaCl and 1 vol MgCl₂

Group 3. *Solutions with three or four salts* (prepared from group 1)

- 25 vol NaCl; 1 vol KCl and 1 vol CaCl₂
- 25 vol NaCl; 1 vol KCl and 1 vol MgCl₂
- 25 vol NaCl; 1 vol CaCl₂ and 1 vol MgCl₂
- 25 vol NaCl; 1 vol CaCl₂; 1 vol MgCl₂ and 1 vol KCl

Group 4. *Effects of pH on ciliary movement*

Control solutions adjusted to pH 3·0, 5·0, 7·0 and 9·0. Adjust some of the control solution to each of the following pH values (approximately) by adding HCl for the lower pH values and NaOH for the higher ones (N/10 for sea water and N/100 for Ringer's).

PRINCIPLE OF THE EXPERIMENT

Living tissues and cells are bathed by solutions which bear a marked similarity to dilute sea water. Biologists have often speculated on the evolution of this chemical environment from the dilute sea waters of the ancient oceans

---

* Ringer's solution for frog: if not available in the laboratory, see Hale (1958) or other handbook for physiological preparations.

where life probably first appeared. It is true that some part of this salt content is important only in providing osmotically active materials and could be replaced by other ions or compounds similarly active osmotically. Many of the ions present, however, are playing highly specific roles. If the balance among these many ions is drastically changed, characteristic effects in tissues may be anticipated. Such widely diversified phenomena as irritability, anesthesia, mortality and growth are modified by balance of ions.

In the latter part of the nineteenth century a pioneer physiologist named Ringer noted that the activity of a perfused frog heart could not long be maintained in an isotonic solution of pure sodium chloride but was maintained for prolonged periods if small amounts of calcium and potassium were added to the solution.

Since Ringer's time it has been found that pure solutions of any of the salts commonly found in living tissues are often as toxic as distilled water, and that the normal activities and responsiveness of cells depend upon a proper balance of monovalent and divalent cations (a physiologically balanced solution). The term *ion antagonism* is used to describe this effect which one toxic ion exerts in counteracting the toxic effects of another.

It is recognized (a) that some ions are more toxic than others, (b) that the precise order of toxicity varies with the species or kind of animal and (c) with the tonicity or concentration of the toxic solution. Further it is noted (d) that a great variety of ions may antagonize the toxic effects of any single ion, (e) that monovalent ions are usually antagonized by divalent ions and (f) that antagonists vary for even such closely related ions as $Na+$ and $K+$.

This ion antagonism is not well understood. Most of the theories attribute toxicity of unbalanced ion solutions and ion antagonism to *effects on the cell membrane*. The cell membrane is looked upon as a precisely organized colloidal emulsion. It is well known that ions vary in their degree of hydration, that some emulsions can be reversed from oil-water to water-oil emulsions by increasing the ratio of calcium to sodium, and that the rigidity or fluidity of protoplasm (sol-gel state of gelatinous material) may be markedly varied by the ratio of monovalent or divalent ions present. Any or all of these facts may be involved in the action of unbalanced ion solutions (Heilbrunn, 1952; Giese, 1962). This emphasis, however, is on possible structural changes in the organization of the plasma membrane. The effect on the ion transport system of the cell may, however, be more significant and must certainly be a part of the disorganization. The life of all cells is associated with a characteristic transmembrane potential which depends on an unbalanced (but quantitatively precise) distribution of different ion species on its two sides. Obviously this will be destroyed when the external medium does not provide the essential ions for its maintenance or when the relative quantities are seriously disturbed.

EXPERIMENTAL DETAILS

First dissect out about two dozen pieces of ciliated epithelium and place in a bowl of sea water (control solution). To do this, open the mussels by cutting the adductor muscles. The gills hang down between the visceral mass and the mantle (which lines the shell and is closely attached to it). With fine scissors cut the gills off near their lines of attachment and then cut transversely to provide pieces which include some of the free margin. The cilia along the free margin and those lining the water tubes are of different sizes and may not be equally exposed to the test solutions; your results will be better if you concentrate on one group of cilia, preferably those along the free margin.

Label your Syracuse dishes and add to each not more than 10 ml of the appropriate test solution. Shake off excess sea water from a piece of gill, touch gill lightly with blotting paper and put it in test solution.

Examine at intervals to determine as accurately as possible when the ciliary activity ceases. This will be most rapid at low pH values (1 min or less) and with some of the single ion solutions (probably within 5–10 min for many of them). The more complex solutions will maintain activity longer and with the three and four ion solutions activity will probably still be evident at the end of the laboratory period. If this is the case, cover your watch-glasses and check during the next day.

With the low pH values and some of the single ion solutions, cilia may have ceased to beat before you have had time to examine the preparation. In this case, repeat with a fresh solution and another piece of gill, watching carefully while activity ceases. Is there any evidence of stimulation of activity just prior to death?

RESULTS

Present your data in a histogram or histograms. The precise values obtained will vary but the order, with respect to the different groups of solutions, will always be the same. The variability in the precise values is probably usually due to transfer of small amounts of sea water to the test solutions when the bits of gill are added to the Syracuse dishes. More consistent results can be obtained by washing in larger amounts of the test solutions, but the added time involved is not justified if one only wishes to establish the principle. The buffering action of sea water creates another variable in the tests designed to show the action of pH on cilia.

In general, most of the single ion solutions will inactivate the cilia within the first hour and in some cases within the first 10 min. You will probably find that the following are most toxic: $NaCNS$, Na_2SO_4, $NaCl$, NaI, $NaBr$, $CaCl_2$ and $MgCl_2$; the double combination of $NaCl$ and KCl is usually as toxic as some of these single ions; the $NaCl$ and $CaCl_2$ is usually just slightly less so. Solutions as the lower pH values are extremely toxic.

TROUBLE-SHOOTING

Students will probably require some assistance with their microscopy, but once the cilia have been identified and the activity observed, the experiment runs on its own.

If the observations are to be continued during the next day, cover the lively preparations with empty Syracuse dishes at the end of the day.

BIBLIOGRAPHY

Fawcett, D. (1961). Cilia and flagella. *In* "The Cell" (J. Brachet and A. E. Mirsky, eds.), Vol. 2, pp. 217–297. Academic Press, New York. [Monographic review of the cytology and physiology of cilia.]

Giese, A. C. (1962). "Cell Physiology," 2nd ed. Saunders, Philadelphia.

Gray, J. (1928). "Ciliary Movement." Cambridge University Press. [Classic account of the earlier work on cilia.]

Hale, L. J. (1958). "Biological Laboratory Data." Methuen, London. [Formulae for Ringer's solution and artificial sea water.]

Heilbrunn, L. V. (1952). "An Outline of General Physiology," 3rd ed. Saunders, Philadelphia. [Discussion of ion antagonism and other effects of single ion solutions.]

Sleigh, M. A. (1962). "The Biology of Cilia and Flagella." Pergamon Press, Oxford. [A monograph of 242 pp.]

C.   Some Effects of Radiation on Cells*

I. PHOTODYNAMIC ACTION

ANIMALS

Only a few drops of human finger blood are required for the major part of the experiment which is a study of photodynamic hemolysis. For the optional part, any readily available protozoan cultures are satisfactory— *Amoeba, Paramecium, Euglena.*

APPARATUS

Blood lancets, sterile, disposable (B-D Microlance).
Test tubes (size about 100 mm × 13 mm).
Stenders (about 1 in. diam.) or Syracuse watch glasses.

* By including the optional procedures under Parts I and II, each section is suitable for a single laboratory period of about 3–4 h duration. If the options are not included the two parts may be done during one laboratory period. In this case it is better to start with Part I and do Part II during the second half of the laboratory period while the erythrocyte suspensions require only periodic examination.

Illuminating apparatus. Many different arrangements may be used—sunlight, 100 W incandescent lamp or other source giving about 500 ft candles. The difficulty is to control the temperature. The simplest arrangement is to use a 100 W desk lamp placed about 2 ft from the rack of test tubes and to create a good flow of air over the preparations with an electric fan. A tidy arrangement consists of a box with frosted glass sides and top with openings at the ends for ventilation and containing a fluorescent tube of suitable illuminating capacity (Fig. 2). A rack is attached at each side so that test tubes can be placed close to the lighted glass windows. Stender dishes or slides can be placed on the top window. If necessary a fan can be used to create an air flow through the box.

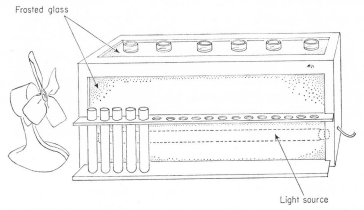

Frosted glass

Light source

FIG. 2. A suggested apparatus for illuminating the preparations used in the experiment on photodynamic action.

A light-proof box or cupboard is necessary for the control preparations. If the laboratory microscopes are normally stored in their carrying cases (as they are in our laboratory), these make very good light-proof boxes which can be readily accessible to the students on the laboratory benches. Alternatively, the preparations may be covered with heavy black-cloth on the table.

CHEMICAL SOLUTIONS

0·01 M Rose Bengal (tetra-bromo-tetra-chloro fluorescein). Dissolve 1 g in 100 ml distilled water and store in dark bottle for a class of about twenty-five students. Solution must be freshly prepared each year.

Buffered saline. Mix equal parts of:

M/15 Na_2HPO_4 (9·5 g/litre)
M/15 KH_2PO_4 (9·1 g/litre)
Isotonic saline (9 g NaCl/litre)

3% Hydrogen peroxide, small amounts of stock solution in Barnes bottles.
M/500 Sodium cyanide (10 mg NaCN/100 ml water) store in Barnes bottles and mark *Caution Poison.*

3 M $Na_2S_2O_3.5H_2O$ (74·4 g/100 ml water) store in Barnes bottles.

0·01 M Eosin (0·65 g/100 ml). Prepare 200 ml for class of twenty-five students. (*For optional part of experiment.*)

PRINCIPLE OF THE EXPERIMENT

Certain dye substances, both natural and artificial, have the capacity to sensitize tissues so that light of wavelengths which normally create no damage whatever cause marked tissue reactions of an injurious sort. Although the process is not completely understood, it appears that the dye molecules become excited by the radiant energy and pass on their energy to activate certain proteins which then become susceptible to photochemical oxidation. The reaction is a non-specific photosensitized oxidation (Davson, 1964). In nature, farm animals may obtain photosensitizing dyes from certain plants; in bright sunlight the white animals may die while the black ones (sheep or pigs) will live. The principles of photodynamic action will be demonstrated in this experiment with suspensions of erythrocytes and (in the optional part) with cultures of protozoa.

Red corpuscles are suspended in a physiological saline solution buffered to pH 6·8 with phosphate buffer. Blood is not normally hemolyzed by this solution in a period of 24 h. Different concentrations of rose Bengal are added to the blood and hemolysis times determined for samples exposed to light and control samples placed immediately in the dark. Temperature must also be controlled.

EXPERIMENTAL DETAILS

Prepare a suspension of finger blood containing about 8 drops of blood in 160 ml of buffered saline. This gives a dilution of approximately 1 : 400. Pipette 9 ml of this into each of ten test tubes.

From the stock solution of rose Bengal (1% or 0·01 M) prepare the following dilutions in isotonic saline: 10^{-3} M, 10^{-4} M, 10^{-5} M, 10^{-6} M. You now have a series of five rose Bengal solutions ranging from 10^{-2} M to 10^{-6} M. By adding 1 ml of these to the test tubes containing 9 ml of blood a series of dilutions, ranging from 10^{-3} M to 10^{-7} M, is obtained. Prepare duplicate tubes for this range of concentrations and immediately place one of the pair in the dark and the other in the illuminating apparatus. Record the time to hemolysis.

Hemolysis is readily detected by observing the print of this page or the sharp edge of a piece of paper through the solutions. When the erythrocytes have ruptured and released their hemoglobin (hemolysis) the solutions no longer appear cloudy (suspended red corpuscles) but perfectly clear and transparent.

To test the effect of oxygen on photosensitivity, prepare duplicate tubes as follows and place one of the pair immediately in the dark and the other in the light.

(a) 9 ml Blood suspension, 3 drops 3 M sodium thiosulphate (reducing agent), 1 ml 10^{-4} M rose Bengal.

(b) 9 ml Blood suspension, 3 drops 3% H_2O_2, 1 ml 10^{-4} M rose Bengal.

(c) 9 ml Blood suspension, 3 drops N/500 NaCN solution (*caution*), and 1 ml 10^{-4} M rose Bengal.

RESULTS

Tabulate the results carefully. In the two higher concentrations hemolysis should be detected in the light within less than 1 to 30 min (depending on the illumination) but will require two or three times as long in the dark. Dye concentrations up to 10^{-5} M will probably produce hemolysis in the light during the laboratory period; the tubes at 10^{-5} M or less in the dark at these concentrations will probably not hemolyze. In the lower concentrations hemolysis may not occur during the laboratory period and the tubes may be left overnight and checked the next morning. Hemolysis may not occur even in this time at the two lowest concentrations. The reducing agent (thiosulphate) should increase the hemolysis time in the light. The peroxide may have no effect in the light but should reduce the time in the dark. Cyanide should increase the time when tubes are in the light. Explain these results as evidence that the reaction is a "non-specific photosensitized oxidation" (Davson, 1964).

OPTIONAL EXERCISE ON PHOTODYNAMIC ACTION

Study the effect of two photosensitizing agents (rose Bengal and eosin) on *Paramecia* or other cultures of protozoa. Prepare your dye dilutions from stock solutions of 10^{-3} M rose Bengal and 10^{-2} M eosin. Add a known amount (e.g. 0·1 ml) of dye to a known amount (e.g. 0·9 ml) of culture in a hollow ground slide or small stender dish and expose to light. Determine the time for cessation of movement at different dilutions. Set up adequate controls in the dark.

II. ULTRAVIOLET LIGHT

ANIMALS

A culture of *Amoeba* is best for the observations of protoplasmic changes under the influence of ultraviolet light. For the optional section (comparative study) a variety of small organisms is suitable; we suggest *Paramecia, Euglena,*

Daphnia, Rotifers, *Tubifex* (oligochaete worms) or *Tubatrix* (vinegar worms, Nematoda).

Micro slides, with depression of about 1·5 mm depth (hollow ground slides).

Illuminating apparatus. Various types of inexpensive ultraviolet lamps are sold for germicidal or laboratory purposes such as the examination of materials for fluorescence. Select one with maximum radiation around 2 500 Å. A suggested arrangement which permits illumination at a series of intensities (distances) is shown in Fig. 3.

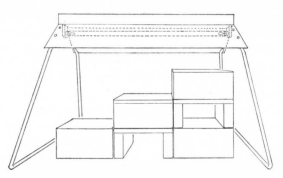

FIG. 3. A suggested arrangement for exposure of cultures to ultraviolet radiation. Adjustments can be easily made to increase the number of intensities. A suitable lamp is the Westinghouse Sterilamp G30T8. A screen should be put in front of the apparatus if it is located where light might be reflected into the students' eyes.

A series of well-defined changes may be observed when naked protoplasm such as that of the *Amoeba* is exposed to ultraviolet radiation. Many of the same changes occur when the temperature is changed to lethal levels. Viscosity changes cause the animal to round up and cease movement; subsequently alterations in the granulation of the protoplasm occur and are associated with permeability changes which lead to the accumulation of water (vacuoles) and eventually the cytolysis (rupture) of the cell. Heilbrunn (1952) argues that the first of these changes is due to release of calcium from the cortex to the interior of the cell and that this is later followed by a general release of the calcium. Doubtless denaturation of protein with a disorganization of the delicate tertiary bonding occurs but release of calcium may be one of the factors involved.

EXPERIMENTAL DETAILS

A mercury vapor lamp is used. Radiation is generated in the vicinity of 2 500 Å. Be particularly careful to protect your eyes from direct *or* reflected radiation. The burn is painful and may cause temporary blindness.

The apparatus is arranged so that hollow ground slides, containing drops of culture fluid, may be exposed at varying distances from the source of radiation, hence at different radiation intensities.

Expose *Amoebae* to intense radiation for brief periods and describe the series of changes which are observed in the cytoplasm. Make careful sketches showing a series of changes in the disintegration of the animals. It is suggested that you expose a preparation at a short distance from the lamp for about 1 min and examine. Make a sketch. If the changes are far advanced, then expose another preparation for a shorter period or at greater distance and again make a sketch. If no changes or only slight changes have taken place, expose for longer periods. In this manner, gradually build up a series of sketches to show the course of events when protoplasm is irradiated in this manner.

OPTIONAL EXERCISE ON ULTRAVIOLET LIGHT

Expose several different kinds of small animals to a series of intensities and record the lethal times in relation to relative intensity. Make notes on behaviour and appearance of the animals. It may be necessary to add culture fluid to compensate for evaporation. Discontinue the experiment after 2 h. Present data graphically by means of histograms.

RESULTS

The course of events in the disintegration of the *Amoeba* was suggested above (p. 136).

In the optional portion of the experiment, no particular differences in resistance may be noted at the higher intensities but at intermediate and lower intensities definite differences should appear. If the highest intensity (exposure distance closest to the lamp) is arbitrarily considered 100, then the relative intensities at increasing distances may be calculated by the inverse square law ($I = 1/D^2$ where I is intensity and D the distance). If now, the exposure time required to kill the various animals is multiplied by the intensity, you will obtain a series of comparative values which are measures of the relative resistances of the animals to ultraviolet radiation. In a typical laboratory experiment the following series of animals was thus arranged in order of decreasing resistance: *Amoeba, Tubatrix, Daphnia, Vorticella*, salmon embryo, *Paramecium* and *Euglena*.

TROUBLE-SHOOTING

Students should be cautioned concerning the ultraviolet lamp and it is best to hang a curtain in front of it. Remember that if the lamp is on the bench nearby, radiation may be reflected from a white or bright table top into the eyes and cause a nasty burn. Students will be interested to detect the odour of ozone produced in the air by the u.v. lamp and this should be brought to their attention.

If the *Amoeba* cultures are rich and the students know how to illuminate their preparations and use a microscope properly, there are no particular difficulties with this exercise.

BIBLIOGRAPHY

Blum, H. F. (1932). Photodynamic action. *Physiol. Rev.* **12**, 23–55. [Review of early literature.]

Davson, H. (1964). "A Textbook of General Physiology," 3rd ed. Churchill, London. [Standard textbook account.]

Giese, A. C. (Ed.) (1964). "Photophysiology." Academic Press, New York. [A two volume monograph covering many aspects of action of light on cells.]

Heilbrunn, L. V. (1952). "An Outline of General Physiology," 3rd ed. Saunders, Philadelphia. [Discussion of protoplasmic reactions to radiation and temperature change.]

Hoar, W. S. (1966). "General and Comparative Physiology." Prentice-Hall, Englewood Cliffs, New Jersey. [Chapter devoted to physiological action of light.]

Hollaender, A. (Ed.) (1954–56). "Radiation Biology." McGraw-Hill, New York. [A three volume monograph.]

Laurens, H. (1933). "The Physiological Effects of Radiant Energy." The Chemical Catalogue Co., Inc., New York. [Older monograph with historical notes on photodynamic action.]

Lea, D. E. (1962). "Actions of Radiations on Living Cells," 2nd ed. Cambridge University Press. [A shorter monograph.]

D. Bioluminescence*

ORGANISMS

A culture of luminescent bacteria may be purchased at small cost from the American Type Culture Collection, 2029 M. Street, N.W., Washington, D.C. Request culture 7744 *Photobacterium fischeri*. Alternatively, the organisms may be isolated from marine fish. Obtain unwashed fish from the fish market, store at about 13°C for a day or two and examine in the dark for luminous spots. Streak some of the material from the luminous spots on a nutrient

---

* Based on Giese (1962a and b) and notes from A. C. Giese, Department of Biology, Stanford University, California, U.S.A.

agar plate. It may be necessary to replate several times until a pure culture is isolated.

CULTURE METHODS

The culture requirements of this organism have been carefully studied (Hill, 1928). Prepare sterile Petri dishes (100 mm × 20 mm) with autoclaved nutrient agar consisting of: 1 g peptone; 1 g glycerol; 2 g agar; 3 g NaCl; 0·5 g CaCO$_3$; 100 ml water (if sea water is used, omit the NaCl).

Add salts and nutrients to boiling water but add the agar after removal from the flame or hot plate; stir until materials are dissolved. Autoclave and cool to about 45°C (warm but not hot to the touch); agitate to maintain suspension of carbonate and pour sufficient into previously sterilized and dry Petri dishes to form a thin layer over the bottom. The carbonate is required to maintain neutrality with organisms which produce acid. When cool the dishes are inoculated with organisms from a vigorous culture by streaking with bacteriological needle or, more effectively, with sterile camel-hair brush. In the latter case a small amount of the 1% glycerol solution (sterile) may be placed on the source culture, and in this way the inoculation will spread large numbers of organisms more evenly over the agar than is possible with the needle.

If the organisms are required over an extended period, subculture at weekly intervals. For any particular class or demonstration prepare the required cultures (about eight per pair of students) 24 h in advance.

APPARATUS

Graduated cylinder (50 ml or 100 ml).
Beakers (250 ml or 500 ml).
Test tubes with test tube rack and rubber stoppers to fit tubes.
Glass tube 1 m long, 1 cm diameter.
Camel-hair brush.
Black light 3 600–4 000 Å (e.g. Westinghouse, 250 W "Purple-X") in an ordinary desk lamp.
Dark room. The experiments must be performed in a light-proof room; a dim red lamp will be required to provide light for reading directions and carrying out the experimental procedures.

CHEMICAL SOLUTIONS

1% Glycerol in sea water (or 3% NaCl) (5 g/500 ml).
M/250 NaCN in dropping bottles (20 mg/100 ml).
4% Urethane in dropping bottles (4 g/100 ml).

"Luminal" solution A. 0·5 g luminal dissolved in 10 ml 0·1 N NaOH and diluted to 500 ml.

"Luminal" solution B. 1 g potassium ferricyanide and 10 ml of 3% H_2O_2 dissolved in 500 ml water.

(Note: "Luminal" may be obtained from the Varnington Chemical Company, 416 North Varney Street, Burbank, California, as *3-aminophthalcyclohydrazide* or from Eastman Organic Chemicals, Rochester 3, N.Y., as *3-amino-2,3-dihydro-1,4-phthalazinedone.*)

0·1 N HCl (8·3 ml concentrated acid/litre).
0·1 N NaOH (4 g/litre).
Crystals of $K_4Fe_2(CN)_6$, about 10 g.

Principle of the Experiment

Several different light-producing reactions will be demonstrated. In part I, the "black" lamp with its short energetic wave band, is played on fluorescent materials to demonstrate this particular phenomenon. Several common materials around the laboratory will probably demonstrate this: for example, dyes such as fluorescein or eosin, dyes in certain fabrics of the students' clothing, phosphorescent rocks, sometimes the students' hair-oil.

In part II, the living light produced through the metabolism of a bacterium is shown to be dependent on a supply of oxygen, and further that the metabolism responsible for the luminescence is inhibited by metabolic poisons such as cyanide and urethane.

In part III, a sharp emission of light appears in a chemical reaction.

In each case photons (packets or quanta of radiant energy) have been released in the reactions and have struck the photosensitive pigments of your eyes to excite the optic system and create the sensation of light. In part I the high energy (ultraviolet) radiation has momentarily displaced electrons from the fluorescent materials and sent them into a high energy state; in returning to ground state during a brief interval, they release this energy in the form of (photons of) light. In parts II and III, some of the energy of a chemical reaction is emitted in the form of light. In the metabolism of the luminescent bacteria, a complex biochemical formed from reduced flavin mononucleotide and a long-chain aldehyde (the complex is referred to as *luciferin*) is oxidized in the presence of an enzyme (luciferase) and light is emitted during the reaction (Hoar, 1966). The supply of flavin mononucleotide is generated in a side chain of the electron transport system; consequently cyanide inhibits the luminescence since it ties up the cytochrome system which is a part of the electron transport chain. Urethane is thought to inhibit through its action on the enzyme luciferase.

EXPERIMENTAL DETAILS

Before proceeding to the dark room, suspend the bacteria from six to eight cultures in the 1% glycerol solution. To do this, add 10–15 ml of the solution to the Petri dish, brush the surface of the agar plate and pour into the beaker. Set the washed cultures aside and they may be rinsed again later for additional bacteria. Add 10 ml of the suspension to each of a series of ten test tubes measuring the amounts with a graduated cylinder. Now proceed to the dark room or put out the main light and wait for dark adaptation to occur in your retinas (what is actually happening in the retina?). When the luminescence on the Petri plates is clearly evident proceed with the experiment. By this time only the top layers of bacteria in the test tubes may be emitting light.

PART I

While your eyes are adapting to the dim light, turn on the black lamp and note what happens when it is directed onto different materials such as fluorescent dyes, phosphorescent rocks or colored fabrics in your clothing.

PART II

Shake one or more of the tubes and note the flash of light. Record the "dimming time" for a 10 ml sample. Shake and repeat to determine how accurately "dimming times" can be measured. The "time to dimming" is a measure of the rate of respiration. Explain in terms of the above discussion. This part of the experiment can be made more spectacular by using a glass tube 1 m long filled with the bacterial suspension.

Now, place four of the suspensions in a test tube rack at eye level and add M/250 NaCN to them as follows: 5 drops, 10 drops, 20 drops and 40 drops. Close tightly with rubber stoppers, shake and record "dimming times". *Avoid getting the cyanide on your fingers;* if this should happen wash thoroughly with soap (alkaline) and water. Compare carefully with the control. At low concentration the cyanide is thought to affect only the rate of respiration; at high concentrations it may combine with luciferin (intensity effect).

Carry out a similar experiment using 4% urethane in amounts of 5, 10, 20 and 40 drops. Compare as before.

PART III

Chemiluminescence is demonstrated by mixing equal quantities of the two "luminal" solutions provided. Pour the mixture over a small amount of ice.

Add a small amount of the KOH solution; add some of the HCl; again add some alkali. Describe what happens after each manipulation.

Again mix equal amounts of the two "luminal" solutions and add a crystal of potassium ferricyanide. Shake.

Add some drops of 0·1 N NaOH to each of the "luminal" solutions and mix.

Other combinations of the materials supplied will suggest themselves during this experiment. Make comparisons as to color, intensity and persistence of illumination.

Results

The findings are largely qualitative. The student should examine some of the literature listed below and familiarize himself with the properties of light and the significance of the experiments which he has performed.

Trouble-shooting

It is obvious that the preparations of the cultures prior to the laboratory must be carried out according to proper bacteriological procedures. Students should again be cautioned in the use of cyanide and instructed to clean all glass thoroughly at the end of the exercise.

Bibliography

Davson, H. (1964). "A Textbook of General Physiology," 3rd ed. Churchill, London. [General discussions of photochemical reactions as well as bioluminescence.]

Giese, A. C. (1962a). "Cell Physiology," 2nd ed. Saunders, Philadelphia.

Giese, A. C. (1962b). "Laboratory Manual in Cell Physiology." The Boxwood Press, Pittsburg, Philadelphia. [An outline for a similar experiment.]

Harvey, E. N. (1960). Bioluminescence. In "Comparative Biochemistry" (M. Florkin and H. S. Mason eds.), Vol. 2, pp. 545–591. Academic Press, New York. [Discussion of the evolution of bioluminescence.]

Hill, S. E. (1928). The influence of molds on the growth of luminescent bacteria in relation to the hydrogen ion concentration, together with the development of a satisfactory culture method. Biol. Bull. mar. Biol. Lab., Woods Hole, 55, 143–150.

Hoar, W. S. (1966). "General and Comparative Physiology," Prentice-Hall, Inc., Englewood Cliffs, New Jersey. [Textbook account.]

McElroy, W. D. and Glass, B. (1961). "A Symposium on Life and Light." Johns Hopkins, Baltimore. [Reviews of many aspects of bioluminescence and discussions of chemiluminescence on pp. 183–205.]

McElroy, W. D. and Seliger, H. H. (1962). Biological luminescence. Scient. Am., 207 (6), 76–89. [Popular account.]

E. Oxygen Equilibrium Curve of Hemocyanin

ANIMALS

A good supply of freshly collected hemocyanin is essential. Dissociation curves developed from stored blood are often steeper than normal due to denaturation of the proteins. Large crabs (*Cancer*), lobsters (*Homarus*) or *Limulus* provide abundant hemocyanin. One large crab provides enough blood for about four students (duplicate experiment with two pairs of students).

APPARATUS

The technique described here is based on a direct visual comparison first described by Pantin and Hogben (1925). It can be easily adapted to a colorimeter or spectrophotometer. We sometimes use the Bausch & Lomb "Spectronic 20" in our introductory laboratory. Many other instruments are equally suitable.

A vacuum pump which creates a difference of 735 mm on the manometer (Fig. 4) is required. If a vacuum line is not present in the laboratory, a good aspirator pump will usually provide the necessary pressure differences. However, a vacuum pump will prove more reliable since water pressures often vary; a single pump, with a suitable series of stopcocks, is adequate for two groups of students. Arrange vacuum as shown in Fig. 4.

A series of test tubes, about 15 mm internal diam.

Clamps and connections as shown in Fig. 4.

CHEMICAL SOLUTIONS

Hemocyanin. Pull one of the large walking legs from the body so that it breaks into the blood sinuses and tears out some of the muscle. The joint between the first and second segment of the walking leg is the autotomy joint and a break here is useless. The exoskeleton of the appendage must be broken at its point of articulation with the body. Do not use the cheliped or pincer as its removal may injure the digestive gland and result in release of pigment which obscures the hemocyanin comparison. Hold the animal over a large funnel (diameter about 12 in.) while amputating the leg; place the animal in the funnel immediately thereafter; its activity will promote bleeding. Blood is collected from the funnel in a beaker.

Now agitate the blood gently in the beaker while a white fluffy clot forms and the blood becomes fully oxygenated (blue). Filter through several layers of cotton gauze (cheese cloth); the blood is now ready to use.

Starch suspension. Put a few grams of soluble starch in a flask of distilled water and shake; some starch should remain in the bottom of the flask.

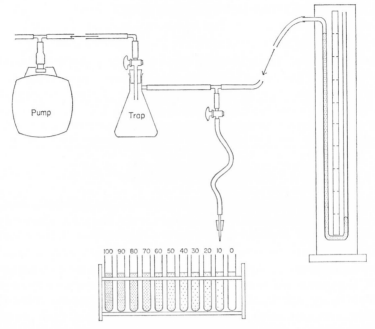

Fig. 4. A suggested arrangement for operating the experiment with two groups of students on one vacuum pump. Both groups should not attempt to adjust the pressure at the same time.

A variety of colors (avoid indicators) such as indian ink, hematoxylin, iodine in KI solution and Orange G dye should be adequate to prepare the blank or "dummy". Only small amounts (about 10/ml) of the colors are required.

Capryl alcohol (2-octanol), small amount in Barnes bottle.

> M/15 Na_2HPO_4 (9·5 g/litre).
> M/15 KH_2PO_4 (9·1 g/litre).
> Sodium hydrosulphite ($Na_2S_2O_4 . 2H_2O$), few grams of solid.

PRINCIPLE OF THE EXPERIMENT

The respiratory pigment, hemocyanin, is blue when oxygenated and colorless when deoxygenated or "reduced". The color change can be readily produced by lowering the oxygen tension and bringing the blood into equilibrium by shaking it; the color change is proportional to the oxygen tension at equilibrium.

In this simple visual method of developing an oxygen equilibrium curve a sample of blood is first completely reduced by bringing it into equilibrium at about 5 mm partial pressure of oxygen (difference of about 735 mm on the limbs of your manometer). A "dummy" or blank solution is then prepared (to match this sample of reduced blood) by mixing dilute starch and dyes. This blank is then mixed with varying amounts of oxygenated hemocyanin to produce a series of colors corresponding to varying dilutions of oxy-hemocyanin. These blank colors (corresponding to percents "saturation" with hemocyanin) are then matched against a sample of blood which is equilibrated at different partial pressures of oxygen to give the relationship between partial pressure of oxygen and percent saturation with hemocyanin.

Experimental Details

Put 5 ml blood and 1 drop of carpyl alcohol in the equilibrating tube and attach to the manometer. Start the vacuum pump and evacuate the vessel, tapping vigorously and constantly until the blue color disappears. This is your standard reference color for reduced hemocyanin. Complete reduction requires a difference of about 735 mm in mercury heights of the two limbs of the manometer. When decoloration is complete, close the tube with the thumb screw and turn off the pump. To determine whether reduction is complete, take 2 ml of blood in a test tube and add a few crystals of sodium hydrosulphite ($Na_2S_2O_4.2H_2O$). The turbidity of blood reduced in this way may not be quite the same as that of the blood reduced with the vacuum pump.

Make up about 50 ml of a solution of water and coloring material to match the color of the reduced blood. This solution is to be used to dilute the blood in making up the color standards. A variety of coloring material is satis-factory. Dilute starch solution with one or two drops of indian ink, Orange G dye, iodine or hematoxylin will usually produce a matching solution. Indi-cators should be avoided.

Prepare a series of color standards by mixing oxygenated blood with diluting solution in different proportions. In this way a color series corres-ponding to percent of saturated hemocyanin is obtained. Thus, a color corresponding to a hemocyanin solution 50% oxygenated is obtained by mixing equal parts of oxygenated blood and diluting solution (Table I).

To obtain an oxygen dissociation curve a 5 ml blood sample is equilibrated with known partial pressures of oxygen. To do this attach the sample to the manometer, establish the required pressure with the pump and tap the tube until the color no longer changes. At atmospheric pressure (760 mm Hg) the partial pressure of oxygen $= 1/5 \times 760 = 152$ mm. If the apparatus is evacuated to a pressure of 100 mm Hg (the difference between the levels of mercury in the two arms of the manometer), the oxygen pressure will then be $1/5 \times 100 = 20$ mm and so on. The color of the blood in the equilibrator

G

TABLE I

Oxygenated blood (ml)	Diluting solution (ml)	Standard % oxygenated hemocyanin	Oxygenated blood (ml)	Diluting solution (ml)	Standard % oxygenated hemocyanin
0·0	5·0	0	3·0	2·0	60
0·5	4·5	10	3·5	1·5	70
1·0	4·0	20	4·0	1·0	80
1·5	3·5	30	4·5	0·5	90
2·0	3·0	40	5·0	0·0	100
2·5	2·5	50			

is then matched against the standards to determine the percent saturation of the blood with oxygen.

Equilibrate the blood at oxygen pressure of 5, 10, 15, 20, 30, 40, 50, 60, 70, and from the data obtained plot the dissociation curve.

Study the effect of pH on the oxygen dissociation curve by using phosphate buffer at pH 6·0 (12 ml $M/15$ Na_2HPO_4 plus 88 ml $M/15$ KH_2PO_4). The 5·0 ml samples can be brought to the desired pH by adding 0·5 ml of buffer. Add 0·5 ml buffer to the blood sample and to each of the standards used above. Repeat the equilibrating at the oxygen tensions 10, 20, 30 and 40 mm. Compare with first curve.

RESULTS

Results from a typical laboratory experiment carried out according to these directions on *Cancer* hemocyanin are shown in Fig. 5. With this technique considerable variation may be expected, but the shapes of the equilibrium curves at normal pH should be very similar from group to group and the Bohr effect (movement of the curve to the right at lower pH) should always be clearly evident. Various factors such as differences in the calcium ion content (Larimer and Riggs, 1964) and temperature (Waterman, 1960) may be responsible for the differences which appear from time to time.

TROUBLE-SHOOTING

Students will probably require assistance at two points. There is sometimes a failure to obtain complete deoxygenation of the hemocyanin because of a failure to *tap vigorously* during the evacuation. Hit the tube on the palm of your left hand and, if the blood is cold, hold in the hand to warm to body temperature. The other difficulty which often arises is in establishing the various oxygen tensions on the manometer. It is not necessary to establish

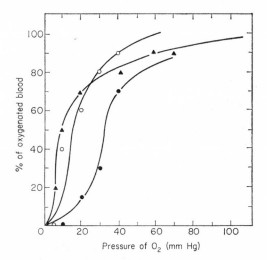

FIG. 5. Class room data obtained with *Cancer* hemocyanin. ▲, Blood as obtained from the crab at pH 7·2; ○, pH 8·0; ●, pH 6·0.

the precise values listed (5, 10, 15 etc.) but it is necessary to have values close to these and values which are known precisely; it is as easy to plot 6, 12 and 18 as it is 5, 10 and 15 or any other series. It should also be noted that if starch has been used in preparing the blank solution, it will tend to settle and the suspension must be shaken frequently if comparisons are to be accurate.

CLEANING UP

We usually cook and eat the crabs!

BIBLIOGRAPHY

Larimer, J. L. and Riggs, A. F. (1964). Properties of haemocyanins. *Comp. Biochem. Physiol.*, **13**, 35–46. [Describes effect of Ca^{++} on crayfish blood.]

Pantin, C. F. A. and Hogben, L. T. (1925). A colorimetric method for studying the dissociation of oxyhaemocyanin suitable for class work. *J. mar. Biol. Ass. U.K.*, **13**, 970–980. [The technique as originally described.]

Prosser, C. L. and Brown, F. A. (1961). "Comparative Animal Physiology," 2nd ed. Saunders, Philadelphia. [Excellent discussion of respiratory functions of blood in chapter 8.]

Waterman, T. H. (Ed.) (1960). "The Physiology of the Crustacea," Vol. 1. Academic Press, New York. [Detailed discussion of equilibrium curves for hemocyanin.]

Welsh, J. H. and Smith, R. I. (1960). "Laboratory Exercises in Invertebrate Physiology," 2nd ed. Burgess Publishing Co., Minneapolis. [Describes procedure for same experiment.]

F.   Active Transport Through Cell Membranes

ANIMALS

The directions are written for the goldfish *Carassius auratus* because of its universal distribution and easy availability. However, the exercise works well with kidneys from a variety of fishes or from frog tadpoles.

APPARATUS

Microscope, slides, cover glasses, dissection instruments (needles, forceps, scissor).

The solutions must be continuously aerated and a cylinder of oxygen is essential. Each pair of students is provided with six stender dishes (about 50 mm diam.). The oxygen is led to these through a series of polythene or rubber tubes provided with valves (such as used by aquarists): hypodermic needles (about 20 gauge) at the ends where the oxygen enters the stenders provide a fine jet of gas to maintain oxygen at a high level in the stenders (Fig. 6).

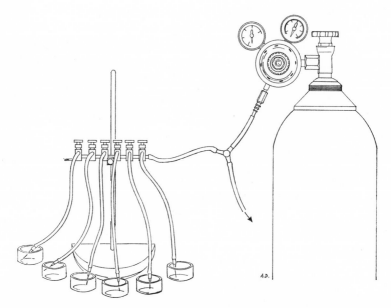

FIG. 6. A suggested arrangement for the oxygenation of the six tissue preparations.

CHEMICAL SOLUTIONS

1. Basic saline solution (basic medium)

NaCl	5·8 g/l (for marine fish 7·8 g/l)
KCl	0·19
$CaCl_2.2H_2O$	0·22
$MgCl_2.6H_2O$	0·20
$NaHCO_3$	1·26
$NaH_2PO_4.H_2O$	0·07

2. Basic saline solution *plus* 2·5 mg phenol red per 100 ml.
3. Basic saline solution *plus* 1·0 mg phenol red per 100 ml.
4. Omit calcium from the basic medium.
5. Omit potassium from the basic medium.
6. Potassium cyanide

M/100	65 mg KCN
	2·5 mg phenol red
	100 ml basic saline
M/500	13 mg KCN
	2·5 mg phenol red
	100 ml basic saline

7. 2,4-Dinitrophenol

M/10 000	18·4 mg DNP
	2·5 mg phenol red
	100 ml basic saline
M/50 000	3·7 mg DNP
	2·5 mg phenol red
	100 ml basic medium

8. Potassium iodoacetate

M/2 000	11·2 mg potassium iodoacetate
	2·5 mg phenol red
	100 ml basic medium

9. *p*-Aminohippurate

M/800	24·5 mg hippurate
	2·5 mg phenol red
	100 ml basic medium
M/2 000	9·7 mg hippurate
	2·5 mg phenol red
	100 ml basic medium

10. Uric acid

M/680	24·7 mg uric acid
	2·5 mg phenol red
	100 ml basic medium

11. Phenol red indicator standards, a series of tubes such as the "La Motte" standardized indicator solutions.

Principle of the Experiment

One of the ways in which materials enter cells or pass through membranes is by *active transport*; the other depends on the physical forces of diffusion and osmosis, i.e. differences in concentration gradient. *Active transport* implies not only the movement from regions of lower concentration to regions of higher concentration (i.e. against a diffusion gradient) but also the involvement of metabolic processes to provide the necessary energy.

In this experiment simple microscopic methods will be used to follow the movement of dye through kidney tubule cells and to note its concentration within the tubules where the color becomes much more intense than in the surrounding medium. In the second part of the experiment a series of metabolic poisons are shown to inhibit or prevent this process. For example, cyanide inhibits the cytochrome system and thus eliminates the ATP production which depends on oxidative phosphorylation; dinitrophenol uncouples oxidative phosphorylation and iodoacetate inhibits one of the glycolytic enzymes (3-phosphoglyceraldehyde dehydrogenase). Failure of the dye to accumulate under these conditions argues for a dependence on the supplies of ATP generated during metabolism.

Experimental Details

It is best to have two goldfish for each pair of students (one is used in part I and one in part II). Before the class begins work, the instructor will demonstrate the proper method of pithing the goldfish, dissecting out the kidney, teasing it in the saline and mounting small pieces for examination.

PREPARATION OF KIDNEY FRAGMENTS

Remove goldfish from tank, grasp the fish in left hand and with the right hand push a dissecting needle through the back part of the skull and destroy the brain and anterior part of the spinal cord. Cut away the body wall on one side and remove the viscera, including air bladder. The kidney will be seen as a somewhat rectangular body in the anterior dorsal area. It may be easily removed with curved forceps. Wash it quickly in the basic medium and tease apart with dissecting needles in the stender of aerated basic medium. Transfer small portions to each of the other five dishes; note the time and see that the fragments are *very finely divided* and aerated.

To examine kidney tubules, transfer small bits of tissue (less than 1 mm to a glass slide), add a drop of the fluid from which the tissue was taken and place a cover glass on the tissue; press lightly with the fingernail to "squash" the tissue flat. The tubules should now be clearly visible under intermediate magnification. Note that the broken fragments of tubules tend to round up at the ends to isolate the lumina from the suspension fluid.

THE EXPERIMENT

Set up six stender dishes as illustrated in Fig. 6 and place about 5 ml of the appropriate solution in each of them. Ensure that the aeration is continuous. For the first half of the laboratory period, use the series of solutions given in part I below; clean up the stenders after about 90 min and then do the second series set out under part II. At the end of the class clean all the glassware thoroughly and leave the hypodermic needles with their plastic tubes to soak in water. The inhibitors used in part II are active in small amounts and can ruin the experiment for the next group of students.

Examine bits of the tissue on glass slides at intervals of 5, 10, 20, 30, 45 and 60 min. Accumulation of dye may be evident at 5 min and is usually maximal at 30–60 min.

Note whether the dye is accumulating in the cells or the lumina or both and record concentrations on an arbitrary scale from minimal ($+$) to maximal ($++++$). Phenol red is an indicator and changes color with the pH. Compare the color with a series of standards in the laboratory. In this experiment an attempt has been made to maintain an alkalinity in the test solutions through the inclusion of bicarbonate.

TEST SOLUTIONS

I. EFFECT OF CALCIUM, POTASSIUM AND OXYGEN ON TRANSPORT

(a) Basic saline medium
(b) Basic saline medium + phenol red 2·5 mg %
(c) Basic saline medium + phenol red 1·0 mg %
(d) Omit Ca^{++} from (b)
(e) Omit K^+ from (b)
(f) Omit O_2 from (b)

II. ENZYME INHIBITION AND PHENOL RED TRANSPORT

Enzyme mechanisms involved in active transport have been studied by the use of compounds known to inhibit specific enzymes in one way or another. In the second part of the experiment prepare a control and compare with saline containing representative inhibitors from the above series as indicated by your instructor. According to the literature, the lower concentration gives partial inhibition while the higher completely inhibits the process.

RESULTS

Tabulate the results carefully. Define *active transport* and discuss the findings of this experiment as evidence for the phenomenon. Consult the literature and comment on the probable point of action of each of the inhibitors.

Uptake of phenol red may be detected within a few minutes as a faint redness of the cells of the tubular epithelium; later a deep redness appears within the tubular lumina. Wasserman *et al.* (1953) describe the effects of calcium and potassium. Discover whether uptake by the cells is blocked or whether it is the secretion into the lumen. According to the literature potassium is required for uptake of dye from the medium while excretion of dye from the cells into the lumen of the tubule requires calcium. Within limits, the uptake increases with increasing potassium; in calcium-free media the dye accumulates within the cells without significant deposition in the tubular urine (Wasserman *et al.*, 1953).

When the tissues are not supplied with oxygen, you should be able to discover that the governing processes are aerobic.

TROUBLE-SHOOTING

There are very few places where this experiment can fail. It is important to make the dissection quickly and to get the kidney fragments into aerated saline promptly. For this reason, it is advisable for the demonstrator to make a dissection, show the students the location of the kidney, and how it is removed and teased in saline. It is also advisable to make a mount and demonstrate the tubules before the students start their work. Later in the laboratory as the dye begins to accumulate this should be shown to students who have not seen it already. Again, the optics of the microscope must be checked, for the lighting is critical if the first evidence of accumulation is to be observed. The class should know that all pieces of tubule will not accumulate dye or do so to the same degree. There is a variation in the physiological capacities of different areas of the tubules; also, the opportunity for penetration varies with the size and degree of fragmentation of the kidney.

CLEANING UP

The stenders should be thoroughly washed after the inhibitors. The plastic tubes and their aerating needles should be left soaking in a beaker of water in preparation for the next laboratory group.

BIBLIOGRAPHY

Forster, R. P. (1948). Use of thin kidney slices and isolated renal tubules for direct study of cellular transport kinetics. *Science, N.Y.*, **108**, 65–76. [The definitive experiments.]

Giese, A. C. (1962). "Cell Physiology," 2nd ed. Saunders, Philadelphia. [General discussions of permeability and active transport.]

Holter, H. (1961). How things get into cells. *Scient. Am.*, **205** (3), 167–180. [Good review paper.]

Jaffee, O. C. (1954). Phenol red transport in the pronephros and mesonephros of the developing frog (*Rana pipiens*). *J. cell. comp. Physiol.*, **44**, 347–361. [Describes the original experiments on competitive inhibition using uric acid and hippurate.]

Wasserman, K., Becker, E. L. and Fishmen, A. P. (1953). Transport of phenol red in the flounder renal tubule. *J. cell. comp. Physiol.*, **42**, 385–393. [Describes the effects of Ca^{++} and K^+ ions.]

G. Salinity and the Volume or Weight of Animals

ANIMALS

Marine or estuarial polychaete worms are preferred although the experiment can also be performed with nudibranchs or other soft-bodied invertebrates. We usually use *Eudistylia vancouveri* (removed from their tubes) but have obtained nice class results with *Nereis*. Twelve animals are required for each group of students.

APPARATUS

The size of the animal may be determined either as weight or volume. Animals weighing 6–10 g may be weighed on a simple balance such as a triple beam balance sensitive to 0·1 g or the volume may be determined in a 100 ml graduated cylinder by observing the rise in fluid level on the addition of the animal to the cylinder. For worms of smaller size, volumes may be determined in a burette (50 or 100 ml capacity, graduations 0·1 or 0·2 ml). Burettes with damaged stopcocks or tips may be cut off and closed at the bottom with a rubber stopper. It is then easy to drain the volume tube together with the animal back into the holding dish by simply removing the stopper.

Ten stacking dishes. Any wide-mouthed containers with capacity over 100 ml are suitable for holding the animals during the experiment—jam jars, stacking dishes (100 mm diameter), plastic ice box containers.

CHEMICAL SOLUTIONS

Sea water of salinity 28–30‰.

Isosmotic sucrose. Note: Nicol (1960, p. 33) provides a nomograph for corresponding concentrations of sucrose and sea water.

Principle of the Experiment

This experiment will illustrate several of the physiological difficulties faced by animals in a hypo-osmotic environment. The body fluids of such animals are hypertonic to the surrounding medium. Water flows in due to differences in water concentration; the animal swells. The student should discover whether swelling is roughly proportional to dilution since the worms are placed in two different dilutions.

If the animal behaved as a simple osmometer swelling should continue for some time in direct relation to the exposure. Decreased rate of swelling may mean that the animal is able to excrete some of the water or that it is able to prevent the swelling due to the elasticity of its tissues. It may also indicate a loss of salt.

Even though the body surfaces are relatively impermeable to salts, they are not likely to be absolutely so. Loss of salt may also decrease the gradients and the failure of the worms to recover when returned to sea water should provide a basis for arguments concerning the loss of salts. The results of the sucrose solution should also provide evidence concerning the permeability to salts.

Experimental Details

Where balances are available, determine the weights of worms in various solutions at the times indicated below. Otherwise follow changes by determining volumes. In either case, first remove adhering water by touching lightly with absorbent paper. Then, either weigh the worm on a Petri dish or place it in a partly filled volume tube and note the change in level of the meniscus. The solution in the volume tube is that particular solution in which the worm is being studied.

As a preliminary to the main exercise, select a worm, determine its size twenty times and estimate the error involved in your method.

Now proceed as follows using two worms for each part of the experiment. Determine their initial volumes in sea water and then place in the following solutions.

1. Sea water control.
2. Distilled water.
3. Equal parts of sea water and distilled water.
4. Equal parts sea water and isosmotic sucrose.
5. Sucrose osmotically equivalent to sea water.

Determine sizes at 10 min intervals for 90 min. At the end of this time return all animals to sea water and re-determine their size at 15 min intervals for 60 min.

Study the percentage change in size with respect to time and with respect to (osmotic) concentration of the surrounding fluid. Tabulate all results on the blackboard. Graph your results and compare with average graph for class results. Discuss factors responsible for observed changes in volume.

RESULTS

If the laboratory time is limited, calculations may be performed later and the calculations and tabulation of class results may be carried out the next day. Figure 7 is a sample graph prepared from data obtained in a class of fifty students. Conclusions follow logically and simply from the statement of the principles of the experiment and the graphed results which emerge.

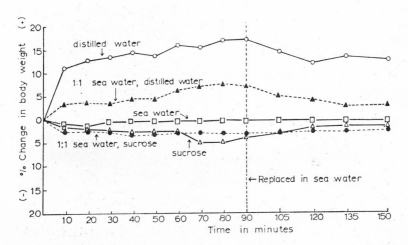

FIG. 7. Change in weight or volume of *Eudistylia vancouveri*. Average values obtained in a class of fifty students.

BIBLIOGRAPHY

The literature is voluminous. The following standard texts contain useful bibliographies.

Hoar, W. S. (1966). "General and Comparative Physiology." Prentice-Hall, Englewood Cliffs, New Jersey.

Nicol, J. A. C. (1960). "The Biology of Marine Animals." Pitman, London.

Potts, W. T. W. and Parry, G. (1964). "Osmotic and Ionic Regulation," Pergamon Press, Oxford.

Prosser, C. L. and Brown, F. A. (1961). "Comparative Animal Physiology," 2nd ed. Saunders, Philadelphia.

H. Physiological Color Changes of Vertebrates

ANIMALS

Frogs.

Fish. Either minnows, goldfish (with some dark, pigmented areas) or small trout are suitable. It is essential to have a species with easily detachable scales which are covered with pigmented epidermis.

APPARATUS

Stacking (preparation) dishes, about 300 ml capacity or glass jars which can be put over individual frogs while their colours are being compared.

Three large containers such as crocks or wooden boxes or aquaria (size about 18 in. × 12 in.). The interiors of two of these are painted black (dull paint) and one is painted white unless it is transparent and can be placed on a white background. One of the black-painted containers must be closed with a light-proof cover while the other is open to the sky or overhead illumination.

Microscopes, glass slides and cover-glasses.

Hypodermic syringe (1 ml capacity or less) with needles (about 22 gauge or greater).

Instruments. Blunt probe, fine forceps, scissor, etc.

CHEMICAL SOLUTIONS

Adrenaline (1 mg/ml).

Acetylcholine (100 mg/ml).

Melatonin (0·5 mg/ml).

Pituitary extract. Some pituitary extracts do not contain melanophore stimulating hormone (MSH). Beef pituitary powder (whole gland) is inexpensive (N.B.C. Research Biochemical, for example) and gives a good response in frogs. Shake about 1 g of powder with about 10 ml frog Ringer solution; let stand for about 30 min and filter.

0·2 M Sodium chloride (1·2 g/100 ml).

0·2 M Potassium chloride (1·5 g/100 ml).

0·2 M Calcium chloride (1·8 g/100 ml).

PRINCIPLE OF THE EXPERIMENT

The chromatophores of lower vertebrates contain several biochemically different types of pigment granules. The black or brown pigments are melanins and the cells which contain them are called *melanophores*; red and yellow pigments are usually carotenoids (sometimes pterins) and the cells which contain them are respectively the *erythrophores* and *xanthophores*. In addition, fish chromatophores often contain silvery particles or crystals of guanine and are called *guanophores* (*leucophores* if the particles are small and *iridiophores* if they are in the form of large reflecting plates). Reflection and refraction of light by these crystalline plates may give the animal a blue color. These several different types of cells will be identified and studied during the microscopy work of this exercise.

In addition, an attempt will be made to identify the factors responsible for changes in the distribution of pigment granules within cells. In the less specialized situations the distribution of the pigment granules depends only on hormones; in the more specialized situations the control is by way of the autonomic nervous system. The frog exemplifies hormonal regulation of the chromatophores; many of the teleost fishes (e.g. trout and minnows) show a predominant nervous control of chromatophores; in some, such as the eel, both hormones and autonomic nervous system are apparently active. The pathways are shown diagrammatically in Fig. 8. There is a rich literature devoted to the pigment cell physiology of lower vertebrates (Waring, 1963).

EXPERIMENTAL DETAILS

I. Place a normal and a blinded frog in each of the following situations.

(a) A clear glass bottle or aquarium on a white background or a large box painted white inside.

(b) A similar container which is black inside and absolutely light-proof.

(c) A similar container (black inside) into which light enters from above. Light must strike only the ventral area of the retina; none should be reflected into the dorsal area (Fig. 8).

To blind the animals, etherize lightly and cauterize the cornea (any standard laboratory anesthetic is equally suitable). To anesthetize, place the frog under a stacking dish or wide-mouth bottle with a small piece of cotton soaked in ether. Leave only until the frog relaxes and is unresponsive to pinching. Remove from jar. Hold back the nictitating membrane of the eye with fine forceps and rub a hot blunt probe over the cornea. It should become opaque. The probe must be heated in an open flame. *Beware* of ether and open flames!

The frogs should recover quickly and comparisons should be made after about 1 day. There should be a small amount of water in the bottom of the containers to keep the animals moist.

II. Describe the color changes which occur when frogs (or/and minnows or trout) are injected with the following substances; for each animal, use about 0·25 ml of the solutions supplied: adrenaline, acetylcholine pituitary, extract (MSH or intermedin), melatonin. The comparisons can be made most readily by selecting frogs of uniform color and placing one animal under each of a series of glass stacking dishes on a moist (saturated paper towels) table top. Include an uninjected control. Observe at intervals over a period of about 2 h. If distinct differences are not evident within 30 min, make another injection.

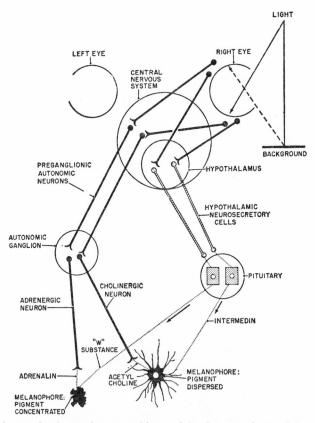

FIG. 8. Diagram for the regulatory machinery of the chromatophores of the eel, *Anguilla*. (From Scharrer, E. and Scharrer, B. (1963). "Neuroendocrinology". Columbia University Press, New York.)

III. Study pigment cells under the microscope. Mount bits of living tadpole skin or skin covered with scales from fish (trout, minnow, goldfish) in a drop of water under a cover-glass. It is not necessary to kill the animals. With fine forceps, single scales or groups of scales can be detached from fish or small bits of skin obtained from tadpoles.

Identify the various types of pigment cells described above and make careful sketches. Describe melanophores as *punctate, stellate* or *reticulate*.

While observing melanophores with pigment in the dispersed or concentrated state, apply each of the following substances and note any changes which occur; adrenaline, acetylcholine, pituitary extract, melatonin, 0·1 and 0·2 M NaCl, KCl and CaCl$_2$.

RESULTS

Well marked color differences should be evident as a result of the different treatments. MSH or intermedin may be the only factor normally involved in the chromatic responses of the frog. As will be evident from the microscopic preparations and from the frog injected with pituitary extract, this factor brings about a dispersion of the melanin and a black or dark animal. Reference should be made to Fig. 8. If the entire chromatic control of the frog is to be explained in terms of this one factor, then it is evident that intermedin is released in large amounts only when the ventral portion of the retina is stimulated but if both the ventral and dorsal areas are simultaneously stimulated no release occurs; in the dark, intermedin is not released and the animal is also light. A melanophore concentrating hormone (MCH) has also been described in some amphibians (*Xenopus*) and fishes, and many writers would explain these reactions in terms of two hormones. MSH is released on stimulation of the ventral portion of the retina while MCH is released when the dorsal areas are stimulated. The evidence supports the view that when release of both hormones is stimulated, the effect of MCH predominates and, further, that in the absence of any pituitary stimulation, the small amounts of MCH produced will override the effects of small amounts of MSH. In addition, it has recently been discovered that melatonin is formed in relatively large amounts in the pineal gland which has long been related to the photic responses of the lower vertebrates. As your results should demonstrate, melatonin is a powerful agent in clumping the pigment within melanophores.

Control is predominantly by way of the autonomic nervous system in the trout or minnow. Figure 8 shows the pathways and your data should show that adrenaline tends to clump the pigment granules while they are dispersed by acetylcholine. These reactions can be demonstrated in the frog even though the animal does not normally depend on the autonomic for color adjustment. The movement of melanophore granules within the chromatophores is probably regulated in the same manner throughout the vertebrates and the responses of frog melanophores to autonomic drugs can be considered pharmacological rather than physiological.

The effects of dilute salt solutions are more difficult to detect in laboratory experiments of this sort. In the melanophores of *Fundulus*, KCl has been observed to concentrate the pigment granules while they are dispersed by

NaCl; opposite effects may be observed in other types of pigment cells (cf. action of NaCl on xanthophores) and in different species of animals (cf. KCl on frog chromatophores). Effects of ions are probably to be explained in terms of their action on the membrane potential which in turn modifies the electrophoretic migration of pigment granules (Hoar, 1966).

TROUBLE-SHOOTING

There is absolutely nothing that can go wrong with the experiment, provided that the animals are not killed with over-anesthetic and provided that the students know how to use a microscope since care is required to demonstrate guanine crystals.

OPTIONAL

Some students may wish to demonstrate more specifically the role of the pituitary by removing it and testing the responses of the hypophysectomized frogs in the three situations used for the blinded animals. The operation is not a difficult one and the instructor may wish to prepare some hypophysectomized animals even though the students may not have time to do this in the laboratory period. Detailed instructions and diagrams may be found in Rugh (1962).

CARE OF EXPERIMENTAL ANIMALS

Check the blinded and hypophysectomized animals daily; remove dead animals, wash out the containers and put in a small amount of fresh water.

BIBLIOGRAPHY

Fingermann, M. (1963). "The Control of Chromatophores." Pergamon Press, Oxford.

Hoar, W. S. (1966). "General and Comparative Physiology." Prentice-Hall, Englewood Cliffs, New Jersey.

Parker, G. H. (1948). "Animal Colour Changes and their Neurohumors." Cambridge University Press.

Prosser, C. L. and Brown, F. A. (1961). "Comparative Animal Physiology," 2nd ed Saunders, Philadelphia.

Rugh, R. (1962). "Experimental Embryology," 2nd ed. Burgess Publishing Co., Minneapolis.

Waring, H. (1963). "Color Change Mechanisms of Cold-blooded Vertebrates." Academic Press, New York.

9 | A Biological Membrane
The Frog and Toad Urinary Bladder

P. J. BENTLEY

The Mount Sinai Graduate School of Biological Sciences, City University of New York, New York, U.S.A.

INTRODUCTION

Animals live in environments of varying physical and chemical composition with which they will tend to equilibrate. These habitats include freshwater rivers and ponds which have low salt concentration, the oceans which have a high concentration of salts, and dry land where water is relatively scarce. Ordinary physicochemical forces, if left unchecked, will thus in fresh water tend to dilute the body fluids and in sea water or on land increase their concentrations. Such changes would soon produce body fluids unsuitable for the maintenance of life and result in the death of the animal. The ability to survive these potentially hostile conditions is due to the properties of the membranes with which the animals are surrounded, enabling them to control what enters and leaves their body fluids.

Biologically membranes may be relatively static structures designed to limit physically exchange from either side; the skins of many fish and mammals could be included in this group. On the other hand, biological membranes may dynamically control what passes across them and even move materials against their physicochemical gradients. Examples of tissues with such dynamic membranes include gills, lungs, guts, kidneys and the skin and urinary bladders of many Amphibia.

The present series of experiments are designed to acquaint you with some of the properties of a dynamic biological membrane and a hormone that may physiologically control its permeability.

EXPT 1. PREPARATION OF THE ISOLATED URINARY BLADDER: VOLUME, PERMEABILITY TO WATER AND STRUCTURE

The aim of this class is to prepare an isolated bladder preparation, get an estimate of the volume of the anuran bladder, and to examine its structure in the histological preparations provided.

APPARATUS

1. The dissecting instruments and apparatus necessary for mounting the bladder are as described under Dissection (see Appendix, p. 172).

2. A coarse balance (weighing to 1 g) suitable for weighing frogs or toads (one instrument for the class will be enough).

3. A well damped balance weighing rapidly to about 1 mg (e.g. Mettler model H4) which can be shared by a number of students but must be near to the preparations.

4. An aquarium aerator or compressed air supply which can be divided to pass air through a water bath and along several thin plastic tubes supplying the bathing Ringer solutions.

PROCEDURE

1. Select two toads and, disturbing them as little as possible, weigh them on the coarse balance provided. Empty the bladder by catheterizing with a piece of plastic tubing (see dissection instructions). When the bladder is empty, weigh again and calculate the water content of the bladder as a percentage of the body weight (bladder empty). Enter the result on the class board or record sheet.

Estimate the mean value for the volume of urine contained in all the toads used in the class. What is the maximum amount of fluid the bladder holds?

If the toads are relatively undisturbed the mean value should be about 15 g per 100 g body weight and the maximum about 30 g per 100 g. The value will, however, vary in different species.

2. Prepare an isolated bladder preparation as described in the Appendix (p. 172). If unsuccessful with your first toad use another.

3. Measure water transfer along an osmotic gradient across the bladder. When the bladder is filled with dilute (1×10) Ringer solution take it carefully out of its test tube of Ringer solution and dry the rubber stopper and glass tubing with a soft paper tissue. Weigh the preparation when suspended from the upper hook on the balance and then replace it in the aerated Ringer solution. Reweigh about 1 h later (depending on the time you have left in the class).

Depending on the condition and size of bladder tissue, the preparation should lose anything from 15 to 50 mg of water in an hour. Greater losses usually indicate that the bladder has a hole in it. Water moves slowly across the bladder wall along an osmotic gradient as it would across a semipermeable membrane limiting the movement of solute relative to that of solvent.

4. Estimate the volume of the bladder by filling it to its maximum distension with fluid. The bladder clearly is capable of great distension and becomes a very thin sac indeed.

5. Examine the structure of the bladder. While you are incubating the bladder, look at the transverse sections of bladder tissue that have been provided. (These are made by fixing the distended bladder in Susa and staining with haematoxylin and eosin.) Observe the prominent epithelial cells which line the mucosal surface of the bladder, the thin serosal layer which can sometimes be seen to contain small blood vessels and muscle cells.

Active sodium transport from the mucosal to the serosal side of the bladder takes place across the epithelial cells and their permeability to water (and sodium) is increased when neurohypophysial hormones are present.

EXPT 2. EFFECT OF NEUROHYPOPHYSIAL HORMONES ON THE PERMEABILITY OF THE BLADDER TO WATER

Hormones released from the neurohypophysis of vertebrates increase the permeability of biological membranes such as the amphibian urinary bladder and skin (not *all* Amphibia) and the renal tubules of most tetrapod vertebrates to water. The mammalian renal tubule responds in this manner limiting urinary water loss and increasing the urine concentration. In the absence of such hormones large volumes of urine are formed: a condition called diabetes insipidus. The response of the isolated amphibian urinary bladder to neurohypophysial hormones is analogous to the response of the renal tubule to this hormone.

APPARATUS

In addition to the equipment and solutions used in expt 1, you will require oxytocin (for *Rana*; e.g. Pitocin, Parke Davis, or Syntocinon, Sandoz) or vasopressin (for *Bufo*, e.g. Pitressin, Parke Davis or oxytocin, but in higher concentration; 20 mu/ml).

PROCEDURE

1. Make two isolated bladder preparations and fill them with dilute (1 : 10) frog Ringer solution. Use the same volume of fluid to fill the bladder throughout the experiment.

2. Measure the water transfer across these preparations for 30 min as you did in expt 1. This serves as a control measurement and checks whether your bladder has any bad leaks.

3. After weighing the preparations move them back to the baths in which they have just been incubated and refill *one* with ordinary 1 : 10 Ringer. Fill the other with 1 : 10 Ringer solution to which has been added 10 mu/ml of oxytocin or vasopressin (preferably oxytocin for *Rana* or vasopressin for *Bufo*).

4. Have ready two more baths of Ringer solution, *one* containing 10 mu/ml of oxytocin if you are using *Rana* or the same dose of vasopressin if you are using *Bufo*. The other bath should *not* contain hormone.

5. After weighing place the bladder filled with ordinary dilute Ringer into the bath containing the hormone and the other (with hormone inside) into the bath where there is no hormone present. Thus one preparation has hormone at the mucosal surface and the other at the serosal surface.

6. Weigh again to estimate the water transfer after 30 min.

The bladder with hormone at the serosal surface should lose 0·1–0·4 g of water, while water transfer from the preparation with hormone at the mucosal surface should not alter significantly as compared with the previous control figures.

7. If time permits wash the preparations in ordinary Ringer solution for 10 min, and then reverse the treatment of the two preparations so that hormone is present at the mucosal surface of the bladder which previously had it at the serosal side and vice versa. Measure water transfer over the next 30 min. The results should check with the previous period and provide you with more convincing data.

CONCLUSIONS

Mammalian neurohypophysial hormones increase the permeability of the bladder to water and the water moves along the osmotic gradient in the same direction as it would in an intact frog with hypotonic urine in its bladder. The hormone can only gain access to the receptors and effectors when placed on the serosal side, so that we can infer that this side has properties which are different from those at the opposite surface. Such physiological asymmetry of two cell surfaces of the same cell occurs widely and may have great functional significance.

EXPT 3. EFFECTS OF AN OSMOTIC GRADIENT ON WATER TRANSFER IN RESPONSE TO NEUROHYPOPHYSIAL HORMONES

In expt 2 you demonstrated an increase in the water transfer across the anuran urinary bladder *in vitro*. This took place from the mucosal to the serosal side of the bladder, and as the frog's urine is hypotonic and at the mucosal surface this represents a physiological response. It is, however, instructive to see what happens to the response when the osmotic gradient is eliminated or if its direction across the bladder is reversed.

APPARATUS AND SOLUTIONS

You will require the same apparatus as in the previous experiments. In addition you will need a hypertonic solution of frog Ringer. This can be made by adding sodium chloride 6·6 g/litre to normal frog Ringer to make a total concentration of 13·1 g/litre. The osmolarity will be about 470 m-osmole/litre compared with 248 m-osmole/litre for normal Ringer.

PROCEDURE

Prepare two preparations of the anuran urinary bladder, filling both initially with dilute 1 : 10 Ringer solution.

1. When the bladders are prepared and you are ready to start the main part of the experiment, empty both preparations of fluid and refill one with the standard volume of normal (not dilute) Ringer solution and the other with the hypertonic Ringer solution.

Weigh the bladders and measure water transfer over the next 30 min as you have done in previous experiments.

2. After measuring the weight changes transfer both weighed bladders to tubes of fresh Ringer solution containing the hormone (oxytocin for *Rana* and vasopressin for *Bufo*) at a concentration of 10 mu/ml. Measure weight changes over the next 30 min.

3. If time permits tidy up your experiment by rinsing both bladders in fresh Ringer for 10 min. Reverse the order of the experiment. Thus the bladder which contained hypertonic Ringer should now contain normal Ringer and vice versa. Measure the water transfer again for 30 min.

In the absence of hormone the bladder filled with hypertonic solution should gain a small (10–30 mg) amount of fluid, while in the presence of hormone it will gain at an accelerated rate (50–150 mg). The weight change in the bladder containing normal Ringer should be very small both in the presence and absence of hormone but may be measurable. Sodium is normally transported from the mucosal to serosal side of the bladder and this may take some water with it. Neurohypophysial hormones increase the rate of sodium transport but it is doubtful if you will be able to detect any significant change in water movement that is associated with this.

CONCLUSION AND NOTES

Neurohypophysial hormones do not increase the rate of water transfer across the bladder in the absence of an osmotic gradient (except the small amount that may accompany actively transported sodium). Such hormones will, however, increase the rate of water transfer in either direction; that is, mucosa to serosa or serosa to mucosa. The rate of transfer in the latter direction is two to three times less than in the former case and this may be apparent if you compare your results in expts 2 and 3. This difference is called "rectification of flow" and may be due to active solute transfer (sodium in this instance) altering the properties of the system and/or the fact that the two sides of the bladder epithelial cells function as two non-homogeneous membranes in series. Such effects can be demonstrated in synthetic model membranes.

Active transport of water (water movement against its diffusion gradient) is not thought to take place in vertebrate tissues. The production of physiologically hypertonic solutions as occurs in the bird or mammal kidney is due to the special arrangement of the renal tubules to form a "countercurrent multiplier" system. Neurohypophysial hormones play a role in this system by controlling the permeability of the tubules to water along an osmotic gradient and thus only indirectly lead to the formation of hypertonic solution. The effect on the bladder and renal tubules is analogous to that of removing a "waterproofing" on the membrane to allow a freer movement of water from one side to the other. It has been suggested that neurohypophysial hormones may open minute pores (about 80 Å in diameter) in the mucosal surface of the epithelial cells allowing water to pass through the cells more readily.

Expt 4. The Effects of Cyanide, Decreased pH and a Sulphydryl Blocking Compound on the Action of Neurohypophysial Hormone

The properties and integrity of living membranes are dependent in various degrees on the composition of the fluids that bath them and their metabolism. These two factors, obviously, may be interrelated. In the present experiments you will test the effects of three different substances on the membrane's response to neurohypophysial hormones. Firstly the effects of cyanide which inhibits metabolism connected with oxidative processes; secondly N-ethylemaleimide (NEM) which irreversably blocks sulphydryl (–SH) groups in tissues, and thirdly a small decrease in the pH of the bathing media.

APPARATUS

In addition to the materials and solutions you have required in the previous experiments you will need a dilute solution of choline chloride (2·02 g/litre; 13 mM), sodium cyanide and NEM solutions of suitable concentrations to make the bathing media up to 2 mM and 1 mM respectively. If the bath contains 35 ml use 0·1 ml of NaCN (0·34 g/10 ml) and 0·2 ml of NEM (0·44 g/20 ml). Carbogen (95% O_2 + 5% CO_2) is used to decrease the pH of the bath.

PROCEDURE

Make two preparations of the isolated anuran bladder. Fill them with the dilute choline chloride solution instead of dilute Ringer solution. This rules out the possibility that any observed effects are indirectly related to changes in sodium transport across the bladder.

1. Bladder A. After weighing place this bladder preparation in a bath of Ringer solution containing 10 mu/ml of oxytocin or vasopressin (depending on the species used). Instead of aerating this solution pass carbogen through the same polythene tubes. This will decrease the pH to about 6·8. Measure the water transferred during 30 min of these conditions.

Bladder B. After weighing place the bladder in a bath of aerated Ringer solution containing the hormone preparation (10 mu/ml) and sodium cyanide to a concentration of 2 mM. Measure the water transferred in 30 min.

Water transfer in bladder A should nearly be reduced to levels normally seen when no hormone is present, while in B normal rates of water transfer expected in the presence of hormone should be observed despite the inhibition of oxidative processes.

2. Empty and refill each bladder with dilute choline chloride solution and wash it for 10 min in clean aerated Ringer solution.

3. Bladder A. Weigh and place in aerated normal Ringer solution with hormone (10 mu/ml) present.

Bladder B. Weigh and place in normal Ringer solution containing NEM at a concentration of 1 mM as well as hormone (10 mu/ml).

The exposure to carbogen should not permanently affect the bladder, so that when returned to a normal pH neurohypophysial hormones should act as usual. NEM irreversably blocks membrane SH groups and water transfer in response to the hormone will decrease to levels approaching those seen with no hormone present.

CONCLUSIONS

The response of the anuran bladder to neurohypophysial hormones does not depend directly on oxidative metabolism and indeed neither has it been possible to measure any changes in the anaerobic breakdown of glycogen or production of lactic acid that may be associated with this response. The energy requirements for the process are too small to measure.

The neurohypophysial hormones contain a disulphide (SS) group which greatly facilitates its activity on the bladder. It is thought that a reaction takes place between this group and SH groups on the membrane. However, NEM may block other essential SH groups in the tissue so this evidence alone cannot be considered conclusive. Other results also suggest that such a disulphide–thiol interchange takes place.

A correct pH is very important for the stability of many biological systems and reactions and it can be seen that even very small changes may have large effects. It has been suggested that this effect on the bladder may be due to a decrease in suitably ionized membrane SH groups thus preventing the interaction of hormone and bladder receptors. Alternatively it is also possible that the change in pH may be reflected inside the cell so that subsequent reactions essential to the effect of the hormone are inhibited.

EXPT 5. TESTING THE ACTION OF AN EXTRACT OF THE FROG'S NEUROHYPOPHYSIS IN STIMULATING WATER TRANSFER ACROSS THE BLADDER

In the previous experiments you have been using commercially available neurohypophysial hormones, oxytocin and vasopressin, which have either been extracted from the pituitary glands of mammals (usually from ox and pig) or have been synthesized to give the same structure. It is, however, pertinent to ask if the frogs or toads themselves have hormones capable of such action. Many anuran Amphibia live in dry terrestrial habitats for much of their lives, a situation where a physiological ability to absorb water from their bladders may conceivably be of advantage in prolonging the animal's survival. Clearly it is not enough to just have the bladder, it must also possess a suitable hormone to elicit the effect.

APPARATUS AND SOLUTIONS

In addition to the basic apparatus for dissecting and mounting the bladder you will need the following.
1. One 1 ml graduated pipette.
2. Two 10 ml graduated centrifuge tubes.
3. One small diameter (approx. 2·5 cm) funnel and matching filter papers.
4. One glass rod of a diameter sufficient to grind tissue in the bottom of the centrifuge tube.
5. A solution of 0·25% acetic acid made up in 0·6% sodium chloride solution.
6. A freshly made solution of sodium carbonate 0·03 g/100 ml.
7. A small beaker suitable for a boiling water bath along with accompanying heating apparatus.

To facilitate the speed of the experiment the demonstrator may prepare an extract of rat pituitary (see procedure (3)).

PROCEDURE

1. Set up two isolated bladder preparations filling with dilute (1 : 10) Ringer solutions.
2. Frog pituitary extract. Weigh and kill a frog or toad by decapitating it, taking care not to get the poison from the poison glands on the animal's

back in your eyes. Dissect out the pituitary gland in the following manner. Place one blade of a pair of coarse scissors into the hole at the back of the skull and cut dorsally along one side of the brain case and then along the other side so that you can lift the roof of the skull and expose the brain. Free the brain anteriorly with a pair of forceps and pull it back with a rolling action so as to expose the floor of the brain case and the cranial nerves. You will see the large optic nerves, cut these. Just behind these nerves the pituitary is attached by a thin stalk to the hypothalamus; this stalk will usually break as you continue pulling the brain back. Remove the brain completely. The pituitary will be left on the floor of the brain case and can be easily identified as a discrete small oval piece of tissue. Remove this with the aid of a pin and pair of fine forceps and place it in 0·25 ml of the 0·25% acetic acid. Grind it up with the aid of the glass rod. Leaving the glass rod in the tube, stuff the tube opening with non-absorbent cotton and place it in the boiling water bath for 3 min. Make up to about 1 ml with hot frog Ringer solution and filter. Add another 0·5 ml of the hot frog Ringer solution to the tube and put this through the filter also. Neutralize the filtrate by adding 0·25 ml of the sodium carbonate solution. The pH should be about 7. You now have an extract of the frog pituitary which should contain active neurohypophysial principles.

3. This section can be done by the class demonstrator or one group of students as it will provide sufficient material for five or six groups.

Weigh and kill a rat dissecting out the pituitary in the same manner as the frog. Extract and bring to pH 7 to 8 in the same way.

4. Measure the passive water transfer across the bladder for a 30 min period as described in the previous experiments. This can be proceeding while you are preparing your extracts but you will need to be quick.

5. Prepare two bathing tubes of Ringer solution. To A add the neutralized extract of the frog or toad pituitary, and to B add a proportion (x ml) of the rat pituitary extract equivalent to the body weight of the frog or toad, i.e.

$$\frac{\text{wt of frog}}{\text{wt of rat}} \times \text{total vol of rat extract (ml)} = x \text{ ml}$$

Usually the amount of hormone stored in tetrapod neurohypophyses is proportional to the body weight and this applies to rats and anuran Amphibia.

6. After recording the passive water transfer add one bladder preparation to each of these tubes (after weighing) and record the water transfer in each for a further 30 min.

The water transfer across the bladder should be considerably accelerated (0·2–0·4 ml) by the addition of the extracts of the frog's pituitary. The response to the rat's pituitary extract should be less than this. However, this response will depend on the size of the frog and the amount of rat pituitary extract used as well as the sensitivity of the bladders. The frog's pituitary will contain far more activity capable of stimulating the isolated bladder, and if this is not apparent after procedure (6) it should be possible to show the difference by using smaller amounts of each extract and/or reducing the measuring time to say 15 or 20 min.

CONCLUSIONS

The frog or toad neurohypophysis contains a biological activity capable of strongly stimulating water transfer across the bladder of the same species. Rat and anuran pituitaries contain similar amounts of hormone on a unit body weight basis but hormone structures are different. Rats contain vasopressin and oxytocin which are polypeptides containing eight amino acids but which differ from each other by two amino acid substitutions in the molecule. Frogs and toads also contain at least two such hormones, one very similar to oxytocin called 8-isoleucine oxytocin and the other 8-arginine vasotocin. Vasotocin, as its name implies, is a combination of oxytocin and vasopressin containing the 5-amino acid ring of the former and the 3-amino acid side chain of the latter. It is more than fifty times as active as oxytocin or vaso-pressin in stimulating water transfer across the frog or toad bladder. Vaso-tocin occurs in birds, reptiles, Amphibia and all the fishes so far examined with the possible exception of some elasmobranchs.

In the Amphibia this hormone is released in response to dehydration and so aids the absorption of any water that is stored in the urinary bladder. In addition it accelerates water uptake through the skin and decreases the rate of formation of urine by the kidney.

NOTES ON THE BLADDER WITH REGARD TO FURTHER EXPERIMENTS

Active sodium transport takes place across the bladder and this gives rise to an electrical potential difference (p.d.) which may be as great as 120 mV, usually 20–50 mV, serosal side positive. You can measure this p.d. in the isolated bladder with the aid of a potentiometer like that used in a pH meter or with a sufficiently sensitive voltmeter. The bladder is connected to either of these instruments by connecting the potentiometer (or voltmeter) to two calomel cells (as used in pH meters and readily obtainable commercially) which are placed in small baths of saturated KCl solution. These calomel cells are then connected to each side of the bladder with KCl-agar bridges. These bridges are made out of fine polythene tubing into which has been sucked hot solution of agar 3% in saturated KCl. This solution sets in the tubes and they can be stored in saturated KCl solution and rinsed with dis-tilled water before use. The p.d. across the bladder preparations can be measured in this way (normal Ringer solution on the serosal side and isotonic NaCl on the other side). If isotonic sucrose or choline chloride is substituted for the mucosal NaCl solution the p.d. will fall away as sodium transport ceases.

BIBLIOGRAPHY

GENERAL

Leaf, A. (1965). Transepithelial transport and its hormonal control in toad bladder. *Ergebn. Physiol.*, **56**, 216–263.

Bentley, P. J. (1966). The physiology of the urinary bladder of Amphibia. *Biol. Rev.*, **41**, 275–316.

STRUCTURE

Peachey, L. D. and Rasmussen, H. (1961). Toad bladder structure and function. *J. biophys. biochem. Cytol.*, **10**, 529–553.

NEUROHYPOPHYSIAL HORMONES

Follett, B. K. and Heller, H. (1964). The neurohypophysial hormones of lungfishes and amphibians. *J. Physiol., Lond.*, **172**, 92–106.

Heller, H. (Ed.) (1963). "Comparative Aspects of Neurohypophysial Morphology and Function." *Symp. zool. Soc. Lond.*, No. 9.

Orloff, J. and Handler, J. S. (1963). The effect of adenosine-3',5'-phosphate (cyclic AMP), theophylline and vasopressin on water movement and sodium transport in the toad bladder. *In* "Hormones and the Kidney" (P. C. Williams, ed.), *Mem. Soc. Endocr.*, No. 13, pp. 89–100. Academic Press, London.

Sawyer, W. H. (1966). Neurohypophysial principles of vertebrates. *In* "The Pituitary Gland" (E. W. Harris and B. T. Donovan, eds.), Vol. 3, pp. 288–306. University of California Press.

Schwartz, I. L. and Livingston, L. (1964). Cellular and antidiuretic aspects of the antidiuretic action of vasopressin and related peptides. *Vitam. Hormon.*, **22**, 261–358.

APPENDIX

ANIMALS

Several species of frogs and toads have been used as a source of isolated bladder preparations. Such species are readily available from biological suppliers and include: *Bufo marinus* (U.S.A. and Australia), *Rana catesbiana* (U.S.A.), *Bufo bufo* and *Rana esculenta* (Europe). The technique can be adapted to species that are available locally and, apart from the families Ranidae and Bufonidae, responses to neurohypophysial hormones have been demonstrated in the Hylidae and Leptodactylidae.

Choice of suitable species is dictated by the size of the animals (and hence ease of dissection) and the season. I have found European frogs and toads to be most sensitive to neurohypophysial hormones from April to October. In other countries such as the U.S.A. and Australia this need not apply as animals are transported from parts of the country where the conditions do not induce hibernation. In my experience *Bufo marinus* and *B. bufo* provide the best preparations as the bladders are larger and easier to dissect. Animals from 20 to 25 g in weight can be used though 50–80 g is optimal. If *Rana esculenta* are used, animals over 40 g should be obtained. With experience smaller animals can be successfully dissected.

CARE OF ANIMALS

When animals in good condition are obtained within a month of the experiments it is not necessary to feed them. *Bufo* are best kept on damp sand at about 21 °C in containers which have a drain at the base. Water can be thrown over the animals daily but will not then lie about in pools. *Rana* should have pools of clean water available.

DISSECTION OF THE BLADDER

Instruments

Blunt-nosed artery scissors, fine curved forceps with *blunt* tips (2 pairs), haemostats (1 pair), razor blade, straight seeker or piece of wire, thin plastic catheter tube (diameter about 2 mM), Petri dish, frog Ringer solution (g/litre): NaCl, 6·5; KCl, 0·25; $CaCl_2$ 0·3; $NaHCO_3$, 0·2 and glucose 1·0.

Bufo

Weigh the animal, then empty the bladder by inserting the thin plastic catheter tube into the cloaca and if possible up into the bladder. Reweigh the toad. The cloacal stimulation alone will usually be sufficient to persuade the toad to empty its bladder. Leave the toad 5–10 min to allow the bladder to contract more completely.

To double pith the toad, hold the animal in a cloth dorsal side upwards and bend the head downwards. Cut into the vertebral column at the base of the skull with a razor blade exposing the nerve tissue. Push a seeker or piece of wire up into the cranial cavity and disintegrate the brain and then push it down the spinal cord. The toad is now ready for dissection.

1. Lay the toad on its back. Cut away the skin on the ventral side of the trunk exposing the abdominal wall.

2. Cut the abdominal wall on either side of the anterior abdominal vein from the fork of the body up to the sternum. Clamp the anterior abdominal vein at its anterior end and pull it and the strip of abdominal wall to which it is attached back so that it lies between the legs. The haemostat is left in

position to anchor down this piece of tissue. The bladder can now be seen attached by its blood vessels to this anterior abdominal vein.

3. Push one side of a pair of forceps under the bladder just to one side of this attachment to the anterior abdominal vein and carefully push it forward until you can grasp one whole lobe of the bladder with the forceps. It is also possible to grasp it by pushing forceps from the other (anterior) side.

4. With the artery scissors now cut the lobe free from the opposite lobe by cutting the tissue in front of the forceps and pulling the bladder gently upwards as you cut. It will have attachments to the rectum, peritoneal tissue and even gonads. Cut through all these tissues to free the bladder. The pieces of excess tissue can be trimmed off later. Place the freed piece of tissue into a Petri dish containing some of the frog Ringer solution. Next grasp the ends of the other lobe of the bladder and free it also.

The bladder may contract and fold up on itself while in the Ringer solution, but it can be straightened out by grasping a piece of attached non-bladder tissue or a piece of bladder near the cut surface and gently stirring it back and forth in the Ringer. You should then be able to distinguish a sac-shaped piece of tissue with a free cut surface on one side.

Rana esculenta

The same dissecting procedure applies except that instead of freeing each lobe of the bladder separately the whole bladder is dissected in *one piece*.

Grasp the tissue by which the bladder is attached to the anterior abdominal vein and lifting it upwards cut it free first downwards towards the rectum and cloaca and still holding it gently upwards free it on each side in turn. Again do not hesitate to cut through organs to which it is attached. This procedure is a more difficult dissection than in *Bufo* and usually only one preparation can be obtained consisting of one or two lobes or parts of these.

MOUNTING THE BLADDER ON A PIECE OF TUBING

Apparatus (see Fig. 1)

1. A piece of glass tubing (about 12 cm long and 0·5 cm diam.) pushed through the centre of a rubber stopper (to fit a 150 mm × 30 mm test tube), one end of the tubing expanded. This can be done by heating the end of the glass tubing in a gas flame and when it is soft push it down vertically on a hard surface. This expanded tip acts as a flange which prevents the bladder from slipping off the end of the tubing. The rubber stopper should have a groove cut down one side to admit a thin piece of plastic tubing which acts as an air line. (The glass tubing should project about 7 cm below the stopper so as to be just below the surface of the Ringer solution.) Wind a wire loop around the top part of the glass tubing and use a rubber band to stop it

coming off the tube. This wire acts as a hook by which the tube plus stopper and bladder can be suspended from the suspension hook of a balance for weighing.

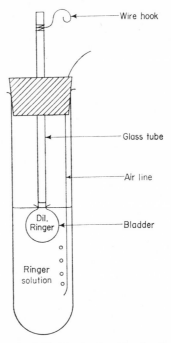

FIG. 1. The frog or toad bladder *in vitro*. For details see text p. 173.

2. Silk thread size 0.
3. 1 ml graduated syringe, needle and plastic tube to fit.
4. Retort stand and clamp.
5. Test tubes 150 mm × 30 mm) and stand.

Procedure

With the aid of a stand and clamp (around the rubber stopper), direct the expanded tip of the tube obliquely (angle about 20°) into the Petri dish containing the bladder. Grasp the cut end of the bladder with a pair of forceps, swing it gently back and forth in the Ringer so that the bladder expands slightly with fluid, then with the aid of a second pair of forceps slip it on to the end of the glass tubing pulling it along the tubing as far as it will go. Turn the tube upside down by swivelling the clamp around, thus preventing the bladder from slipping off the tube. Tie the bladder to the tube with silk thread making two or three loops around the bladder tissue and making sure that no free edges of bladder are left below the tie. Put the preparation in a test tube of Ringer and fill the bladder with 1–1·5 ml of dilute (1 × 10) Ringer solution using the syringe and attached plastic tubing. Hold the preparation up and see if there are any obvious leaks. If any holes are near the top of the bladder it may be possible to tie these off with another piece of thread. Next, with the aid of forceps, slide the ring of thread attaching the bladder (and so push the bladder) down towards the tip of the glass tube. Place the bladder and attached tubing into a test tube (150 mm × 30 mm) containing enough Ringer solution to just cover the bladder (about 35 ml). The fluid in the bladder should not build up hydrostatically in the tubing; if it does, remove some with the syringe. Place the air line in position with the tip at the bottom of the test tube. Be careful not to puncture the bladder with the air line as you push it into the test tube. A temperature of 20–25°C is optimal, and room temperature should thus normally suffice, though if necessary a water bath can be used to attain such a temperature.

The preparation is now ready for the experiments. With practice this entire procedure can be performed in 5–10 min but initially you will take much longer. The experiments have been designed to allow you at least an hour. Take your time and if necessary use another toad and try again. The main aim of expt 1 is for you to gain sufficient skill and dexterity to set up the preparation. This is not only essential if you are to perform the next four experiments but, if you are interested in biological research, may provide you with a useful tool later on.

10 | Temperature and the Goldfish Intestine

M. W. SMITH

*Department o Physiology, Institute of Animal Physiology,
Babraham, Cambridge, England*

There is much evidence to show that the active transport of both electrolytes and non-electrolytes, across the intestinal mucosa of different animals, is mediated partly through the action of enzymes. Any abrupt change in temperature should therefore cause an immediate and pronounced change in the rate of transport of various substances. But the goldfish enjoys an additional privilege denied most other multicellular organisms, the ability to adapt its metabolism and transport processes to suit any environmental temperature from 0 to 40°C. The following experiments show some of the ways transport phenomena in the goldfish intestine respond to short and long term changes in temperature.

The first section deals with apparatus and experimental techniques common to all the experiments, and the second section sets out the individual experiments.

I. Apparatus and Experimental Techniques

ANIMALS

The goldfish intestine is small compared with intestines of many other laboratory animals and it is necessary to use fish weighing 50–70 g to provide intestines suitable for easy eversion.

APPARATUS

1. *High input impedance electrometer* to measure potentials of 0–10 mV. The Vibron electrometer (Electronic Instruments Ltd) is suitable for this purpose. Potentials can be read directly from the electrometer and noted down on paper, or a permanent record of changes in potential can be obtained by feeding the output voltage from the electrometer to a potentiometric pen recorder ("Xactrol", Ether Ltd, or "Servoscribe", S. Smith & Sons).

H

2. *Standard reference electrodes* (Electronics Instruments Ltd, RG23/1) are half filled with a saturated solution of potassium chloride. To the end of each electrode is attached a length of soft polythene tubing ("Portex", Portland Plastics Ltd, NT/2 SH80) filled with 2·5% w/v agar in 0·9% w/v sodium chloride solution. There should be a good excess of these units and all should be stored with agar bridges dipping into 0·9% w/v sodium chloride

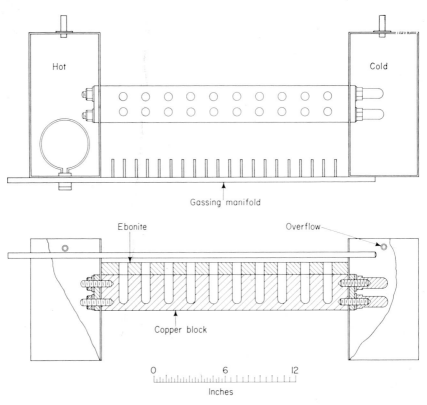

FIG. 1. Temperature gradient, described originally by Selwyn (1961), made by Mr D. V. Barker to the design of Dr G. D. Greville (A.R.C. Institute of Animal Physiology, Babraham, Cambridge).

solution with their leads connected together. Electrodes are matched before the experiment and pairs chosen which give the smallest potential, measured when both bridges dip into the same solution of sodium chloride. This junction potential is usually of the order of 0·5 mV and must not exceed 1 mV. The lead from the reference electrode to the "high" inlet of the electrometer should be shielded. The electrometer and stands holding the reference electrodes must be earthed.

3. *Temperature gradient.* The apparatus used is shown in Fig. 1. A copper rod is bathed with ice water at one end and heated water at the other. The copper projects into the cold bath to aid temperature equilibration with the cold water. Both solutions are well stirred. Insulation of the copper is essential to maintain a constant gradient. Holes are drilled in the copper at intervals so that two tubes can equilibrate to any one temperature. Ten different temperatures can be used and the gradient varied by changing the temperature

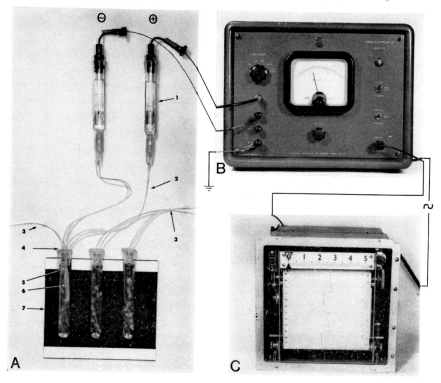

FIG. 2. Basic assembly used to record transmural potentials of goldfish intestine. A. Electrode assembly; B. Vibron electrometer; C. Ether pen recorder. 1, Reference electrodes; 2, agar bridges; 3, gassing tubes; 4, perspex stopper; 5, polythene cannula; 6, everted intestinal sac; 7, heated copper bar.

of heated water. Mild steel may be used instead of copper to reduce the cost of construction but if this is done particular care must be taken to avoid corrosion.

The arrangement of apparatus used in the experiments described below is shown in Fig. 2. The intestine is tied to a polythene cannula which is held by a pinch fit in a hole drilled through a plastic stopper. This stopper fits very loosely in the incubation tube and has three extra holes drilled through it, one for the oxygenator, one to let excess gas escape and the third for an agar bridge, connected via one reference electrode to the "high" input of the electrometer. Plastic stopper and accessories can be lifted clear and placed in another incubation tube within a few seconds.

CHEMICAL SOLUTIONS

Sacs of everted goldfish intestine are incubated in bicarbonate saline (Krebs and Henseleit, 1932). One litre of this solution is made from stock solutions as shown in Table I.

TABLE I

Chemical	Stock solution (g/litre)	Vol taken (ml)
Sodium chloride	171·6	40
Potassium chloride	21·3	20
Magnesium sulphate (MgSO$_4$.7H$_2$O)	14·7	20
Sodium dihydrogen orthophosphate (NaH$_2$PO$_4$.2H$_2$O)	9·15	20
Calcium chloride	14·1	20
Sodium bicarbonate		2·1 g
Glass distilled water		to 1 000 ml

The stock solution of calcium chloride is made by first dissolving about 15 g of dried calcium chloride in 500 ml of glass distilled water and then standardizing this solution by titration against 0·1 N silver nitrate solution (16·98 g/litre). The remaining solution is then diluted with distilled water to give 14·1 g CaCl$_2$/litre. The stock solution of calcium chloride is added last, when the volume has been made up to just less than 1 litre. Sodium bicarbonate is dissolved in the saline and, where specified, glucose is added to give a final concentration of 5 g/litre. This solution is gassed with 95% O$_2$ + 5% CO$_2$ and must be used the same day. Solutions stored for any length of time should be stoppered to stop loss of CO$_2$ with consequent precipitation of calcium as calcium phosphate.

PREPARATION OF EVERTED SACS

Goldfish are killed by decapitation just below the gills. The body wall is opened by cutting down each side as near to the dorsal muscle as possible. Blunt ended forceps are used to hold connective tissue at the cut surface and to pull away the intestine, liver and genitalia from the swim-bladder and body wall. The rectum is cut free and the mixture of tissues transferred together to a Petri dish containing bicarbonate saline (with 5 g glucose/litre), gassed with 95% O_2 + 5% CO_2. Holding the anterior end of the intestine (identified by a prominent gall-bladder) with one pair of forceps, the liver and genitalia are eased away with a second pair of fine forceps. It is important not to stretch the intestine unduly at this stage and to handle as little as possible. When a length of intestine 10–15 cm has been cleared, cut this free and remove the intestinal bulb, the first 2–3 cm of the intestine. The remaining piece of anterior intestine is divided into two or three lengths of about 5 cm, each of which is then everted on a metal rod. The metal rod is 1 mm in diameter and covered with tightly fitting polythene tubing, the end of which projects 1–2 mm beyond the end of the rod. This is closed to make a smooth round end by pressing between two fingers after softening the polythene in a match flame. The piece of intestine to be everted is pulled gently over the rod, and a needle and thread pushed through the end of the intestine and polythene projecting beyond the rod. The thread is tied and the intestine pulled back over itself into the saline. Pulling must always be gentle or the intestine tears away from the thread holding it to the polythene. Forceps used to handle the intestine at this stage should have smooth ends. Once everted, the intestine is cut free and tied on to a polythene cannula made small enough for the intestine but with an internal diameter large enough to let an agar bridge pass through. The inside of the everted intestine is rinsed with bicarbonate saline from a syringe and emptied by blowing gently down the cannula. The sac is formed by tying the intestine as far from the cannula as possible. The completed sac is now ready to be filled with the solution under test and can then be incubated.

DIFFICULTIES AND HOW TO AVOID THEM

1. *Agar bridges.* The junction potential begins to increase after 2–3 weeks use and potentiometric readings become erratic. At this time salt is seen to deposit within the agar which must then be replaced. Sometimes very small air bubbles become trapped in the free end of the agar bridges and this also causes the potential to change. This difficulty is overcome by careful cutting of the bridge with a razor blade so that the agar projects a little way beyond the end of the tubing. If the potential remains erratic, then probably the interference is electrical in origin. Extra leads to earth and/or putting the electrometer on a different plug from the other apparatus eliminates this difficulty.

2. *Temperature gradient.* Any liquid spilling over the edge of the incubation tubes and falling onto the copper, causes potential readings to become erratic. Condensation on to cold tubes (those at 15°C or below) can also cause

trouble. Loose caps should be fitted to all incubation tubes which are being equilibrated with gas.

3. *Fish*. There is some evidence that intestines give variable results from Marcht o June and possibly in October. These are times of the year when the environmental temperature would normally be changing quite markedly and should be avoided if possible.

4. *Cleaning apparatus*. It is suspected that chromium ions poison intestinal preparations and apparatus must not be cleaned with chromic acid. Wash all glassware in a dilute solution of "Pyroneg", Diversey (U.K.) Ltd, Barnet, Herts., and then boil for 15 min in Permutit water before drying in an oven.

II. EXPERIMENTS

EXPERIMENT 1

To measure transmural potentials at different incubation temperatures using intestines from fish acclimatized to 8 or 25°C.

Idea

Transmural potentials measured in the presence of glucose, give an indirect measure of the rate of sodium transport across the tissue. If the potentials of an 8°-acclimatized intestine differ in any way from those of a 25°-intestine, this will show that goldfish mucosal cells can modify their sodium transport in response to a changed environmental temperature.

Procedure

Use bicarbonate saline containing 5 mg/ml glucose for this experiment. Fish have been acclimatized to 8 or 25°C for at least 1 week prior to the experiment. Prepare three or four everted sacs from the anterior intestine of the 8°-acclimatized fish. Put about 0·1 ml of the bicarbonate saline in each sac and leave the sacs in the same medium gassed with 95% O_2 + 5% CO_2 for 10 min at room temperature. Measure the potential of each sac, moving the agar bridge gently within the sac to get the highest reading, then transfer the sac showing highest potential to the cold end of the temperature gradient (about 7°C). Record the potential until it is stable, then transfer sac and bridges to the next tube (about 10°C). Repeat this operation for all ten tubes, the highest temperature being not greater than 30°C. Repeat the whole experiment using sacs prepared from the anterior intestine of a fish acclimatized to 25°C. Plot $\log_{10}$ potential versus reciprocal incubation temperature measured in T for both intestines. Figure 3 shows the results which might be expected.

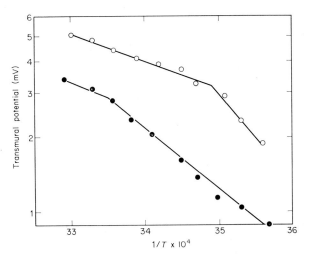

FIG. 3. Transmural potentials measured at different incubation temperatures using intestines from fish previously acclimatized to 8° (–O–), or 25°C (–●–).

Conclusions

(a) What is the immediate effect of temperature on the transmural potentials; is the increase linear throughout? (b) How does acclimatization to a high environmental temperature affect the behaviour of potential with temperature? (c) Compare potentials (i.e. sodium transport) of the two fish measured at incubation temperatures equal to their previous environmental temperature. (d) If compensation has occurred, is it complete or not? Classify the type of compensation according to Precht (1958).

EXPERIMENT 2

To determine the time needed to acclimatize a cold fish to warm water and how to stop it.

Idea

Acclimatization is, by definition, a change in cell organization which takes some time to become complete. It is probably associated with changes in enzyme synthesis. Puromycin stops enzyme synthesis and would be expected to retard acclimatization, measured in this instance by changes in the potentials of goldfish intestine.

Procedure

Take two fish kept at 8°C for at least 1 week and place them in water at 25°C. Kill one after 10 h and the other after 20 h in the warm water. Repeat the procedure of expt 1. The intestine taken from the fish kept in warm water for 20 h should have acclimatized but the one kept in warm water for only 10 h should still behave like an 8°-intestine.

Repeat the experiment of keeping an 8°-acclimatized fish at 25°C for 20 h but this time inject intraperitoneally, at the time of transfer, 10 μg/g puromycin dihydrochloride (National Biochemicals Corporation) dissolved in 0·05 ml 0·9% w/v solution of sodium chloride. Repeat the procedure of expt 1 and plot the results from the three fish as before. Sample results are shown in Fig. 4.

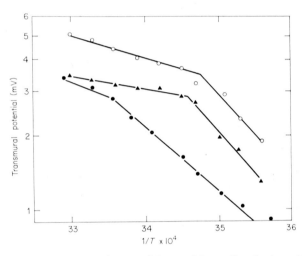

FIG. 4. Time course of changes in potential caused by acclimatization of an 8°-fish to 25°C. The cold-adapted fish had been placed in water at 25°C for 10 h (–O–) or 20 h (–●–, –▲–), before starting the experiment. In one case, (–▲–), puromycin (10 μg/g goldfish) was injected intraperitoneally at the time of transfer to warm water.

Conclusions

(a) Is acclimatization complete 10 h or 20 h after raising the environmental temperature of the fish? (b) Does puromycin affect acclimatization, measured by the incubation temperature at which a change is seen in the slopes of potential versus temperature plots? (c) Does puromycin change the absolute potentials compared with the intestine kept at 25°C for only 10 h and, if so, how would you explain this change?

EXPERIMENT 3

To measure the effect of glucose on transmural potentials at different incubation temperatures using intestines from fish acclimatized to 8 or 25°C.

Idea

Glucose is known to increase the transmural potential of intestinal preparations from mammals. If this mechanism is present in the goldfish, can
it be changed by previous acclimatization of the fish to different temperatures?

Procedure

Make up bicarbonate saline with no glucose and add glucose (5 mg/ml)
to part of this medium. Use two fish acclimatized for at least 1 week, one
to 8°C and the other to 25°C. Prepare sacs from the 8°-acclimatized fish as
in expt 1. Put saline containing glucose in each everted sac. Choose four

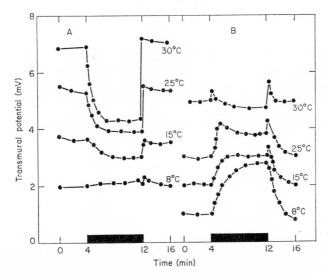

FIG. 5. Effect of glucose on transmural potentials of goldfish intestine measured at
different incubation temperatures (8, 15, 25 and 30°C), using fish acclimatized to 8°C (A)
or 25°C (B). Solid bars show the time during which intestines were incubated in medium
containing no glucose.

incubation temperatures to study 8, 15, 25 and 30°C and equilibrate bicarbonate saline, with and without glucose, at each temperature. Incubate a sac at
8°C, first in the glucose-containing medium and then in the glucose-free
medium. Leave the sac for 8 min in the glucose-free medium and then return
it to the original medium. Record the change in potential which occurs immediately the sac is replaced in the glucose-containing medium. Repeat the
operation at the other temperatures and then with an intestinal sac taken
from the fish acclimatized to 25°C. Plot the potential as shown in Fig. 5.

H§

Conclusions

(a) At some incubation temperatures the transmural potential is permanently increased by the presence of glucose in contact with the mucosa. (b) The transmural potential can be inhibited by the presence of glucose when measured at incubation temperatures below the previous body temperature of the fish. (c) Acclimatization of a fish to warm water increases the inhibitory action of glucose on the transmural potential.

EXPERIMENT 4

To measure the serosal transfer of glucose and relate this to the transmural potential of the goldfish intestine.

Idea

The active transport of sodium and sugars is closely related, though how this connexion operates is a matter of controversy. Sodium transport across goldfish intestine (reflected by the transmural potential) can be changed by altering the incubation temperature. The transport of glucose might be expected to change in a similar way to the potential.

Procedure

Take three fish acclimatized to 8°C for at least 1 week. Form three sacs from one fish intestine and put exactly 0·1 ml of bicarbonate saline containing 5 mg/ml glucose into each sac. Incubate the three sacs at 15, 22 or 30°C for 1 h in bicarbonate saline containing 5 mg/ml glucose. Record the highest potential for each sac and, at the end of incubation, squeeze the contents out of each sac into weighed bottles. Reweigh the bottles. The fluid recovered is equal to the difference between the two weights. Weigh each sac and estimate the glucose in the serosal solutions as follows.

Estimation of glucose

Take 0·05 ml of each sample and dilute to 2·5 ml with distilled water. Take 0·2 ml of this diluted solution and add 5 ml of glucose reagent (Boehringer Biochemical Test Combination, C. F. Boehringer & Soehne, GMBH, Mannheim). Leave the solutions in the dark for 35 min and then read the colour formed in a spectrophotometer at 436 mμ. These optical densities are compared with others obtained by adding 0·1, 0·2, 0·3 and 0·4 ml of a 0·1 mg/ml standard solution of glucose to 5 ml of glucose reagent.

Repeat the whole experiment with the remaining two fish, randomizing the sacs so that, by the end of the three experiments, the first, second and third sac has each been incubated at 15, 22 and 30°C. Calculate the glucose concentration in the serosal solutions and the amount transferred/1 h/100 mg intestine. Plot the mean potential at each incubation temperature against the mean glucose transfers. Sample results are shown in Fig. 6.

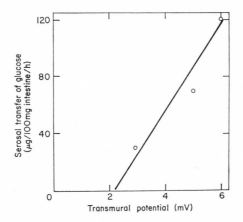

FIG. 6. Transfer of glucose by intestines taken from 8°-acclimatized fish incubated at 15, 22 or 30°C, plotted against the corresponding transmural potential. Each point is the mean of three determinations.

Conclusions

(a) At 30°C glucose is transported against its concentration gradient, clearly demonstrating active transport. (b) At lower incubation temperatures the concentrating effect at the serosal surface of the sacs is less obvious but there is still a positive transfer of glucose. (c) The glucose transfer is roughly proportional to the transmural potential but the line does not pass through the origin. (d) The metabolism of glucose may reduce the net transfer of glucose.

SUGGESTIONS FOR FURTHER WORK

1. Repeat expt 4 using 3-methylglucose which is not metabolized. Find out if this affects the general pattern of potential versus transfer.

2. The active transport of amino acids is also closely connected with sodium transport. Alanine behaves like glucose in increasing the transmural potential of goldfish intestine. Measure the serosal transfer of alanine (Aqvist, 1947) and relate that to the transmural potential.

3. Acclimatization of goldfish to a high environmental temperature reduces the transport of threonine and valine. Test if this is so for alanine.

REFERENCES

Aqvist, S. E. G. (1947). A micromethod for the determination of alanine in proteins. *Acta physiol. scand.* **13**, 297–300.

Precht, H. (1958). Concepts of temperature adaptation of unchanging reaction systems of cold-blooded animals. *In* "Physiological Adaptation" (C. L. Prosser, ed.), pp. 50–78. American Physiological Society, Washington, D.C.

Selwyn, M. J. (1961). An apparatus for maintaining a range of constant temperatures. *Biochem. J.* **79**, 38P.

BIBLIOGRAPHY

SODIUM TRANSPORT

Curran, P. F. (1965). Ion transport in intestine and its coupling to other transport processes. *Fedn Proc. Fedn Am. Socs exp. Biol.* **24**, 993–999.

SUGAR TRANSPORT

Crane, R. K. (1965). Na$^+$-dependent transport in the intestine and other animal tissues. *Fedn Proc. Fedn Am. Socs exp. Biol.* **24**, 1000–1005.

Csáky, T. Z. (1965). Transport through biological membranes. *A. Rev. Physiol.* **27**, 415–450.

AMINO ACID TRANSPORT

Rosenberg, I. H., Coleman, A. L. and Rosenberg, L. E. (1965). Role of sodium ion in the transport of amino acids by the intestine. *Biochim. biophys. Acta* **102**, 161–171.

Wiseman, G. (1964). "Absorption from the Intestine". Academic Press, London and New York.

GOLDFISH

Mepham, T. B. and Smith, M. W. (1966). Regulation of amino acid transport across intestines of goldfish acclimatized to different environmental temperatures. *J. Physiol., Lond.* **186**, 619–631.

Smith, M. W. (1964). Electrical properties and glucose transfer in the goldfish intestine. *Experientia* **20**, 613–614.

Smith, M. W. (1966). Sodium-glucose interactions in the goldfish intestine. *J. Physiol., Lond.* **182**, 559–573.

Smith, M. W. (1966). Influence of temperature acclimatization on sodium-glucose interactions in the goldfish intestine. *J. Physiol., Lond.* **182**, 574–590.

Smith, M. W. (1967). Methionine transfer across goldfish intestine acclimatized to different temperatures. *Experientia* **23**, 548–549.

Smith, M. W. (1967). Influence of temperature acclimatization on the temperature dependence and ouabain-sensitivity of goldfish intestinal adenosine triphosphatase. *Biochem. J.*, **105**, 65–71.

11 | Hunger in Insects
Taste Threshold Rise in Blowflies after Feeding

L. BARTON BROWNE

*C.S.I.R.O., Division of Entomology, Canberra, A.C.T.,
Australia*

ANIMALS AND APPARATUS

SPECIES OF BLOWFLY

Some species of blowflies are more suitable than others. The following are desirable characteristics.

1. The fly should respond decisively, by labellar extension, to tarsal contact with sufficiently stimulating sugar solutions.

2. "24 h starved"* flies should have a low glucose threshold, 0·5 M or less.

3. The fly should have a reliably negative response to water for at least some minutes after it has been allowed to become water satiated.

Phormia regina and *Lucilia cuprina* are known to be satisfactory species. *Lucilia sericata* is usable but a bit slow in its response. Most *Calliphora* species and the housefly *Musca domestica* are not satisfactory, having poorly defined responses to chemical stimulation.

WAXED STICKS

The flies are used mounted on waxed sticks. These are made as follows. The terminal inch of a 6 in. length of $\frac{1}{10}$ in. diameter copper wire is dipped alternately into molten paraffin wax and cold water. The process is repeated until the wax is about $\frac{1}{2}$ in. in diameter. These sticks may be held in blocks of wood provided with appropriate sized holes.

PRE-TREATMENT OF FLIES

Best results are obtained with flies in the third day of adult life. Flies can conveniently be kept in glass jars with a wire gauze insert in the lid but care must be taken to avoid overcrowding. On their first day they are provided

---

* The designation "24 h starved" flies is used for convenience. This is not a precise description of the state of the flies as they have had access to dry filter paper with some glucose on it until within a few hours of being used. A period of 24 h has elapsed, however, since they were last provided with filter paper freshly soaked in glucose solution (see Pre-treatment of flies).

only with a dry filter paper. On their second day of adult life, 24 h before their use on the third day, the flies are supplied with a filter paper soaked with distilled water which is replaced after about 15 min by one soaked with a

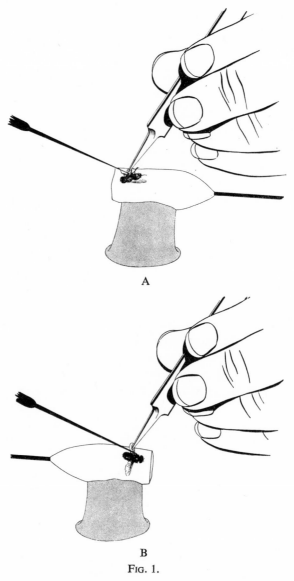

A

B

FIG. 1.

glucose solution. The concentration of glucose supplied should be the lowest one which gives good survival. This may vary a little from species to species and with the temperature at which the flies are kept, but will be within the range 0·1–0·3 M. If it is necessary to keep flies past the third day fresh glucose-soaked filter paper should be provided each day. In some species these older flies may prove less satisfactory than flies 3 days old.

Flies should receive the following treatment on the day of the class. Preferably several hours before and at least 1 h before the flies are to be used, the previous day's glucose-soaked filter paper is removed and replaced

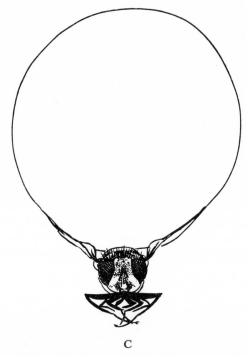

C

FIG. 1. A and B. Fly being affixed to waxed stick with a warm needle. C. End-on-view of a fly mounted on a waxed stick showing the dorsal surface of the thorax in firm contact with the wax. The fly should not hang loosely from its wing tips.

with a water-soaked paper. About 15 min later the flies are anaesthetized with carbon dioxide and are affixed to the waxed sticks in the way shown in Fig. 1. The period of carbon dioxide anaesthesia should be kept to a minimum. Each pair of students should receive sixty flies already mounted on waxed sticks.

INJECTION APPARATUS

The injection of measured amounts of trehalose solutions into the haemocoels of flies is effected with an Agla micrometer syringe. This is fitted with a fine glass needle constructed by drawing out 3–4 mm outside diameter Pyrex tubing to a diameter of about 0·1 mm. This needle is joined to the syringe by means of an appropriate sized piece of pressure tubing. Injections should be made under a dissecting microscope.

CHEMICAL SOLUTIONS

1. Glucose solutions used for testing threshold run in doubling concentrations from 0·0625 M up to 2·0 M. This series of solutions is conveniently made by preparing a 2·0 M solution (360 g/litre) and by obtaining the remaining solutions by a series of halving dilutions.

2. 1·0 M Fucose (164 g/litre). This is a relatively expensive sugar; make only the quantity of solution required.

3. 1·0 M Trehalose (378 g/litre).

IDEAS AND PRINCIPLES

GENERAL

The behavioural responses of lower animals are largely of a stereotyped nature and it is instructive to consider the mechanisms by which these are regulated so as to conform with the requirements of the organism. A suitable response for a study of this kind is that of blowflies to sugar. Tarsal contact with a sugar solution elicits extension of the labellum. Contact of the labellar

FIG. 2. A fly feeding on an acceptable solution.

lobes with the solution causes the lobes to be spread on the surface of the liquid which is then imbibed (Fig. 2). The imbibed solution goes mainly to the crop of the fly and is released into the foregut over a period of some hours.

The present series of experiments is concerned with the rise in taste threshold which occurs after the fly has fed and with some aspects of the mechanisms involved in the rise. It represents, in short, a study of hunger in a lower animal.

TASTE THRESHOLD AND ITS DETERMINATION

A blowfly is deemed to have responded positively to a solution if tarsal contact causes the fly to extend its labellum. The taste threshold of a population is defined as the concentration to which 50% of flies respond positively. For strict determination of taste threshold it is necessary to use large batches (often in excess of 100) of water-satiated flies for each test concentration and to plot the percentage responding against concentration. When threshold is determined in this way each fly contacts only one concentration and has, therefore, completely non-sugar-adapted tarsal chemoreceptors. Smaller numbers of flies can be used if, at the expense of some accuracy, ascending thresholds are obtained. Each fly is tested briefly first on the lowest concentration of the series and if no response is obtained it is tested on the next higher concentration and so on until a positive response is obtained. Thresholds obtained in this way tend to be higher than the true threshold because of the partial adaptation of the tarsal receptors which has been caused by the contact with concentrations below the threshold.

In the present experiments ascending thresholds of individual flies are obtained before and after various treatment. In this circumstance it is possible to obtain significant results from very few flies by recording the number of doubling steps by which threshold of each fly changes and determining whether the mean number of steps is significantly different from zero.

The use of doubling steps in the series of test solutions is justified by the fact that the scattering of thresholds of a population of blowflies is not significantly different from a normal distribution when plotted against the log of concentration.

EXPERIMENTAL DETAILS

A series of separate but related experiments is described. The experiments are first described separately. Secondly, a suggested order for carrying out the various parts of the experiments so that they fit into a 3 h period is given. The number assigned to the groups of flies mentioned in the text below are referred to again in Table I.

1. THRESHOLDS OF THE SAME FLIES DETERMINED AT TWO TIMES SEPARATED BY 1 H (CONTROL FOR OTHER EXPERIMENTS)

Allow eight flies (group 1) to drink to repletion on water. This is achieved by touching the tarsi of each fly on the surface of distilled water and allowing the fly to remain in contact with the solution until it withdraws its labellum. Not all flies will respond positively to water. For a number of hours after drinking to repletion flies should respond to water for only a few seconds if at all. Next obtain an ascending threshold to glucose for each of the eight flies. The tarsi are first touched on the surface of distilled water and the fly is again allowed to drink to repletion if it responds. The tarsi are then touched momentarily ($<$ 1 sec in most species but longer is required in a slow responding species like *Lucilia sericata*) to the surface of a 0·06 M solution of glucose. If the fly fails to respond by labellar extension it is transferred to the next higher concentration and so on until it extends its labellum. When labellar extension occurs tarsi of the fly should be removed from the solution before the labellar lobes can make contact with the surface. The fly is then again given contact with water and if it responds positively, as rarely happens, it is kept in contact with water until the labellum is withdrawn. It is then tested on the concentration of glucose higher than that to which it previously gave a positive response. If the response to this higher concentration is a definite one the threshold concentration for that fly is considered to be the one to which it originally responded positively. Any fly which in this initial determination of threshold fails to respond to 0·5 M glucose should be discarded and replaced, as should any which fails to give a clear-cut response or is any way aberrant in its behaviour. Re-determine threshold for each of the eight flies 1 h after the previous determination. For each fly the number of doubling concentration by which the threshold has increased or decreased between the two determinations is recorded. Decreases in threshold are scored as negative increase. The method of analysing the results is outlined below. Thresholds should change only slightly, if at all, during the elapsed hour.

2. THRESHOLD BEFORE AND AFTER FEEDING ON 2 M GLUCOSE

The experimental design is similar to that described for the previous experiment. The thresholds of eight flies (group 2) are determined as before but this time each fly is allowed to feed to repletion on 2 M glucose immediately after the first determination of its threshold. The thresholds are again determined after 1 h has elapsed. A substantial increase in threshold should occur.

3. THRESHOLD BEFORE AND AFTER FEEDING ON 1 M FUCOSE

Fucose is not metabolized by blowflies but is readily imbibed. A 24-h starved fly which feeds to repletion on a 1 M solution of fucose remains metabolically starved. Thus fucose is a tool by which the effects of the nutritional state of the tissues may be dissociated from the other effects of sugar intake. A rise in taste threshold after fucose feeding of the same order as that after glucose feeding would indicate clearly that the metabolic state of the tissues is not an important factor in the determination of taste threshold.

Accordingly an experiment identical with that described above, except that the flies are fed 1 M fucose instead of 2 M glucose, will be carried out (eight flies, group 3). A substantial increase in threshold should again occur.

4. THE EFFECT OF THE CONCENTRATION OF TREHALOSE IN THE HAEMOLYMPH

Trehalose is the main blood sugar of blowflies and the last of this series of experiments is designed to determine whether taste threshold is controlled by the trehalose concentration of the haemolymph. In this the effects of injections of trehalose in the haemocoel are investigated. The thresholds of sixteen flies are determined and 1 h later eight (group 4a) of these are injected

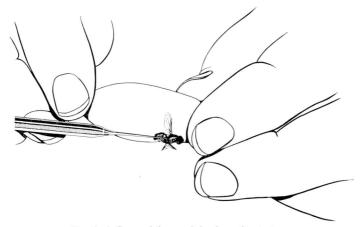

FIG. 3. A fly receiving an injection of trehalose.

with 1·5 μl of 1·0 M solution of trehalose; the injection being made reasonably slowly into the metathorax in the region of the metathoracic spiracle (Fig. 3). The remaining eight flies (group 4b), which act as controls, are stabbed with a solid needle similar in diameter to that used for the sugar injection. The blood trehalose concentration of the trehalose injected flies is greater (by up to a factor of 2) than that in flies fed glucose 1 h before (group 2). The threshold of each fly is determined 15 min after injection or stabbing. The thresholds of the groups should not differ markedly either from one another or from their original thresholds. The thresholds should be significantly lower than those of sugar fed flies.

SUGGESTED ORDER FOR CARRYING OUT THE SERIES OF EXPERIMENTS

Students should work in pairs. The experiments described can be performed comfortably in a 3 h period only if the suggested order is followed. The approximate times to be taken for each operation are given (Table I). The times in parentheses indicate the number of minutes which should have elapsed since the commencement of the experiments. If the initial "watering" of the flies takes less than the allotted 30 min, these times should be adjusted accordingly.

TABLE I

Suggested order for carrying out experiments

The group numbers given refer to those given above in the detailed descriptions of the experiments

	Student A	Student B
30 min (0–30 min)	Satiate *all* flies (groups 1, 2, 3 and 4) with water. Allow several flies to drink at the same time. This is achieved by supporting the waxed sticks on plasticine columns. The operation may take less than 30 min, if so pass on. Times given for subsequent operations should, however, be adhered to.	
15 min (30–45 min)	Thresholds* of eight flies (group 1)	
30 min (45–75 min)	Thresholds* of eight flies and feed on 2 M glucose (group 2)	Thresholds* of eight flies and feed on 1 M fucose (group 3)
15 min (75–90 min)	Thresholds* of eight flies (group 4a)	Thresholds* of eight flies (group 4b)
15 min (90–105 min)	Thresholds of eight flies (group 1)	
30 min (105–135 min)	Threshold of eight flies (group 2)	Threshold of eight flies (group 3)
15 min (135–150 min)	Inject eight flies with trehalose (group 4a) and stab eight more (group 4b)	
15 min (150–165 min)	Threshold eight flies (group 4a)	Threshold eight flies (group 4b)

* Discard flies with initial thresholds > 0·5 M.

SAMPLE RESULTS

Tables of fundamentally the same design are used for recording the results of all four experiments. A sample table for the effects of glucose feeding (expt 2) is given below (Table II). Flies which fail to respond to a 2 M solution are assigned a threshold value of 4 M.

In this example the mean increase in the number of doubling concentrations is 2·9.

For expt 4 the table requires an extra column in which is recorded the time of day at which the flies received their injections.

TABLE II

Fly	Initial threshold	Time of day at which initial determination of threshold is made and at which flies feed on glucose	Threshold after treatment	Time of day of second threshold determination	No. of doubling concn increase in threshold
1	0·5	3·09	2·0	4·09	2
2	0·25	3·13	4·0	4·13	4
3	0·125	3·16	2·0	4·16	4
4	0·5	3·19	1·0	4·19	1
5	0·25	3·21	4·0	4·21	4
6	0·5	3·24	2·0	4·24	2
7	0·5	3·27	2·0	4·27	2
8	0·25	3·30	2·0	4·30	3

The significance of the effect of any of the treatments can be tested by carrying out t tests (Snedecor, 1956, p. 85 *et seq.*) to determine whether the mean number of doubling concentrations by which threshold changes differ significantly from zero. Comparisons between effects of different treatments can be effected by carrying out t tests between the relevant means.

FIG. 4. A general view of the arrangement for determining ascending threshold.

TROUBLE-SHOOTING

The major troubles with which this series of experiments may be afflicted are outside the student's control and cannot be rectified during the course of the class. The most frequently encountered difficulty is that the flies may have high initial taste thresholds to glucose, in which case many flies would have to be discarded. This happens when a batch of flies differs from the norm in such a way that a usually satisfactory pre-treatment results either in under or over starvation.

When thresholds are high scaled down experiments should be carried out with those flies with thresholds of 0·5 M or less. In extreme cases the acceptable limit should be raised to 1·0 M.

CONCLUSIONS

1. Taste thresholds to glucose rise after flies have fed to repletion on 2 M glucose. Some consequence of feeding has therefore caused thresholds to rise.

2. A non-metabolizable sugar (fucose) also causes a marked rise in the threshold to glucose. The metabolic state of the tissues is therefore not a significant determinant of threshold.

3. Elevation by injection of the blood trehalose to a level at least comparable with that reached after glucose feeding fails to cause a significant rise in threshold. The concentration of trehalose in the blood is not the factor determining sugar threshold.

4. The elimination of the previous two possibilities suggests that the site of action of glucose as an elevator of taste thresholds to glucose is in the gut.

FURTHER IDEAS

A number of additional behavioural experiments dealing with the general problem of the control of hunger and thirst can be carried out using blowflies mounted on waxed sticks. A few examples are outlined below.

1. Demonstration of sugar acceptance and salt rejection. The taste thresholds to a series of sugar solutions are obtained and these compared with thresholds to the same sugar solutions made up in a sodium chloride solution instead of water. Rejection thresholds can also be obtained to a series of sodium chloride solutions of different concentrations made up in a sugar solution of a concentration to which the flies respond positively (Dethier, 1955).

2. Relationship between concentration of sugar solutions and the duration and rate of intake. Flies (plus waxed sticks) are weighed before and after feeding on several different concentrations of sugar solutions. The duration of feeding is recorded and the rate calculated.

3. The effect on taste threshold of the concentration and volume of sugar solution imbibed. The taste thresholds of flies are determined after feeding on measured drops of sugar solutions of different concentrations (Evans and Barton Browne, 1960).

4. The effect of imbibing one sugar on the thresholds to others.

5. The relationship between the threshold to sugar and its nutritional value (Hassett *et al.*, 1950).

6. The control of water intake. A study similar to that described above may be made to investigate the factors controlling water intake (Evans, 1961; Dethier and Evans, 1961; Barton Browne, 1964).

BIBLIOGRAPHY

Barton Browne, L. (1964). Thirst in the blowfly, *Lucilia cuprina*. *Nature, Lond.*, **202**, 1137–1138.‡

Dethier, V. G. (1955). The physiology and histology of the contact chemoreceptors of the blowfly. *Q. Rev. Biol.*, **30**, 348–371.‡

Dethier, V. G. (1962). "To Know a Fly", 119 pp. Holden-Day Inc., San Francisco.*

Dethier, V. G. and Bodenstein, D. (1958). Hunger in the blowfly. *Z. Tierpsychol.*, **15**, 129–140.†

Dethier, V. G. and Evans, D. R. (1961). The physiological control of water ingestion in the blowfly. *Biol. Bull. mar. biol. Lab., Woods Hole*, **121**, 101–116.‡

Evans, D. R. (1961). Control of the responsiveness of the blowfly to water. *Nature, Lond.*, **190**, 1132.‡

Evans, D. R. and Barton Browne, L. (1960). The physiology of hunger in the blowfly. *Am. Midl. Nat.*, **64**, 282–300.†‡

Evans, D. R. and Dethier, V. G. (1957). The regulation of taste threshold for sugars in the blowfly. *J. Insect Physiol.*, **1**, 3–17.†

Hassett, C. C., Dethier, V. G. and Gans, J. (1950). A comparison between nutritive values and taste thresholds of carbohydrates for the blowfly. *Biol. Bull. mar. biol. Lab., Woods Hole*, **99**, 446–453.‡

Snedecor, G. W. (1956). "Statistical Methods", 5th ed. Iowa State College Press, Ames, Iowa.§

* A very good popular account of experiments on chemoreception in blowflies.
† Papers describing the work from which the present experiments are derived.
‡ Papers concerned with the suggested further experiments.
§ Statistics textbook: *t* test etc.

12 | Allatectomy of the American Cockroach, *Periplaneta americana* (L.)

DAVID H. CHEN

Insect Physiology Laboratory, Entomology Research Division, ARS, U.S. Department of Agriculture, Beltsville, Maryland, U.S.A.

INTRODUCTION

The corpora allata (c.a.) of the American cockroach (*Periplaneta americana* (L.)) are endocrine glands of importance to the metabolic processes of the insect. They are believed to secrete the juvenile hormone that regulates growth (Bodenstin, 1953), the gonadotropic hormone that maintains reproduction in the female (Chen *et al.*, 1962), as well as hormones that affect lipid metabolism (Vroman *et al.*, 1965) and the production of the female sex attractant (R. T. Yamamoto, unpublished data). Removal of the corpora allata (allatectomy) results in the interruption of one or more of the described processes, unless the insects are treated with biologically active materials or by the implantation of active c.a. Thus, allatectomy of the American cockroach is a valuable surgical technique for various types of physiological and biochemical research.

The procedure described in the following paragraphs should be carried out in three or more separate sessions of about 3 h each in order to achieve a reasonable degree of success in allatectomy. The initial session should be devoted to gathering and assembling equipment for the experiment, mounting the insect, and familiarizing oneself with the external and internal structures related to the operation. Furthermore, practice in removing the c.a. from a few sacrificed insects to gain competence in the operation is also a vital step before venturing further. The second session (soon after the first to allow for continuity) should be devoted to the actual operation from initial anesthetization through the final suture. If time is permitted, practice at least until consistency in revival of the insect from the operation is achieved. The third session should occur sometime after the operation has been proved to be successful. Cessation of production of oöthecae will serve as a convenient indicator to successful allatectomy. In carrying out the gonadotropic hormone test, described in the text, a check on alternate days to determine whether the insect has produced an oötheca should reasonably verify the success of

I

the allatectomy. Therefore, the third session may take place some 21–35 days after the operation. If the surviving insects remain suitable for testing, then injections, transplantations, etc., may be tried at this time.

MATERIALS AND METHODS

The following is a list of required materials and equipment necessary to complete allatectomy of the American cockroach.

1. Ringer's solution. 7·5 g NaCl, 0·35 g KCl, 0·21 g $CaCl_2$ in 1 liter distilled water.

2. Forceps. Two pairs Dumont No. 5 jeweller's.

3. Microscope. Binocular dissecting (10 × to 30 ×).

4. Lights. Strong microscope lamp with focusing lens.

5. Anesthetic. Source of continuous carbon dioxide from cylinder.

6. Dissecting dish. Special paraffin dish with a depressed area to allow for continuous supply of carbon dioxide and mounting of insect (see Fig. 1A).

7. Insect pins. Size no. 3 (1 dozen).

8. Bubble chamber. A 250 ml Erlenmeyer flask partially filled with water to estimate the carbon dioxide flow during the operation (a gauge may be substituted here) (see Fig. 1B).

9. Antiseptic solution. 70% ethyl alcohol.

10. Antibiotic. Streptomycin sulfate crystals.

11. Cotton balls on swab sticks. 1 dozen.

TECHNIQUE FOR ALLATECTOMY

Familiarity with the anatomy of the head and neck is vital in performing an allatectomy. The c.a. consist of a pair of small, transparent, bulbous glands each attached to the brain by a stalk, the corpora cardiaca (c.c.); they are located ventroposterior to the "brain" (supra-esophageal ganglion) and lie dorsolateral to the esophagus. The brain, corpora allata, and corpora cardiaca are sometimes called the brain–c.a.–c.c. complex. Normally the complex is situated deep within the head; however, if the student slightly extends the neck anteriorly and depresses the apex of the head, using the base as a fulcrum, he can shift the c.a. to a position nearer to the region of the neck. With the c.a. in this position, incision into the neck and removal of the c.a. can be accomplished without too much difficulty (see Fig. 2A and B).

Mounting the insect on the operating dish is one of the most critical steps in the entire operation. Correct pinning ensures the proper location and exposure of the c.a., shortens the operation time, minimizes loss of "blood" (hemolymph), and increases the chance of postoperative survival of the animal.

After first anesthetizing the insect with carbon dioxide (2–3 min) in a separate chamber, place the cockroach on its ventral side in the depression of the paraffin dish. Next, regulate the gas flow from the CO_2 tank to an optimum level to keep the insect under sedation by observing the amount of water agitation produced in the bubble chamber. (Since carbon dioxide is heavier than air, it tends to remain in the depression where the insect is

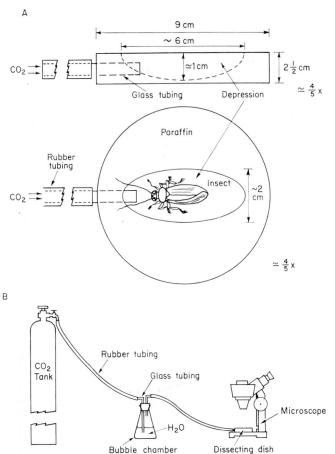

Fig. 1. A. Paraffin dissecting dish. B. Physical set-up.

anesthetized for operation.) If the insect appears to revive, supply more CO_2; however, the valve may become frozen if an excess amount of gas is used, so use considerable caution in regulating the valve.

You will need six pins for the pinning process. Place two pins between the head and the thorax, one on each side of the insect (thoracic pins). Place two more crosswise so as to form an X somewhat posteriorly along the

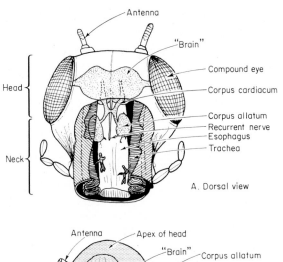

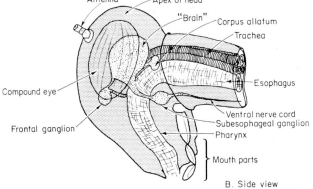

FIG. 2. Dorsal view (A) and side view (B), greatly enlarged and diagrammatic.

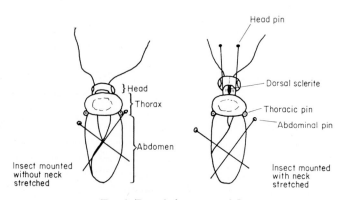

FIG. 3. Dorsal views. $\times \simeq 1\cdot5$.

sides of the abdomen (abdominal pins). Use remaining two pins (head pins) to stretch the neck and depress the head by placing them just posteriorly on each side of the head and guide anteriorly (with the pin tips more or less stationary) for about 1 or 2 mm; then secure the head by pressing the pins down firmly into the paraffin (see Fig. 3).

After the insect is firmly pinned, clean the dorsal surfaces of the head, neck, and thorax with cotton saturated with 70% ethyl alcohol. Place the entire preparation under the dissecting microscope. Adjust microscope to 15 × magnification, make an incision along the anterior edge of the dorsal cervical sclerite (a brownish chitinized integument that forms the dorsal covering of the neck). With a pair of forceps, pull the dorsal sclerite back posteriorly (ripping the dorsal integument) and expose the interior of the neck. Do not cut or remove the integument, since upon completion of the operation it is replaced in the original position to facilitate healing. If the insect bleeds a little, use a swab to remove some of the excess "blood" and replace it with one or two drops of Ringer's solution. (The solution aids in replenishing the body fluids as well as "clearing the field" at the site of the operation.)

The first internal tissues encountered are the large silvery, coil-like tracheae. Carefully ease them aside, away from the midline, to expose the esophagus (an orange-brown tissue underlying the tracheae). Next, trace the esophagus anteriorly until the bluish-white colored c.c. appear. At the end of each c.c. one should find the transparent, bulbous c.a. Clear away the small nerves connected to the c.a. with a pair of forceps and pinch off the c.a. along with a small portion of the c.c. to insure complete allatectomy. Then remove each c.a. carefully from the insect and place on a depression microscope slide for further examination or for other studies.

Place a few crystals of streptomycin sulfate in the wound and replace the dorsal sclerite in its original position. Next release head, abdominal and thoracic pins in that order. Remove the insect from the dissecting dish and transfer it into a marked container supplied with food (dog biscuits) and water (a vial filled with water stoppered with cotton) for future observation. In a few minutes the insect should revive if the trauma has not been too severe. For optimum results aim to complete an operation in about 5–8 min. Mortality rates vary with the individual operator, developmental stage of insect, and conditions during the operation. About 20–25% mortality is average when working with adult female American cockroaches.

EXPECTED RESULTS

If young, mated, oöthecal-bearing female adults are to be used in the experiments, the most useful indicator for success of the allatectomy is

1§

termination of the oötheca production (production of eggs in an egg capsule). We now know that the c.a. play a role (either direct or indirect) in post-maturation development of ovaries of the American cockroach. Thus, in a way, production of oöthecae would be dependent upon whether the c.a. had released the gonadotropic hormone necessary to induce ovarian development and maturation. Allatectomy should terminate production of oöthecae since the gonadotropic hormone would then be absent.

If the allatectomy is successful and the insect survives, allow 21–35 days to permit regression and resorption of all terminal oöcytes. If two or more oöthecae are produced during this time, consider the allatectomy unsuccessful. (It should be pointed out that if fragments of c.a. are left within the body cavity of the insect, oöthecal production will be maintained as if the glands were still present.)

At any time autopsies can be performed to observe any changes taking place since the operation. A very noticeable change in the mature female cockroach will be complete regression and resorption of each of the developing terminal oöcytes of the ovaries. By making a ventral incision along the midline of the abdomen, the ovaries can be exposed and any such changes noted. A convenient method of comparison is to note size, shape, and coloration of each terminal oöcyte from representative experimental and control groups. If the allatectomized insect is injected with crude Cecropia extracts, a change in length of oöcytes can be noted, as shown in Table I (also see Fig. 4A and B).

TABLE I

Effect of injected crude Cecropia extract on ovarian growth of allatectomized American cockroaches

Treatment injection 50 μl	No. of insects injected	surviving	Length of largest oöcyte (mm)*
Cecropia extract	24	23	$3 \cdot 18 \pm 0 \cdot 13$
Peanut oil (controls)	24	24	$1 \cdot 33 \pm 0 \cdot 07$

* Mean ± standard deviation, 3 replicates. (From Chen *et al.*, 1962.)

PHYSIOLOGICAL EXPERIMENTS ON THE ALLATECTOMIZED COCKROACH

Scores of different experiments can probably be conducted with allatectomized cockroaches. One that immediately comes to mind involves implanting pairs of functionally active c.a. into an allatectomized insect to see whether it reverts to the previous homeostatic state (Chen *et al.*, 1962). Another is injecting natural extracts such as Cecropia "oil" (Williams, 1956) from a giant silkworm moth, farnesol, or synthetic compounds such as farnesyl methyl ether or 10,11-epoxyfarnesenic acid methyl ester, etc. to see whether

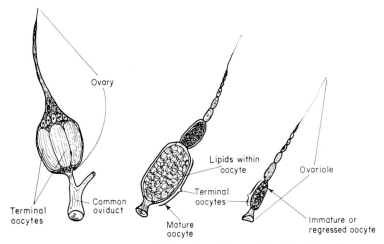

FIG. 4. Gross structures of the cockroach ovary (greatly enlarged).

the ovaries can be reinduced to develop (Chen *et al.*, 1962; Bowers *et al.*, 1965). Biochemical studies can also be undertaken to determine quantitative and qualitative differences between allatectomized and normal cockroaches (Vroman *et al.*, 1965). Other experiments can be set up to clarify various phenomena yet to be explained, such as the relationship of the accessory glands to the c.a., the hormonal and enzymatic mechanisms involved in ovarian development, production of oöthecae, growth and maturation of the insect, the possibility of a c.a.-ovarian feedback system, presence of sex hormones, and countless others that need further investigation.

CONCLUSION

The c.a. are exceedingly important to the insect, but much research is still needed to further our understanding of the function of these fascinating glands. However, they are only a small part of the complex system involving hormonal interactions, most of which still are not very well understood by the endocrinologist. With practice, allatectomy of the American cockroach can become a routine operation to permit the scientist to carry out many simple or even sophisticated experiments limited only by imagination, ambition, and techniques available to the operator.

REFERENCES

Bodenstein, D. (1953). The role of hormones in moulting and metamorphosis. *In* "Insect Physiology" (K. D. Roeder, ed.), pp. 879–931. Wiley, New York.
Bowers, W. S., Thompson, M. J. and Uebel, E. C. (1965). The juvenile and gonadotropic hormone activity of 10,11-epoxyfarnesenic acid methyl ester. *Life Sciences*, **4**, 2323–2331.

Chen, D. H., Robbins, W. E. and Monroe, R. E. (1962). The gonadotropic action of Cecropia extracts in allatectomized American cockroaches. *Experientia*, **18**, 577.

Vroman, H. E., Kaplanis, J. N. and Robbins, W. E. (1965). Effect of allatectomy on lipid biosynthesis and turnover in the female American cockroach, *Periplaneta americana* (L.). *J. Insect Physiol.*, **11**, 897–904.

Williams, C. M. (1956). The juvenile hormone of insects. *Nature, Lond.*, **178**, 212–213.

13 | Hormonal Control of Excretion in an Insect

S. H. P. MADDRELL

Department of Zoology, University of Cambridge,
England

ANIMALS AND APPARATUS

Four freshly fed fifth-stage larvae of *Rhodnius prolixus*; an unfed fifth-stage larva; a binocular dissecting microscope; micrometer eyepiece for use with the latter; focusing microscope lamp; dissecting dish; wax-lined Petri dish; liquid paraffin (B.D.H. "heavy", density = 0·865–0·890 g/litre); squirt bottle filled with Ringer's solution; fine entomology pins (Flatters & Garnett, No. 20); fine glass rods made by pulling out 4 mm glass rod; several fine glass pipettes made by pulling out glass tube to a tip of internal diameter 0·5–1 mm; one wide-mouthed glass pipette (internal diameter at tip of 4–5 mm); a length of rubber or polythene tubing which can be attached to the glass pipettes; pair of No. 5 watchmakers' forceps; pair of ordinary fine forceps; pair of fine scissors (iridectomy scissors are ideal but larger pairs can be used).

CHEMICAL SOLUTION

Ringer's solution of the following composition: 9·82 g NaCl, 0·77 g KCl, 0·50 g $CaCl_2$, 0·18 g $NaHCO_3$, 0·10 g NaH_2PO_4. These salts are dissolved in distilled water and made up to 1 litre. NaCl, KCl and $CaCl_2$ can be dissolved simultaneously but the $NaHCO_3$ and NaH_2PO_4 must be dissolved separately, each in a fairly large quantity of water, before they are added to the rest of the solution.

IDEA AND PRINCIPLE BEHIND THE EXPERIMENT

This experiment sets out to demonstrate that the rate of excretion of an insect can be very dramatically increased and that this increase is caused by the appearance in the insect's blood (haemolymph) of a very active hormone. The insect used for this experiment is *Rhodnius*, a blood sucking bug, which takes very large meals in order to tide it over the periods when it may not be able to find a host. When it has taken one of these enormous meals (which can be up to twelve times its own body weight) it is rather unmanoeuvrable and its blood rapidly becomes diluted by the watery blood meal. It therefore produces a copious flow of dilute urine which both reduces its size and restores the normal concentration of its blood.

In order to show that this rapid excretion (or diuresis) is hormonally controlled you are to set up isolated preparations of the insect's Malpighian tubules, the organs responsible for the fast excretion. These preparations can then be used to test samples of haemolymph for the presence or absence of a factor accelerating the rate at which they secrete fluid.

N.B. It is recommended that you carefully read the following instructions and the section on trouble-shooting (p. 214) before you actually begin the experiment.

EXPERIMENTAL DETAILS

Take a sample of haemolymph from a fed insect by cutting off or nicking a mesothoracic leg near its base and squeezing the insect gently. Take up the drop of haemolymph in a glass pipette fitted with a length of tubing and blow the drop out under liquid paraffin in the wax-lined Petri dish. If it clings to the surface, sink it with a fine glass rod. Put the dish on the stage of the binocular microscope, one of whose eyepieces contains a micrometer, and using transmitted light measure the diameter of the drop and, assuming it to be spherical, calculate its volume. You will require a drop of about 4 μl which is a drop of diameter slightly less than 2 mm. Set this sample aside while you dissect out the set of Malpighian tubules which are to be transferred to it. Pin the fed insect down in a dissecting dish half-filled with wax by holding its legs as shown in Fig. 1. If you use fine pins bent at right angles at a point about two-thirds of their length from the head, the pins lie flat to the surface of the wax and so do not get in the way of the subsequent dissection. Light the insect with a focused spot from the microscope lamp. Taking a pair of fine watchmakers' forceps, push one of the points through the insect's abdominal wall at the spot marked X in Fig. 1 until it lies along the line X–Y. Grasp this length of dorsal abdominal wall and tear it back but not quite off so that a strip of abdominal wall is reflected as shown in Fig. 2. Wash away the blood meal that escapes from the torn midgut with Ringer's solution from a squirt bottle. After flooding the dissection with more Ringer's solution, pin the abdomen open as shown in Fig. 2 using bent pins as described above. Now grasp the end of the pale green midgut (*AG* in Fig. 2) with the forceps and with a fine glass rod break the tracheal connexions between the Malpighian tubules (*MT* in Fig. 2) and this expanded part of the midgut. By manoeuvring this part of the midgut with the forceps it will be possible to move the narrow dark-coloured part of the midgut (*PG* in Fig. 2) and the coiled Malpighian tubules which cling to it so that the tracheal connexions between the tubules and the

abdominal wall can be cut, again by snapping them with a fine glass rod. Next
cut through the midgut with fine scissors between its narrow and expanded
parts. Holding the cut end of the narrow length of the midgut so as to steady
the mass of tissue cut away the posterior part of the rectum leaving the anterior
part attached to the preparation. This is most easily done by cutting round
the edge of the rectal gland which surrounds the connexion of the midgut with

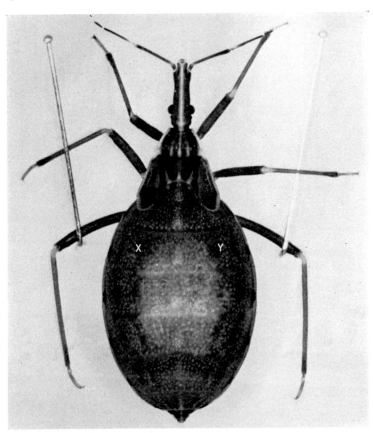

FIG. 1. A fed *Rhodnius* larva pinned down ready for dissection.

the rectum and which appears thicker and whiter than the rest of the rectal
wall (see Wigglesworth, 1931). The preparation is now free and can be picked
up in a drop of Ringer's solution with a wide-mouthed pipette and transferred
to the paraffin-filled Petri dish. Watching the operation under the dissecting
microscope and lighting the preparation from below, pull the mass of tubules
out of the drop of Ringer's solution with a fine glass rod and push them into
the drop of haemolymph. The lining of the part of the rectum which is included

in the preparation is hydrophobic; push it to the surface of the drop where it will spread out along the surface. If the preparation is successful, a droplet of fluid will appear from the short rectal cone within a minute or two and the

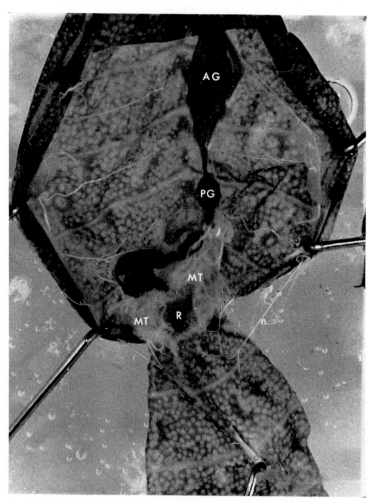

Fig. 2. Partly dissected *Rhodnius* larva. *AG*, Anterior expanded part of the midgut (light green in colour); *PG*, narrow posterior part of the midgut (usually dark red in colour); *MT*, mass of Malpighian tubules; *R*, rectum.

preparation will look like the one shown in Fig. 3. If no fluid appears, try again until you get a successful preparation.

When you have made a viable preparation, measure the diameter of the the droplet of secretion at intervals and so construct a volume/time graph.

If at the end of an hour or an hour and a half the rate of secretion has not nearly fallen to zero, reduce the size of the drop of haemolymph by sucking some out with a glass pipette. When secretion does slow or stop, suck away most of the haemolymph bathing the tubules and replace it with a drop of haemolymph taken from an unfed insect. Follow the rate of secretion over the next 15 min or so and note that the rate of secretion does not increase. Again suck away most of the haemolymph and replace it this time with a sample of

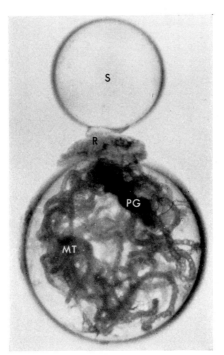

FIG. 3. An isolated preparation of Malpighian tubules (*MT*). *S*, The drop of secretion; *R*, internal surface of that part of the rectum included in the preparation; *PG*, the coiled posterior part of the midgut. This preparation had been secreting for about 1 h so that the drop of secretion is a good deal bigger than the one you will see soon after the preparation is made.

haemolymph taken from a fed insect which is still producing a copious flow of urine. After about 5–10 min the rate of secretion should rise rapidly to a maximum rate which may be maintained for 30 min to 1 h depending on the size of the sample and the extent to which it is diluted when mixed with the haemolymph already bathing the tubules. If you have time, test similarly a sample of haemolymph taken from a fed insect which is no longer producing urine (one fed more than 6 h previously); in this case the haemolymph will again be found to be inactive.

The results of this experiment can most clearly be presented as a graph in which the volume of the droplet of secretion produced by the Malpighian tubules is plotted against the time and the points indicated at which various samples of haemolymph were added. Such a result is shown in Fig. 4.

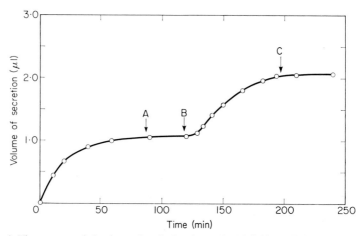

FIG. 4. The secretory behaviour of an isolated set of Malpighian tubules. At A a sample of haemolymph from an unfed insect was added to the preparation, at B the sample added was taken from an insect fed about 1 h previously, while at C was added a sample of haemolymph taken from a fed insect in which diuresis had stopped.

TROUBLE-SHOOTING

Clearly, the main difficulties involved in this experiment have to do with the satisfactory preparation of the isolated sets of tubules. It is not easy to make a satisfactory preparation at the initial attempt and so you are advised not to take too long over it, firstly so that you quickly learn what not to do, and secondly because Malpighian tubules are rather rapidly damaged by being kept for prolonged periods in Ringer's solution. Remember that the Malpighian tubules of *Rhodnius* have two regions, a distal length which is fairly opaque and easy to see and a basal length which is more transparent and so easy to damage inadvertently. Cutting tracheal connexions with a glass rod rather than with a scalpel or fine scissors is much less likely to lead to damaged tubules.

Occasionally it is found with an otherwise successful preparation that there is some fluid on the rectal lining and the drop of secretion tends to mix with it and run back into the drop of haemolymph. If this happens tease this fluid off with a fine glass rod or suck it off with a pipette.

CONCLUSIONS FROM THE EXPERIMENT

Only samples of haemolymph taken from animals which are producing a copious flow of watery urine will accelerate the function of the isolated set of Malpighian tubules. It may be concluded that during diuresis the haemolymph contains a factor which accelerates secretion by the tubules which it does not contain at other times.

FURTHER EXPERIMENTS

EXPERIMENT 1

Apparatus

Five freshly fed *Rhodnius* larvae; five pairs of fine forceps; five clamps and stands; ten wax-lined watch-glasses half-filled with liquid paraffin.

Method

The experiment described above demonstrates the existence of a diuretic factor. This experiment sets out to find the source of the factor. The factor released into the haemolymph must travel from its source to the Malpighian tubules at the tip of the abdomen. So, if fed insects are constricted at various positions on their bodies, diuresis will continue only if the source of the diuretic factor and the tubules are on the same side of the constriction. It is suggested that you constrict one insect at each of the following positions: at the neck, at the middle of the prothorax, at the middle of the mesothorax, and at the junction of the thorax and abdomen. Include one unconstricted insect as a control. Constrict the insects with fine forceps held shut with clamps. Attach the clamps to clamp stands so that you can suspend the insects and collect the drops of urine produced in paraffin-filled watch glasses. The unconstricted insect can be held by its prothoracic legs. Use two watch glasses alternately for each insect so that you can collect drops in one while measuring the diameter of a pooled drop in the other. Plot a volume/time graph for each insect. You will find that the constriction of an insect at any position in front of the mesothorax has no effect at all but that when the constriction is on the mesothorax or behind it, diuresis slows immediately and stops within 30–45 min (typical results are shown in Fig. 5). This experiment shows that the diuretic factor is released into the haemolymph at some point behind the prothorax; since a constriction on the mesothorax stops diuresis either the source is in the mesothorax or there is some centre there whose integrity is essential for the release of the factor from a source further back in the animal. In fact, the latter interpretation proves to be correct (see Maddrell, 1966), the diuretic factor being made in the large fused ganglionic mass in the mesothorax but released from the surfaces of the nerves just behind it.

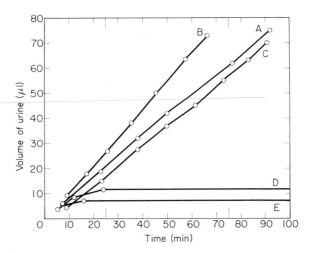

FIG. 5. Urine production in insects constricted at various positions on their bodies. A, Unconstricted control; B, constricted at the neck; C, constricted at the prothorax; D, constricted at the mesothorax; E, constricted at the junction of the thorax and abdomen.

EXPERIMENT 2

You can show that this piece of nervous tissue contains a very large amount of the diuretic factor in the following experiment.

Apparatus

Two short lengths of glass rod of diameter 4 mm; a rubber bung size $6\frac{1}{2}$ with two holes drilled in it; alumina powder or other abrasive powder; a *Rhodnius* larva.

Method

In this experiment you are required to remove a mesothoracic ganglionic mass from a *Rhodnius* larva, grind it up in a little Ringer's solution and test the resulting homogenate on an isolated set of Malpighian tubules prepared as described on p. 210. The grinding up of such a small piece of tissue as the mesothoracic ganglionic mass is an interesting problem itself. One solution is to make a very small pestle and mortar as follows. Take a short length of 4 mm glass rod and heat one end of it in a Bunsen flame until it has a rounded end. While this piece is cooling, heat another piece for a longer time until it has a sizeable lump of molten glass at its tip. Push the rounded end of the first piece of glass into the molten end of the second and pull it away again before they fuse. This will give you a small depression in one piece which will exactly fit the tip of the other. Allow both pieces to cool. Push the mortar into a hole in the rubber bung and roughen the working surfaces of the pestle and mortar by working them together with a little fine carborundum powder and water in the mortar. Clean and dry them both before you use them. The pestle can be kept in the other hole in the rubber bung when not in use (Fig. 6).

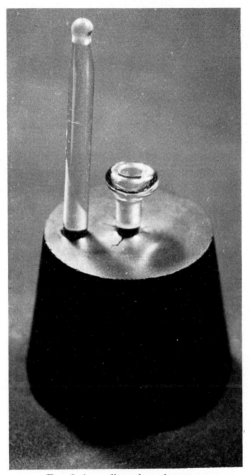

Fig. 6. A small pestle and mortar.

To remove a ganglionic mass from a *Rhodnius* larva, pin the insect down in a dissecting dish under Ringer's solution and open its thorax from the dorsal surface to reveal the mass lying on the floor of the mesothorax (*MTGM* in Fig. 7). Cut the nervous connexions round it and remove it with fine forceps. Transfer it with a little Ringer's solution to the mortar and break it up thoroughly with the pestle; this is best done watching the process under the dissecting microscope. Remove the resulting homogenate with a fine glass pipette and test it on a set of isolated Malpighian tubules. The tubules will respond with alacrity and secrete at their maximum rate for some hours.

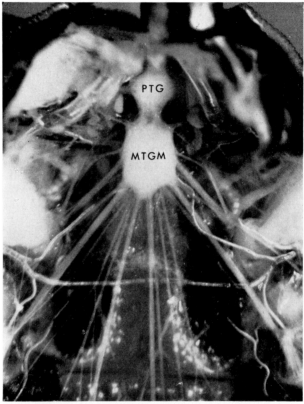

FIG. 7. Dorsal view of the nervous system of the thorax. The nervous tissue was whitened for the photograph by flooding it with absolute alcohol. *PTG*, Prothoracic ganglion; *MTGM*, mesothoracic ganglionic mass.

In fact, nearly all the diuretic activity of the ganglionic mass is contained in two groups of neurosecretory cells (nerve cells which secrete hormones) found near the back of the ganglionic mass; so concentrated is the diuretic factor in them that it can be detected at a dilution of at least 100 million times (Maddrell, 1963, 1964).

CLEANING UP

Pour away the liquid paraffin from the wax-lined Petri dish and clean the dish with disposable tissues. Cover the dish with its lid. Wash out the dissecting dish with tap water and dry it. It is especially important to clean and dry steel instruments which have come into contact with Ringer's solution. Clean and dry the working surfaces of the pestle and mortar and push a tube over them to seat on the rubber bung to keep the dust off them.

BIBLIOGRAPHY

Buxton, P. A. (1930). The biology of a blood-sucking bug, *Rhodnius prolixus*. *Trans. R. ent. Soc., Lond.*, **78**, 227–236. [Describes how to feed *Rhodnius* and how to maintain them.]

Maddrell, S. H. P. (1963). Excretion in the blood-sucking bug, *Rhodnius prolixus* Stål. I. The control of diuresis. *J. exp. Biol.*, **40**, 247–256.

Maddrell, S. H. P. (1964a). Excretion in the blood-sucking bug, *Rhodnius prolixus* Stål. II. The normal course of diuresis and the effect of temperature. *J. exp. Biol.*, **41**, 163–472.

Maddrell, S. H. P. (1964b). Excretion in the blood-sucking bug, *Rhodnius prolixus* Stål. III. The control of the release of the diuretic hormone. *J. exp. Biol.*, **41**, 459–472. [These three papers give a description of most of the experiments outlined here. Rather more on the interpretation and discussion of the results and rather less on how to do the experiments.]

Maddrell, S. H. P. (1966). The site of release of the diuretic hormone in *Rhodnius*— a new neurohaemal system in insects. *J. exp. Biol.*, **45**, 499–508. [Describes the search with the electron microscope for the actual points of release of the diuretic hormone.]

Stobbart, R. H. and Shaw, J. (1964). Salt and water balance: excretion. *In* "The Physiology of Insecta" (M. Rockstein, ed.), Vol. 3, pp. 189–258. Academic Press, New York.

Wigglesworth, V. B. (1931). The physiology of excretion in a blood-sucking insect, *Rhodnius prolixus* (Hemiptera Reduviidae). II. Anatomy and histology of the excretory system. *J. exp. Biol.*, **8**, 428–442. [Useful picture of the excretory organs of *Rhodnius* on p. 429.]

14

A. The Use of the Kymograph

B. The Clam-heart Technique of Bioassay for Acetylcholine

C. Preparation of Nerve Extracts for Bioassay of Bound and Free Acetylcholine

D. The Function of the Cardioregulator Nerves in the Crayfish

E. Pharmacology of the Crayfish Heart

F. Spontaneous Activity of the Crayfish Hindgut and its Control by Drugs

ERNST FLOREY

Department of Zoology, University of Washington, Seattle, Washington, U.S.A.

A. The Use of the Kymograph

In this age of mechanoelectric transducers and electronic recording instruments, the use of mechanical recording devices has been more and more neglected and many principles of the proper use of the kymograph and of its accessories have been forgotten. Consequently, the conviction is spreading that kymographs are not very suitable as recording devices, and the word "old-fashioned" has become a strong weapon in an unjust endeavor to abandon their use altogether and to ban kymographs from the physiology laboratory.

The following instructions are offered in the hope that they will help to restore the lost confidence in the classical tool of the physiologist, and to help the beginner to see the enormous potential of the kymograph as a universal recording device.

TYPES OF KYMOGRAPHS

The main feature of a kymograph is a metal cylinder mounted on a rotatable spindle. This is driven by a motor. Some kymographs have spring wound motors, others have electric motors.

Cheap spring wound motors tend to slow down as the spring unwinds. Their speed is governed by an adjustable brake. This consists often of external, exchangeable, rotating vanes of different sizes. The velocity of their rotation is limited by their air-resistance. The better spring wound motors are provided with several reducing gears. Constant speed is maintained by a governor similar to that used in spring wound watch motors. Electric kymographs have always constant speed because of the inherent frequency control provided by the a.c. line current. Electric kymographs, like their better mechanical counterparts, are provided with gears to allow several speeds of rotation of the drum.

The drum is to be covered with suitable paper on which the records are then inscribed by the stylus of the recording lever.

Two types of inscribing are commonly used: (1) soot writing, and (2) ink writing.

1. The Soot Writing Technique

PREPARATION OF THE DRUM FOR RECORDING: THE APPLICATION OF THE KYMOGRAPH PAPER

Glossy white paper must be selected for this purpose. The drum, removed from the kymograph, is laid onto the paper and the proper area is marked off and cut out. The paper is cut to allow about 3 cm overlap. In order to apply the cut paper strip to the drum, lay it, glossy side down, on the table and moisten the non-glossy (now upper) surface with a sponge and place the drum (which lies on its side) over its center. Lift the two ends of the strip up and join them on top of the drum. Orient strip and drum in such a way that the top of the drum faces away from you. The ends of the kymograph paper must then overlap so that the end of the left half lies over that of the right half. Apply a fast drying glue or cement to the end strip of the right half and press the end flap of the left half of the kymograph paper over it. The procedure is depicted in Fig. 1.

As the paper dries, it stretches and tautly fits the drum. The seam is arranged in such a way that the writing stylus cannot be caught by the edge of the paper when the drum turns in the normal clockwise direction.

SMOKING THE DRUM

When illuminating or natural gas is bubbled through benzene, it picks up enough benzene vapor to give a very sooty flame when ignited. The benzene–gas mixture can be conducted (by way of rubber tubing) to a piece of glass tubing with a narrow orifice (about 2 mm diameter). The arrangement is shown in Fig. 1. When the gas is turned on and the gas–benzene mixture is ignited where it emerges from the glass nozzle, the resulting sooty flame can be directed against the rotating drum; the kymograph paper will not burn

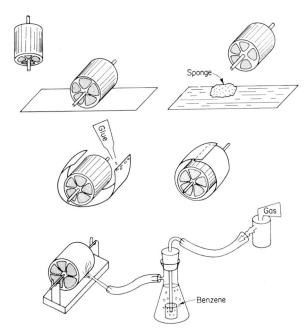

FIG. 1. How to fasten the paper to the drum and how to "smoke" it. If there is not sufficient time to prepare the drum in advance, the paper can be fastened with adhesive tape and the moistening can be omitted. The paper will not be as smooth, however, and the writing tip of the lever might get caught on the tape.

because the metal drum below it conducts the heat away. It is best to place the kymograph drum with its spindle on a stand, as illustrated in Fig. 1, so that it can be rotated horizontally. By moving the flame back and forth the paper can be covered with an even, thin layer of soot. Care must be taken not to touch the paper surface afterwards. The drum is now ready to be mounted on the kymograph.

ADJUSTING THE LEVER

Before a freshly prepared drum is used for recording, the lever and writing stylus must be moved into proper position. It is important that the lever be adjusted so that it moves in the plane of the tangent of that point at which the writing stylus touches the circumference of the drum (see Fig. 2). Both kymograph and the stand holding the lever must be absolutely vertical. Even so the tip of the stylus tends to leave the paper as it moves up or down from the original horizontal position in which it touches the paper. This is due to the fact that the curvature of the drum and that of the arc through which the recording stylus move are at right angles to each other. To avoid the con-

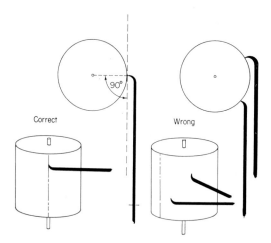

FIG. 2. Diagrams to illustrate the correct placement of the writing lever and some of the common misuses of the kymograph.

sequences of this geometry, levers and styli have been designed that compensate for this and keep the stylus tip on the kymograph drum. Two mechanisms are employed: (1) springs, and (2) double pivoting joints. The springs have the advantage of simplicity but the disadvantage that the pressure with which the tip is pressed against the drum varies: it is greatest with the lever in the horizontal position. The most common arrangement uses spring-like material for the writing stylus itself: paper, celluloid or plastic. Other constructions use a rigid stylus but incorporate a metal spring in the writing arm of the lever which keeps the stylus pressed against the drum.

Levers with a double pivoting arrangement have the great advantage that the stylus writes with constant pressure. Two types are in use. The first employs a Cardanic suspension of the lever. This is modified so that the writing arm of the lever is attached to a freely rotatable spindle that is not vertical but inclined towards the drum so that the writing arm of the lever "falls" against the drum (Fig. 3). The effective weight of the lever arm and the degree of inclination of the spindle determine the pressure of the stylus on the drum. The second type of "constant pressure" lever looks like a conventional type of lever except that the writing tip is mounted on a pivoting hook, as shown in Fig. 4. The latter type of lever can easily be made in the laboratory from a bit of soft glass tubing and sealing wax. It is particularly suited for use with delicate heart preparations and organs that exert only small forces on a lever.

Here are instructions to make an isotonic, light lever with a pivoting "constant pressure" stylus. If you do not already have a proper heart lever

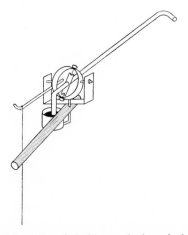

FIG. 3. Diagram of an ink writing gimbal lever; the lever is doubly suspended so that it falls against the drum. In this ink writing version the lever consists of steel capillary tubing; one end dips into an ink well. Note that the load arm is attached to the suspension ring and is not a continuation of the writing arm of the lever.

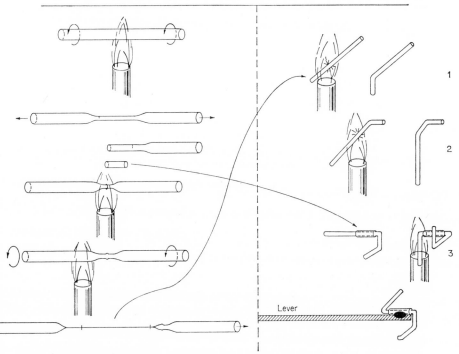

FIG. 4. Diagrams to illustrate the manufacture of a constant pressure stylus. The procedure is explained in detail in the text.

K

available, you can make one from a stick of wood, 0·5 cm in diameter, and a drinking straw (natural, paper or plastic): simply stick a pin through the straw about 5 cm from one end and insert it into the rounded end of the wooden stick. If you have proper kymograph accessories available, select a light heart lever.

Prepare a pivoting writing tip as follows. Heat the middle region of a piece of soft glass tubing (5–8 mm diameter) over the Bunsen burner while continually rotating it with your fingers. Wait until it is soft and pliable, then remove it from the flame and stretch until the thinnest region is no more than about 2 mm in diameter. Nick the center with a file and break the tubing at that point. Nick one of the capillary points again about 15 mm from the tip and break this off. Hold this short piece of capillary with forceps and touch it at both ends to the lower part of the flame. Withdraw it from the flame the instant the flame changes color at the point of contact. The edges of the capillary are now firepolished and smooth.

Next, pick up the two separated parts of the drawn out glass tubing and fuse them over the flame. Now apply the flame to a region to one side of the point of fusion and as soon as the flame turns yellow, pull and move the glass out of the flame all in one motion. This will produce a fine capillary. Break off an 8 cm portion of this.

Now reduce the flame. Hold the thin capillary with one hand at one end and let it touch the flame at a point about 15 mm from the other end. If the flame is touched properly, that is, at its periphery, the heating will be localized and the glass will soften at that point only. Be careful to hold the capillary horizontal. The tip will now drop downward at a right angle. As the tip begins to droop, remove the glass from the flame.

Now hold the capillary at the bent tip in such a way that all parts of the tubing are horizontal. Touch it to the flame as before, but at a point about 15 mm inward from the bend. This will accomplish a second bend of 90°.

Slip the long arm of the bent capillary through the piece of 2 mm capillary prepared before. Now hold, with two fingers, both pieces of tubing so that the bend rests against the shoulder of the short capillary. Turn them so that the terminal, bent portion of the inner, thin capillary points upward. Touch the thin capillary to the flame just where it emerges from the other end of the wider, short capillary. Remove from the flame immediately when the bending begins but allow this to complete a right angle.

All that is left to do now is to touch the very tip of the hook part of the bent inner capillary to the flame to melt the rough edges into a tiny bead.

The writing tip is now ready to be mounted onto the lever. Simply attach it with a drop of molten sealing wax.

When properly balanced (see below) levers of this type do not require more than a pull of 20 mg from the moving organ.

FIXING THE RECORDS

The soot-blackened kymograph paper with the inscribed traces of recorded lever-movements must be fixed in order to make the records permanent. For this purpose the paper must be carefully removed from the kymograph drum and be submerged in a fixative. The procedure is shown in Fig. 5.

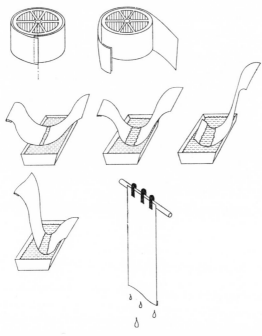

FIG. 5. Diagrams to illustrate the procedure involved in fixing a kymograph record. For details see text.

Do not remove the paper while the drum is still on the kymograph. Remove the drum first from its stand and spindle and set it on a paper-covered table top. Locate the seam where the paper strip had been glued together. With a razor blade make a cut just above the edge of the underlying end of the paper strip. Avoid cutting into the metal surface of the drum. Be sure to place a finger over the first part of the cut so that the paper strip does not suddenly snap off the drum and fall, sooty side down onto the table. Remove the paper strip from the drum, being careful to touch it only near the cut edges (the former seam).

Now, with the sooty side facing upwards, dip the strip into the fixing solution. This is done as follows. First lower the middle portion until it just touches the surface. As the fixative penetrates through the soot from below, immerse further, allowing the liquid to pass over the surface of the middle portion. Now gradually pull the paper strip through the solution, keeping it submerged—first one way towards the left, then the other way towards the right. Pull it through the fixative once again and hang it up to dry on that end which had last been in the fixative.

PREPARATION OF THE FIXATIVE

The most widely used fixative consists of a solution of shellack in alcohol. Dissolve 1 unit weight (e.g. 500 g) of shellack in 2 vol (e.g. 1 liter) of alcohol (96% denatured) and add to each 100 ml of solution 1 ml of castor oil. The latter addition makes the dried film of lacquer more flexible and prevents cracking when the papers are rolled up for storage.

A convenient and clean method of transferring the fixing solution from the storage container to the fixing trough and back is shown in Fig. 6.

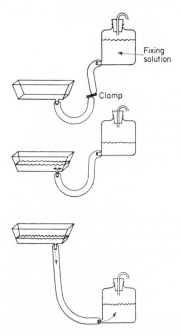

FIG. 6. Method of transfer of fixing solution. The fixing trough has at its bottom an inlet-outlet tube. This is connected by way of rubber tubing with the aspirator bottle that contains the fixative. By raising or lowering the bottle, the trough can be filled or drained. Note the air inlet through the stopper.

2. THE INK WRITING TECHNIQUE

There can be no question about the advantages of ink writing kymography. No smoking apparatus is required. The drum can be prepared quickly for recording and the records can be stored without requiring fixation.

The drawbacks of ink writing are that the friction of an ink writing stylus is greater than that of a soot writing one. When levers are used that feed the ink writing stylus by capillary action, clogging occurs not infrequently. When simple ink boats are used as attachment to the writing tip, the changing weight, as the ink is used up and evaporates, changes the load on the lever and alters the recording conditions.

The best kinds of levers are those which use as the writing arm a stainless steel capillary tube that is fed from a stationary ink reservoir, and which have the writing arm cardanically suspended (gimbal lever, as shown in Fig. 3). Although the manufacturers recommend a non-glossy writing surface, glossy paper must be used when minimal friction is required.

Ink writing levers must be thoroughly cleaned at the end of each experiment. After ink container and capillary have been cleaned with distilled water, they should be stored in alcohol. If there is any suspicion that the ink to be used contains dust, it must be filtered before use. Only slow drying, recording ink should be used. Ordinary ink, as used in fountain pens, is unsuitable.

GENERAL HINTS ON THE USE OF THE KYMOGRAPH APPARATUS

1. Prepare a hand rest to facilitate writing on the kymograph drum. A horizontally held short metal rod held by a clamp on a suitable, independent table stand is very convenient. The height of the rod should be set so that the hand resting on it can comfortably reach a place just to the left or below the recording writing tip of the lever.

2. Select a lever that is suitable for the particular preparation. The contractions of strong muscles should not be recorded with a light heart lever! Some preparations require a counterweight to keep the muscle extended and to facilitate relaxation after induced contractions. The light heart levers to be used for delicate hearts (lamellibranchs, crayfish) and other "weak" organs should be carefully balanced before the organs are connected. Balancing is best done with pieces of plasticene or suitably sticky wax.

3. Although the connecting thread must be securely attached to the organ from which one wishes to record, the other end of the thread should not be tied on to the lever unless one is dealing with a tough and mechanically very resistant organ. It is better to attach the thread by simply pressing it into a small lump of wax affixed to the load arm. Should the lever, in the course of an exciting experiment, be jolted or accidentally hit, this will not tear the organ but merely release the thread.

4. Set the drum at the lowest possible position on its spindle so that it can later on be raised when the first round of recording has been completed.

5. Before beginning the recording make sure that the drum is securely fastened and is not in danger of slipping.

6. Adjust the writing lever so that its tip touches the paper near the upper margin of the drum just to the right of the seam where the paper had been glued together. Make sure that the lever is in a horizontal position when the preparation is attached and in its normal, resting position. When recording from a beating heart, the lever should be horizontal when the heart is in diastole. Only if this precaution is rigidly and consistently observed, can the records later be interpreted properly. Remember that the recording is curvilinear, that is the y-axis is represented by a semicircle the radius of which is given by the length of the writing arm of the recording lever.

As has been stated before, it is essential that the plane of the up-and-down movements of the writing arm lies parallel to the tangent through the drum radius that goes through the writing tip (see Fig. 2).

When adjustments have to be made, be sure to leave the thread slack that connects the load arm of the lever to the preparation. Otherwise the inevitably jerky movements might tear and injure it.

7. On the upper left margin of the paper covered drum (just to the right of the seam) write the date, your name, the kind of animal and preparation used and other information concerning the nature of the forthcoming experiment. Make it a rule to follow this procedure whenever you start with a "new drum". Nothing is more embarassing later, than to be confronted with a record that has no identifying marks on it: the recorded heart beats may have been those of a crayfish or of a clam.

8. Equally important: calibrate the "speed" of the drum before you start recording. Although special timers are available that place time marks on the kymograph paper as this revolves, these are not really necessary if one takes the precaution of marking off suitable time intervals, such as 1 min, 10 sec, or even 2 sec in the case of fast turning drums.

B. The Clam-heart Technique of Bioassay for Acetylcholine

This is the most specific, convenient and rapid bioassay technique. The ventricle of a clam is isolated and suspended for mechanical recording in a suitable organ-bath of known volume. Known and unknown amounts of acetylcholine (ACh) are added to the bath and their effects on the heart are compared. Equal effects indicate identical amounts of ACh present in the bath. A simple calculation permits determination of the amount of ACh originally present in the extracted tissue.

Preparation of the Heart (Fig. 7)

Best results are usually obtained with species of the genus *Protothaca* or *Tapes*, but other genera, such as *Mya, Mercenaria* (=*Venus*), *Cyprina* and *Ostrea*, can be used also. The following genera of lamellibranchs are unsuitable: *Pecten, Mytilus, Modiolus, Anodonta, Crassostrea, Serripes, Tresus, Solen, Dinocardium, Clinocardium, Saxidomus* and *Chlamys*. These statements rely on observations by the author and on the reports by Welsh and Taub (1948), Welsh (1954), Hughes (1955), and Greenberg (1964).

Animals obtained live at fish markets are perfectly suitable. They should be kept in cool (10–15°C) sea water that is aerated. They will live for several weeks without food. In an aquarium with non-circulating sea water, not more than two animals should be kept per liter of sea water.

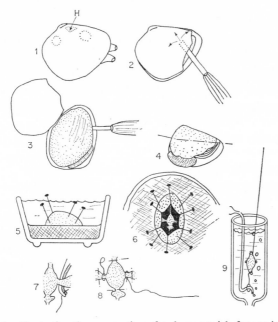

Fig. 7. Sketches illustrating the preparation of a clam ventricle for use in the bioassay of acetylcholine. (1) Outline of the animal with indication of the siphons, the attachments of the adductor muscles and of the heart (*H*). (2) and (3) A screwdriver is used to free the organism from its attachments to the shell. (4) The dashed line indicates where to cut off the dorsal portion of the animal which is to be mounted (5) in a dissecting dish. (6) A top view of the dissecting dish; a longitudinal incision has been made and the dorsal body wall and pericardium have been retracted laterally, exposing the ventricle and the lateral attachments of the auricles. (7) and (8) Details of the heart showing the tips of forceps used in tying the ligatures (7) and the position of the cuts that will free the ventricle; the bulbous structure below the ventricle is the accessory heart. The muscle chamber is shown in (9); the ventricle is anchored on the tip of a long hypodermic needle through which air is bubbled into the bathing saline solution.

For the dissection the following instruments are needed: one screwdriver; one pair of large, one pair of fine scissors; two pairs of small, curved forceps. A dissecting microscope of low power (5 or 10×) is helpful. One also needs fine thread and about ten pins.

The dissection should be carried out with the preparation under sea water. A glass bowl, about 5 cm deep and of about 15 cm diameter with a bottom of black "dissecting wax" (at least 1 cm thick), is most convenient for this.

1. Find a suitable animal and gently tap the edge of the shell with the handle of the screwdriver until a small fragment breaks loose. Now insert the blade of the screwdriver and scrape along the inner surface of one halfshell until the closer muscles are detached. Now remove the remaining portion of the broken halfshell taking care not to injure that part of the animal that lies close to the hinge. With the aid of the blade of the screwdriver free the animal from the other half shell.

2. With the larger pair of scissors cut through the animal in such a way that the entire ventral portion of the animal with its foot can be removed.

Now transfer the dorsal part of the animal to the dissecting dish and pin it down, dorsal side up.

3. With the fine scissors make a superficial sagittal cut along the dorsal body wall. This exposes the pericardial cavity. Retract the body wall laterally.

4. Slip the tips of a pair of curved forceps underneath the junction between one of the auricles and the ventricle. Open its jaws slightly and grasp the tip of a short length of thread. Pull the thread through and, using the other pair of curved forceps, tie a ligature around the proximal portion of the auricle, leaving the junction itself intact.

5. Prepare another piece of thread by tying a small loop at one end. Use it to tie a ligature around the other auricle thereby attaching the loop. Cut through the auricles distal to the ligatures and sever the arteries and the gut anterior and posterior to the ventricle. The ventricle is now free and can be removed (with the proper lengths of thread attached) to the muscle bath.

MOUNTING THE HEART AND RECORDING APPARATUS (FIG. 8)

MOUNTING THE HEART

For the muscle chamber and heart holder the following are needed: the barrel of a 2 ml hypodermic syringe, the barrel of a 1 ml tuberculin-type syringe, a hypodermic needle (No. 17–No. 20) at least 6 cm long, a 10 cm length of thin rubber tubing to be slipped over the nozzle of the 2 ml syringe and a spring clip or pinch cock to be clamped onto the tubing. Plastic syringes are preferable because their flanged ends can be easily cut off. In the case of the tuberculin syringe this facilitates slipping over it the rubber tubing that

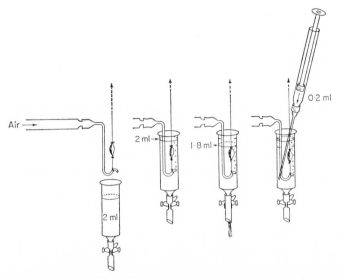

FIG. 8. Muscle chamber and heart holder, as explained in the text, are shown on the left. Also shown is the method of adjusting the level of fluid in the chamber preparatory to the application of ACh and of test samples. The diagram on the right shows how the test samples and ACh are applied.

supplies compressed air, in the case of the 2 ml syringe barrel this reduces the extra volume and length above the calibrated portion.

The 2 ml barrel is held upright by a suitable clamp mounted on a rack and pinion device. The 1 ml barrel with the hypodermic needle attached is held horizontal by another clamp. The hypodermic needle is bent downwards, its tip is bent S-shaped, so that it forms a hook.

The loop attached to the heart preparation is slipped over the hook while the muscle chamber (the 2 ml barrel) is kept lowered below the tip of the needle. The thread attached to the other auricle is attached to the writing lever (see below).

Now the muscle chamber must be filled with sea water and raised to totally submerge the preparation. The air flow through the tuberculin syringe and needle-hook should be adjusted to produce a stream of small air bubbles.

THE RECORDING APPARATUS

The heart preparations are rather delicate. Only if the recording device offers minimal frictional resistance can adequate records be obtained. Heart levers writing on smoked kymograph paper are to be preferred over ink writing ones. In any case, only glossy kymograph paper should be used. The levers must be of the "constant friction" type (see p. 224 and Figs. 3 and 4).

PROCEDURE

1. PREPARATION OF PRIMARY STANDARDS

Select twenty clean test tubes of at least 20 ml capacity, Set them into a rack. With the aid of a 10 ml pipette add to each of eight tubes 9 ml of buffered artificial sea water of pH 6·5 (see Appendix). Cover all test tubes. From a fresh stock solution of acetylcholine chloride (see Appendix) transfer 1 ml into the first test tube, using a 1 ml pipette (blow out type). Gently blow air through the pipette to mix the contents of the test tube. Draw the solution up into the pipette, and blow it out. Repeat five times. Now blow more air through the pipette, holding the tip of the pipette against the bottom of the test tube. The air should displace enough of the solution so that this rises to the top of the test tube and rinses off any drops of an incompletely mixed (thus more concentrated) ACh solution. Using a gummed label or a wax pencil, mark the test tube "ACh 10^{-4}".

Now draw exactly 1 ml of the freshly mixed solution of ACh 10^{-4} into the pipette, withdraw the pipette from the test tube and wipe it with a fresh piece of tissue paper. Immerse the tip of the pipette into the next tube and blow out and repeat the mixing procedure. Be sure to keep the covers over the other test tubes! Remember that 1 drop of an ACh solution of 10^{-4} that accidentally splashes over into another tube will establish there an ACh concentration of about 5×10^{-7}, a concentration that is more than a hundred times stronger than the minimum concentration required to completely stop the test heart!

Continue the stepwise dilution until you have the following standard concentrations: 10^{-4}, 10^{-5}, 10^{-6}, 10^{-7}, 10^{-8}, 10^{-9}, 10^{-10}, 10^{-11}. Be sure to label all test tubes after the mixing is completed.

2. ESTABLISHING THE RANGE OF SENSITIVITY

It is now necessary to find the minimal concentration of ACh that will cause complete cessation of the heart beat. For this as well as the subsequent bioassay it is necessary to know the precise concentration of ACh in the bathing chamber of the test heart. The following procedure should be followed. Fill the bath with exactly 2 ml of sea water and then submerge the heart and aeration needle by raising the bath to the necessary level (see Fig. 8). Adjust the air to the desired flow rate (this should provide a continuous stream of fine bubbles but not so strong as to cause spraying). Now mark the level of the fluid. Remove 0·2 ml with a tuberculin syringe and mark this level also. For exceptionally large hearts you may have to use a larger bath chamber and use 5 ml of sea water from which you withdraw 0·5. In either case, the upper mark indicates 10 vol, the lower mark 9 vol.

When the test heart has established a regular heart rate, add (see below)

1 vol of ACh 10^{-11} to 9 vol of bathing solution, using a tuberculin syringe and squirting the ACh solution into the bath with the needle submerged. Do not aim at the heart. The air bubbles help in the mixing process and within a few seconds the heart will be bathed by a solution of ACh 10^{-12}. It is likely that no effect is noticeable, but there are exceptionally sensitive clam ventricles which will show a diminution of amplitude even at this low a concentration of ACh.

After 1 min, drain the bath and from a wash bottle rapidly fill the bath. Drain again, fill, drain once more and then carefully fill to the 10 vol mark. Wait for at least 1 min. Now drop the level of bathing fluid to the 9 vol mark. Add 1 vol of ACh 10^{-10}. After mixing this will give a concentration of 10^{-11}. After 1 min drain the bath, fill with sea water, drain again, fill, drain once more and then fill to the 10 vol mark. Wait for at least 1 min before the next addition of ACh.

Proceed with the addition of higher and higher concentrations until you find the one that causes complete cardiac arrest.

3. PREPARATION OF THE TEST STANDARDS

The bioassay using the clam ventricle is very accurate and it is necessary to have standard solutions that differ in their ACh concentration by not more than 20%. Such standards can now be prepared economically since you know the sensitivity of the test ventricle. What is needed now is a series of dilutions covering the range between the minimal concentration that causes cardiac arrest (as determined in procedure 2) and the next lower standard concentration. For instance, if ACh 10^{-9} (final dilution) stops the heart, then the test standards need to cover the range between ACh 10^{-8} and 10^{-9} (the final concentrations reaching the heart will thus be 10^{-9}–10^{-10}).

The following test standards will be needed designating the maximum standard concentration as determined by procedure 2 as 10^{-n}:

$1 \cdot 0 \times 10^{-(n+1)}$ $1 \cdot 6 \times 10^{-(n+1)}$ $2 \cdot 9 \times 10^{-(n+1)}$ $5 \cdot 0 \times 10^{-(n+1)}$ $8 \cdot 5 \times 10^{-n(+1)}$
$1 \cdot 2 \times 10^{-(n+1)}$ $2 \cdot 0 \times 10^{-(n+1)}$ $3 \cdot 5 \times 10^{-(n+1)}$ $6 \cdot 0 \times 10^{-(n+1)}$ $1 \cdot 0 \times 10^{-(n)}$
$1 \cdot 4 \times 10^{-(n+1)}$ $2 \cdot 4 \times 10^{-(n+1)}$ $4 \cdot 2 \times 10^{-(n+1)}$ $7 \cdot 2 \times 10^{-(n+1)}$

These test standards are easily prepared as follows. First take a clean 100 ml or 125 ml Earlenmeyer flask, add 99 ml of buffered (pH 6·5) artificial sea water (see Appendix) and 1 ml of the ACh standard $10^{-(n-2)}$. For example, if the minimum concentration causing stopping of the heart beat was ACh 10^{-9}, add 1 ml of ACh 10^{-7} to the 99 ml of artificial sea water. This gives a concentration of 10^{-n} (or 10^{-9} in the example quoted).

Now transfer with suitably accurate pipettes the following quantities into the remaining twenty test tubes: 1·2, 1·4, 1·6, 2·0, 2·4, 2·9, 3·5, 4·2, 5·0, 6·0 7·2 and 8·5 ml. To each of these tubes add enough buffered (pH 6·5) artificial sea water, to give a total volume of 10 ml. Thus you add 8·8, 8·6, 8·4, 8·0, 7·6, 7·1, 6·5, 5·8, 4·0, 2·8 and 1·5 ml. Carefully label all tubes.

4. ESTABLISHING THE RANGE OF EFFECTS

Before the beginning of the bioassay proper, it is advisable to establish the effects of the different standard concentrations of ACh. If afterwards extracts of unknown ACh content are applied, it is very easy to tell, at least approximately, what the range of the contained ACh concentration is, as long as the effect is not supramaximal. This saves much time in matching the effect with that of known ACh standards.

Apply, in subsequent trials, the entire series of test standards, from $1·0 \times 10^{-(n+1)}$ through $1·0 \times 10^{-n}$. Follow the following schedule, which, in fact, is the same that will be employed in the bioassay proper. Allow the heart to beat undisturbed for 1 min. If the beat is steady and regular, stop the kymograph (turning off the motor or disengaging the clutch, whichever is more convenient). Lower the bath level to the 9 vol mark. Add 1 vol of test standard concentration $1·0 \times 10^{-(n+1)}$. Wait for exactly 30 sec. Turn on the kymograph and record for exactly 1 min. Turn off the kymograph, drain the bath, fill with sea water, drain, fill with sea water, drain once more and fill with sea water to the 10 vol mark. Wait another 30 sec, or until 30 sec after the drum was stopped, then turn on the kymograph and record the heart beat for 1 min. During this minute flush the syringe you used to apply the ACh standard and then fill it with 1 vol of the next higher test standard concentration $(=1·2 \times 10^{-(n+1)})$. Proceed as described before until all test standards have been applied.

Note. It is imperative that no air bubbles are trapped in the syringe when the standard (and later on when the unknown extract dilutions) are applied. As this air is expelled into the bath it pushes out the fluid contained in the needle and introduces a sizeable error: the needle volume must not be added to the bath. Make sure that you expel all air from the syringe when you adjust the contained solution to the 1 vol mark (in most cases this will be 0·2 ml).

5. THE BIOASSAY PROPER (FIG. 9)

If the extracts to be assayed have been made up to have a concentration of 1 g tissue (wet weight) in 10 ml of extract $(=1 : 10)$ or (10^{-1}), prepare dilutions of 10^{-2}, 10^{-3} and 10^{-5}. If the extract concentration is not 1 : 10 but another ratio, make it first up to 10^{-1} or 10^{-2} before diluting further by factors of 10, 100, etc. Apply extracts in the same manner as you applied the standard ACh concentrations. Always add 1 vol to 9 vol of bathing solution. Keep the same time schedule as described in section 4 of this outline.

It is very likely that one of the concentrations of a given extract will give an intermediate depression of the heart rate. Looking over the established range of effects of various ACh concentrations (test standards) you can readily select an ACh test standard that will give a slightly smaller effect. If you find this to be the case, apply the extract again (same concentration as before), and next apply a concentration of ACh that gives a stronger effect.

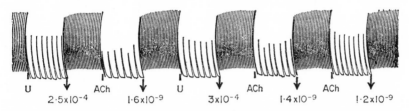

U　　　　ACh　　　U　　　　ACh　　　ACh
2·5×10⁻⁴　　1·6×10⁻⁹　　3×10⁻⁴　　1·4×10⁻⁹　　1·2×10⁻⁹

FIG. 9. Example of an actual bioassay record obtained with a ventricle of *Protothaca staminea*. U, Extract of unknown ACh content; ACh, known acetylcholine. The figures refer to the final concentrations (g/ml) in the bath. ACh $1·6 \times 10^{-9}$ has a stronger action than U 3×10^{-4}. ACh $1·4 \times 10^{-9}$ is only slightly more active than U 3×10^{-9} but ACh $1·2 \times 10^{-9}$ is definitely less active. Two interpretations are permissible: (1) U 3×10^{-4} = ACh $1·4 \times 10^{-9}$; (2) U 3×10^{-4} = ACh $1·3 \times 10^{-9}$ (the average of $1·2 \times 10^{-9}$ and $1·4 \times 10^{-9}$). The results can thus be stated as: $4·6 \times 10^{-6}$ g or 4·6 ($\pm 12·5\%$) μg/g, and as $4·33 \times 10^{-6}$ g or 4·33 μg ($\pm 7·15\%$)/g respectively. By comparison, U $2·5 \times 10^{-4}$ is slightly less active than ACh $1·2 \times 10^{-9}$ and more active than ACh $1·0 \times 10^{-9}$ (not shown); thus its activity is intermediate between the two ACh concentrations and the result of $4·4 \times 10^{-6}$ g or 4·4 μg ($\pm 10\%$)/g. (From Florey, 1967).

The aim in the bioassay is to "bracket in" the extract, so that the record of its effect is preceded by that of a lower, and followed by that of a higher ACh concentration. This procedure defines the lower and upper limit of the possible ACh concentration present in the extract. The more closely matched, the better will be the agreement in the actual ACh concentrations between unknown and test standards.

It is important to know that the differences in the effects of various ACh concentrations become larger the closer the concentrations come to that which causes complete cessation of the heart beat. Where great accuracy is required it is advisable, therefore, to adjust the extract concentrations by suitable dilution (4×10^{-3}, or $6·5 \times 10^{-2}$ etc.) so that their effects nearly match those of near maximal concentrations of the ACh test standards.

The sensitivity of a test heart may vary with time. For this reason it is not possible to rely on the range of effects established under procedure 4. It is necessary to alternate between application of test standards and of extract throughout the entire bioassay procedure.

6. CALCULATIONS

From the results of the bioassay it is easy to calculate the ACh content of the original tissue. This is done in the following manner.

Decide which test standard gives the same effect as the optimal extract concentration. If you find that a given extract concentration has effects intermediate between two test standards that differ by 20%, you can assign to it a standard concentration 10% lower than the higher of the two test standard concentrations. For instance, if the effect of an extract $2\cdot5 \times 10^{-4}$ is smaller than that of ACh 6×10^{-9} but larger than that of ACh 5×10^{-9}, you can equate the extract concentration of $2\cdot5 \times 10^{-4}$ with an ACh concentration of $5\cdot5 \times 10^{-9}$ (accuracy $\pm10\%$). *Note.* The accuracy of the assay should always be given. It is roughly equal to the percent difference between the effectiveness of the extract and the nearest higher and the nearest lower ACh standard, or $\pm0\cdot5$ times the percent difference between the nearest higher and lower ACh standards tested.

When you have established the ACh concentration that corresponds in effectiveness to that of the particular extract concentration, multiply the ACh concentration with the reciprocal of the extract concentration. For example, in the case given above the extract concentration of $2\cdot5 \times 10^{-4}$ has the same effect as ACh $5\cdot5 \times 10^{-9}$ ($\pm10\%$). The ACh concentration of the extracted tissue therefore is

$$5\cdot5 \times 10^{-9} \times \frac{1}{2\cdot5 \times 10^{-4}} \quad \text{or} \quad \frac{5\cdot5 \times 10^{-9}}{2\cdot5 \times 10^{-4}} \quad \text{or} \quad \left(\frac{5\cdot5}{2\cdot5}\right) \times 10^{-9(-4)}$$

$$=2\cdot2 \times 10^{-5}(\pm10\%) \text{ g ACh per g of tissue.}$$

It is customary to express the ACh content in terms of μg of acetylcholine chloride per g wet (or dry) weight of extracted tissue. In the example given the ACh content of the extracted tissue would thus be $22\cdot0$ ($\pm10\%$) μg/g, since 1 μg is equal to $1\cdot0 \times 10^{-6}$ g.

7. DETERMINATION OF SPECIFICITY OF THE ASSAY

Several compounds can accomplish inhibition of the clam ventricle and it is possible that the effect of a tissue extract is due to a component other than ACh. This is particularly true if the extract had to be applied in relatively high concentration or if the assay indicated only a low ACh content of the tissue. So far, no compound has been found that is more effective than ACh in inhibiting the clam ventricle. Of the ones that have been tested, carbamyl choline is the most active. On the heart of *Mercenaria* (=*Venus*) *mercenaria* it has 1/80 of the activity of ACh (Welsh and Taub, 1948). Table I lists the

TABLE I

Relative molar quantities of various cholinesters that cause inhibition equivalent to that produced by a molar quantity of acetylcholine equal to 1

	Mercenaria (Welsh and Taub, 1948)	*Protothaca*
Acetylcholine	1	1
Carbamylcholine	80	18
Propionylcholine	105	37
Benzoylcholine	15 000	292
Butyrylcholine	625	4 800
Acetyl-β-methylcholine	1 100	541
Choline	14 000	58 000

relative effectiveness of various compounds as tested on the hearts of *Mercenaria* and of *Protothaca*. From these data it is quite evident that if any of the compounds shown were present in an extract, and if the inhibitory effect were entirely due to this compound, its amount in the extracted tissue would have to be many times larger than that of the amount of ACh indicated by the assay. Thus, if the assay indicated 1 μg of ACh per g and the activity were due to propionylcholine, about 100 μg of this compound must have been present in 1 g of extracted tissue, and if the compound were acetyl-β-methylcholine the assay would indicate 1 000 μg/g.

From such considerations one may conclude that the assay becomes the more specific for ACh the higher the amount of (apparent) ACh found in the assay. It is very unlikely that an effect corresponding to 100 μg of ACh per g of extracted tissue is actually due to propionylcholine, much less to acetyl-β-methylcholine or choline; if this were so the tissue would have contained no less than 10 mg of propionylcholine, 100 mg of acetyl-β-methylcholine or 1·5 g of choline!

To test for specificity in the case of lower yields of ACh, the following procedures are recommended.

(a) *Biological procedures*

To test whether the active agent is a cholinester, add a small, measured amount of lyzed erythrocytes of human or horse blood to a quantity of extract. The erythrocytes of both species contain acetycholinesterase of high specificity. Blood should be drawn into a heparinized syringe; oxalate or citrate should be avoided because they may affect the calcium activity of the extract. One ml of blood is sufficient for 44 ml of extract. Centrifuge the blood at 1 000 g for 10 min, siphon off the plasma and save it. Add 9 vol of distilled water to the 1 vol of red blood cells. Stir until a homogeneous mixture is obtained. Add 1 part of this to 9 parts of an aliquot of extract. Shake and allow to stand at room temperature for 30 min, then place the mixture into a boiling water bath for 2 min in order to inactivate the enzyme. The subsequent bioassay should indicate that all ACh has been destroyed by the procedure. Remaining activity is due to compounds other than ACh and is most likely not due to a cholinester. The erythrocyte cholinesterase will not appreciably interfere with butyrylcholine and benzoylcholine, however. These compounds can be destroyed by serum-cholinesterase. To the extract, previously treated with erythrocyte-cholinesterase, add 1 part of serum and incubate at room temperature for 30 min, then place the tube into boiling water for 2 min. If the subsequent bioassay indicates that the inhibitory activity has disappeared it is likely that the agent responsible for the previously obtained inhibition was either buytryl or benzoyl choline. Further tests would have to be performed to identify the esters.

(b) *Pharmacological procedures*

Clam hearts have weak cholinesterase activity. They can be sensitized to ACh and closely related cholinesters by the application of anticholinesterase compounds. The sensitivity towards ACh usually increases two- to fivefold. At the end of the bioassay, add eserine ($=$physostigmine salicylate) to the washing and bathing solution to give a final concentration of 10^{-5} g/ml. No eserine needs to be added to the test standards or the extract samples. Allow the eserine to take effect by bathing the heart for 30 min in eserine-sea water (10^{-5}), then repeat the bioassay. If the inhibitory effects of the extract(s) is due to ACh, the results of the assay should be the same as those obtained before the application of eserine. If a significantly different value is obtained, it is to be assumed that part or all of the activity are due to a cholinester other than ACh.

Several drugs are known to block the action of ACh on the clam ventricle. Of these mytolon chloride ($=2:5$ bis (3′-diethylaminopropylamino)-benzoquinon bisbenzyl chloride; in some published papers referred to as benzoquinonium chloride) is the most potent and requires a final concentration of not more than 10^{-6} g/ml to block the action of ACh in concentrations up to 10^{-8} g/ml. The other effective agents are methantheline or banthin ($=\beta$-diethylaminoethyl-9-xanthene carboxylate methobromide) phenyltriethylammonium iodide and 3-hydroxyphenyltriethylammonium iodide. These should be applied in a concentration about 500 times stronger ($=5 \times 10^{-5}$ g/ml) for a blocking action similar to that of mytolon 10^{-6} g/ml. (Quantitative data have been reported in papers by Luduena and Brown, 1952; Welsh and Taub, 1953.)

It is always advisable to make use of one or the other of these blocking agents at the end of the bioassay period to make certain that the activity seen in the assays is indeed due to ACh or at least due to a related cholinester. If the minimal extract concentration that caused complete inhibition of the heart beat before the application of the blocking agent still causes inhibition, this must be due to agents other than ACh.

(c) *Combined chromatography–bioassay*

The easiest method of identification of ACh in the tissue extracts is by means of paper chromatography. This can be carried out on Whatman No. 1 paper or filter paper of equivalent quality. The solvent should be neutral in order to minimize hydrolysis of the cholinesters. Because of the great sensitivity of the clam ventricle to ACh it is possible to carry out the chromatography with very small amounts of tissue extract. Even if the tissue contains not more than 1 μg of ACh per g, no more extract than what corresponds to 10 mg of tissue needs to be applied to the paper. If the ventricle used for the bioassay responds well to ACh 10^{-9}, it is sufficient to extract the cut out strips of the developed chromatogram with 5 ml of buffered sea water. Provided all the ACh is found within one such strip, the final concentration in the eluate would be no less than 2×10^{-9}, and even if the ACh should be distributed over three consecutive strips, enough would be present in the eluates to be detectable in the bioassay.

The technique of paper chromatography is explained on p. 347; therefore no details are given here. The most suitable solvents are water saturated butanol, and a mixture of 5 vol of propanol, 2 vol of benzyl alcohol and 2 vol of water. With these neutral solvents no acid hydrolysis of ACh takes place and the formation of secondary esters is avoided.

If an extract of 100 mg tissue per ml contains acetylcholine-like activity equivalent to that of 0·1 μg of ACh per ml (the original tissue thus contained 1 μg/g), not more than 0·01 ml of the extract need be spotted onto the paper. A spot of authentic acetylcholine chloride, at least 0·01 ml of a solution of 10^{-6}, should be placed near the extract spot. Obviously, the experiment is easier if larger amounts of ACh can be applied.

After development, the papers are air dried (this should be done under the fume hood). The paper strip is then divided into ten equal sections (covering the region from the point of application of the spots to the solvent front) and the strips are shredded into 10 ml beakers. Five milliliters of buffered artificial sea water are then added to each beaker and 2 h allowed for extraction. The eluates thus obtained can then be tested on a clam ventricle. With saturated butanol, ACh migrates to an R_F of 0·1, with propanol-benzyl alcohol-water (5 : 2 : 2) it can be found at R_F 0·45–0·5.

The procedure is sketched in Fig. 10. For a more conclusive proof of the identity of the eluted compound with ACh it is advisable to apply two extract spots and to elute only the paper sections above one of them for bioassay.

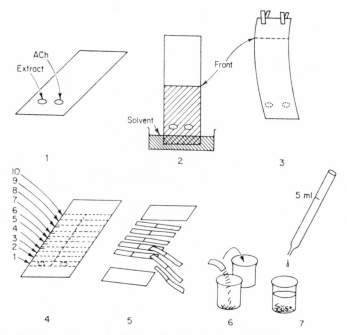

FIG. 10. Sketches of the procedure involved in the identification of tissue acetylcholine by combined paper chromatography and bioassay. (1) The extract and ACh are spotted onto the paper. (2) The chromatogram is developed (the air tight enclosure is not shown). (3) It is removed from the chromatography chamber and dried. (4) The region between origin and "front" is then divided into ten sections, and (5) these are cut out. (6) The left and right portions of each section are then shredded and placed into 10 ml beakers. (7) To each beaker 5 ml of buffered sea-water are added for the elution of ACh. The eluates are tested on the clam ventricle.

When the area to which the activity has migrated has been ascertained in the assay, elute the corresponding area above the other spot with distilled water, allow most of it to evaporate and apply the concentrated eluate to another solvent for development with another solvent. The method has been successfully used to identify ACh in extracts of *Octopus* nerve tissue (Loe and Florey, 1966).

APPENDIX

1. COMPOSITION OF ARTIFICIAL SEA WATER, BUFFERED TO pH 6·5

NaCl453, MgCl$_2$ 52, KCl9 CaCl$_2$ 11 mM, make up to 1 liter. To 1 liter of this add 56 ml of 0·2 N Tris-acid maleate and 44 ml of 0·2 N NaOH.

It is best to prepare this from the following stock solutions: 5 M NaCl (292·2 g of NaCl in 1 liter); 1 M MgCl$_2$ (203·3 g of MgCl$_2$.6H$_2$O in 1 liter); 1 M KCl (74·5 g of KCl in 1 liter); 1 M CaCl$_2$ (111 g of CaCl$_2$, or 147 g of

$CaCl_2 . 2 H_2O$ in 1 liter); 0·2 M Tris-acid maleate (19·6 g of maleic anhydride and 24·2 g of Tris in 1 liter); 0·2 N NaOH (8·0 g of NaOH in 1 liter).

Proceed as follows. Into a 1 000 ml volumetric flask pipette 90·6 ml of 5 M NaCl, 52 ml of 1 M $MgCl_2$, and 9 ml of 1 M KCl. Add distilled water to a level of about 100 ml below the 1 000 ml mark. Close the flask and shake. Now add 11 ml of 1 M $CaCl_2$, close the flask and shake. When the solution has come to rest, add distilled water up to the 1 000 ml mark. Pour the solution into a polyethylene (or Pyrex) bottle of 1 250–2 000 ml capacity.

Into a 100 ml measuring cylinder pour 56 ml of Tris-acid maleate and fill to the 100 ml level with 0·2 N NaOH. Pour the contents of the cylinder into the bottle that contains the salt solution, close the bottle and shake. Label the bottle indicating the molar composition of the artificial medium, the date and the name of the person who prepared the solution.

2. ACETYLCHOLINE STOCK SOLUTION

It is best to obtain preweighed ACh. Ampules containing 100 mg of acetyl-choline chloride can be obtained from Merck Inc. With a glass file, break the ampule and drop it (including the top) into a polyethylene bottle of 100–125 ml capacity. Add 100 ml distilled water (should be slightly acid, pH 5), close the bottle and shake. Carefully label the bottle stating the name of the compound (acetylcholine chloride), its concentration (10^{-3} g/ml of distilled water), the date and the name of the person who prepared the solution. This stock solution should be kept in the refrigerator; it will be stable for several weeks.

BIBLIOGRAPHY

Florey, E. (1967). The clam-heat bioassay for acetylcholine. *Comp. Biochem. Physiol.* **20**, 365–377.

Greenberg, M. J. (1964). A compendium of responses of bivalve hearts to acetyl-choline. *Comp. Biochem. Physiol.* **14**, 513–539.

Hughes, B. (1955). The isolated heart of *Mya arenaria* as a sensitive preparation for the assay of acetylcholine. *Br. J. Pharmac.* **10**, 36–38.

Loe, P. R. and Florey, E. (1966). The distribution of acetylcholine and cholines-terase in the nervous system and in innervated organs of *Octopus doflein*. *Comp. Biochem. Physiol.*, **17**, 509–522.

Luduena, F. P. and Brown, T. G. (1952). Mytolon and related compounds as antagonists of acetylcholine on the heart of *Venus mercenaria*. *J. Pharmac. exp. Ther.* **105**, 232–239.

Welsh, J. H. (1954). Marine invertebrate preparations useful in the bioassay of acetylcholine and 5-hydroxytryptamine. *Nature, Lond.* **173**, 955–956.

Welsh, J. H. and Taub, R. (1948). The action of choline and related compounds on the heart of *Venus mercenaria*. *Biol. Bull. mar. biol. Lab., Woods Hole* **95**, 346–353.

Welsh, J. H., and Taub, R. (1953). The action of acetylcholine antagonists on the heart of *Venus mercenaria*. *Br. J. Pharmac. Chemother.* **8**, 327–333.

C. Preparation of Nerve Extracts for Bioassay of Bound and Free Acetylcholine

One frog; dissecting pan; strong pair of scissors; pair of small forceps; balance, accurate to 1 mg; weighing paper; 10 ml frog-Ringer solution; 5 ml pipette, graduated to 0·1 ml; three test tubes; 500 ml beaker; test tube stand; glass homogenizer, 10 ml capacity; Bunsen burner; wire mesh screen.

Introduction

The acetylcholine (ACh) of nerve tissue occurs in two major fractions: (a) free acetylcholine and (b) bound acetylcholine. The free ACh cannot readily be determined; it is destroyed by the choline esterase as soon as the nerve cells are broken down during homogenizing, i.e. during the procedure that permits separation of free and bound ACh. Bound ACh, on the other hand, can be readily determined and so can the total amount (= free + bound) of ACh.

When nerve tissue is homogenized in an isotonic saline, its free ACh is free to diffuse out of the broken cells, but as it does so it comes in contact with membrane-bound cholinesterase and is destroyed. What remains is the ACh that is bound to certain cell structures, presumably enclosed by membranes (= vesicles). This bound ACh can be released by agents that break down cell structures or that denature proteins. Thus, bound ACh can be released by boiling, treatment with trichloroacetic acid or by "hypo-osmotic shock", i.e. by exposure of the homogenate to a hypo-osmotic medium.

If nerve tissue is dropped directly into boiling distilled water, the cholinesterase is inactivated almost instantly. At the same time the membrane structures of the nerve cells are sufficiently altered to permit outward diffusion of all ACh, that which was formerly bound, and that which was free already. Thus, boiling releases the *total ACh* into the extracting medium.

If isotonic homogenates are boiled, their bound ACh is released and remains in the extract because cholinesterase is destroyed by the boiling.

Method

Decapitate and pith a frog, expose the two sciatic nerves, free them, and remove them from the animal. Weigh each nerve and note the weights. Add about 200 ml of water to the beaker and bring the water to a boil. Multiply the weight of the nerve (expressed in grams) by 100 and add this amount of water to a test tube. For example, if the nerve weighed 33 mg (=0·033 g) add 3·3 ml (=100 × 0·033) of water to the test tube. Place the tube into the boiling water and drop in the nerve, using a glass needle. Remove the test tube 1 min later and allow it to cool. Label the test tube immediately ("SN b ad 1 : 100"—meaning sciatic nerve, boiled, aqua distillata, 1 : 100).

Fill a beaker with crushed ice, pre-cool the glass homogenizer (pestle inserted), add Ringer solution in an amount equal to 100 × the weight of the other sciatic nerve. (Example: if this nerve weighs 28 mg or 0·028 g, add 2·8 ml.) With a suitable glass needle, insert the nerve and then homogenize it, keeping the homogenizer ice cold.

Allow the homogenate to stand for 1 h, then transfer an aliquot of perhaps 1·5 ml to a test tube and label this "SN h ub R 1 : 100" (meaning sciatic nerve, homogenized, unboiled, Ringer solution 1 : 100). Place the homogenizer with the remaining homogenate into the boiling water and heat for 2 min to liberate the bound ACh. Allow the tube to cool and label it "SN h b R 1 : 100" (meaning sciatic nerve, homogenized, boiled, Ringer solution 1 : 100).

Assay

Determine the ACh content of each extract on the clam ventricle, as outlined in Exercise 14B. Expect the total ACh in the original nerve tissue to amount to about 5–10 μg of ACh per g wet weight ($= 5$–10×10^{-6} g), thus a final dilution in the heart muscle chamber of 10^{-3} should have an effect equal to that of a final ACh concentration of 5×10^{-9}–1×10^{-8}.

Remember *SN b ad* gives you the *total ACh, SN h b* the *bound ACh*. By subtracting the value obtained for bound ACh from that of the total ACh you obtain the free ACh. Test SN h ub to convince yourself that the bound ACh is physiologically inactive.

Bibliography

Birks, R. I. and MacIntosh, C. F. (1961). Acetylcholine metabolism of a sympathetic ganglion. *Can. J. Biochem.* **39**, 787–827.

Hebb, C. O. and Krnjevic, K. (1962). The physiological significance of acetylcholine. *In* "Neurochemistry", 2nd ed. (K. A. C. Elliott, I. H. Page and J. H. Quastel, eds.), pp. 452–521. Thomas, Springfield.

MacIntosh, F. C. (1963). Synthesis and storage of acetylcholine in nervous tissue. *Can. J. Biochem.* **41**, 2552–2571.

Mann, P. J. G., Tennenbaum, M. and Quastel, J. H. (1939). Acetylcholine metabolism in the central nervous system. *Biochem. J.*, **33**, 822–835.

Quastel, J. H.(1962). Acetylcholine distribution and synthesis in the central nervous system. *In* "Neurochemistry", 2nd ed. (K. A. C. Elliott, I. H. Page and J. H. Quastel, eds.), pp. 431–451. Thomas, Springfield.

Schallek, W. (1945). Action of potassium on bound acetylcholine in lobster nerve cord. *J. cell. comp. Physiol.* **26**, 15–24.

D. The Function of the Cardioregulator Nerves in the Crayfish

As in all decapod crustaceans, the heart muscle of the crayfish contracts in response to nerve impulses sent out by nerve cells located in the *cardiac ganglion*; the heart beat is *neurogenic*. By complex interactions, involving synaptic transmission and electrotonus, the ganglion cells of the heart ganglion coordinate their activity in such a way that they produce at regular intervals bursts of nerve impulses. The cardiac ganglion is situated within the heart muscle. In the European crayfish, *Potamobius astacus* (formerly *Astacus fluviatilis*), there are sixteen neurons in the cardiac ganglion (Alexandrowicz, 1929). This, among decapod crustaceans, is the largest number of heart ganglion cells known; other species have smaller numbers. Our knowledge of the function of the heart ganglion cells stems largely from the studies on the nerve cells in the cardiac ganglion of palinurid lobsters (reviewed by Maynard, 1960, 1961; Hagiwara, 1960). Of the nine ganglion cells, five function as *pacemakers*, that is they are spontaneously and rhythmically active and dictate their rhythm to the other four cells which in turn act as motoneurons whose axons innervate the heart muscle cells. These "follower" cells also influence the behavior of the pacemaker cells by collateral connections. It is very likely that the heart ganglion of crayfish is organized in a similar manner, but no details are known.

The central nervous system exerts control over the activity of the heart ganglion by means of the cardioregulator nerves; in this way it controls, indirectly, the strength and frequency of heart beats.

In crayfish there are, bilaterally, two regulator nerves: one causes inhibition, the other acceleration. They will be referred to as *inhibitory nerves* and *accelerator nerves* respectively. The normal innervation pattern seems to be that of one axon in each nerve, so that the heart ganglion is reached by a total of two inhibitory and two accelerator axons (Florey, 1960). Recently, however, it has come to light that there are individuals within an otherwise "normal" population of crayfish (*Pacifastacus leniusculus*) which have in their "accelerator" nerves not one but three axons: two accelerator and one inhibitory axon. It is thus very possible that variants to the "normal" patterns will be found. In this sense the following laboratory exercise may well lead to a valuable contribution to the research literature.

The dissection is delightfully simple and the preparation can be set up within a few minutes. The experiments provide a most convincing demonstration of excitatory as well as inhibitory effects of neurons and, at the same time, illustrate the role of cardioregulator nerves in the case of a neurogenic heart beat.

The experiments involve electrical stimulation of the exposed cardioregulator nerves, perfusion of the heart with various solutions, and isotonic recording of the heart beat which is used as an indicator of the activity of the heart ganglion. The following interpretation is useful. The frequency of heart beats indicates the frequency of electrical activity (burst of nerve impulses) of the heart ganglion. The amplitude of each heart beat indicates the number of nerve impulses (motoneurons of the heart ganglion) per unit time. The duration of the individual contractions indicates the duration of the "burst" or the repetitive spike discharge that reaches the muscle over the motor axons coming from the heart ganglion.

EQUIPMENT AND SUPPLIES

One kymograph (writing speed about 2 mm/sec), one light isotonic heart lever of the constant friction type (see p. 224); one, but preferably two electronic stimulators capable of delivering 0·5 msec pulses of up to 10 V and frequencies up to 50 per sec. One, but preferably two, double electrodes with platinum tips; one, but preferably two, simple micromanipulators for electrode positioning. Note: no shielding cage is required and the electrode cables need not be shielded. One small piece of "tacky" wax or plasticene; one piece of thin sewing thread (1 ft length) to which a pin is attached whose tip is bent into a hook; one old pair of strong scissors; one pair of small, curved forceps; one dissecting needle; one medicine dropper without rubber bulb; three ring stands; one separatory funnel of 500 ml capacity and equipped with a one hole rubber stopper through which a glass tube is inserted so that it reaches almost down to the stopcock of the funnel when the stopper is tightened; one ring clamp to hold the separatory funnel; one clamp to hold the medicine dropper; one clamp to hold the crayfish; one 10 in. length of rubber tubing to be attached to the stems of the funnel; one screw clamp to be placed over the rubber tubing to adjust the flow of solution; one glass adaptor to connect the rubber tubing with polyethylene tubing of 1–2 mm inner diameter; one 1 ft length of polyethylene tubing; one dish to collect waste solution that drips from the preparation.

Saline medium: crayfish solution, buffered to pH 6·5 (see Appendix, p. 254).

THE SET-UP

The arrangement of the experimental set-up is illustrated in Fig. 11. Prepare the kymograph drum as described on p. 222. Mount heart lever and crayfish clamp on rings stand (1). Mount medicine dropper on rings stand (2). Mount the ring clamp near the top of ring stand (3). Insert the separatory funnel with tubing attached.

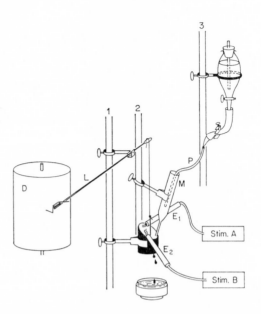

Fig. 11. Arrangement for stimulation of cardio-accelerator nerves, perfusion of the heart and for mechanically recording the heart contractions. The light writing lever (*L*) is mounted on ring stand 1. The preparation is mounted on the same stand. To facilitate the placement of the perfusion cannula (*M*) this is held on a second ring stand (2). A ring clamp mounted on ring stand 3 holds the separatory funnel that serves as constant pressure perfusion reservoir. The perfusion fluid is delivered to the cannula via polyethylene tubing (*P*). E_1 and E_2 are the two electrode holders; the electrode positioners, or micromanipulators, are not shown. The two stimulators (Stim. A and Stim. B) are represented by rectangles. The perfused fluid is allowed to drip into a collecting vessel. *D* represents the kymograph drum. For further detail see Fig. 14.

When properly adjusted, the crayfish clamp occupies the lowest level, the clamp holding the medicine dropper the next. The clamp holding the heart lever should be above that and the ring clamp holding the separatory funnel should occupy the highest position.

Close the stopcock of the separatory funnel, remove the stopper and fill funnel with crayfish solution.

Put the rubber stopper with its glass tube in place and tighten it. Close the screw clamp, then open the stopcock. Now gradually open the screw clamp until a flow rate of about 1 drop every 2 sec is established. Be sure to expel all the air from the tubing. This can be accomplished by squeezing the tubing above the screw clamp and forcing the air up into the separatory funnel. Close the stopcocks.

Balance the heart lever by placing a small lump of wax or plasticene on the load arm.

THE PREPARATION

The dissection and the position of the cardioregulator nerves are illustrated in Figs 12 and 13.

With the old scissors cut off all the legs from a healthy, lively crayfish. Cut along the cervical groove as shown in Fig. 12, but avoid cutting through any of the internal organs. Pull the rostral end of the exoskeleton forward and downward, enough to expose the stomach retractor muscles. Cut through them and pull further: the entire stomach and gut together with the liver and most of the gonads will come out and can be discarded. Be sure to hold the animal upside down, so that any escaping digestive juices can flow out of

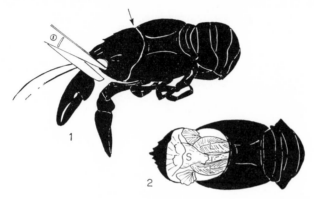

FIG. 12. (1) A crayfish being prepared for evisceration. The scissors cut along the cervical groove indicated by the arrow. It is advisable to cut off the legs before commencing with this operation. (2) When the cut has been made the "head" of the animal can be pulled forward and downward; with it the viscera (liver, L; stomach, S; intestine, i) are pulled out.

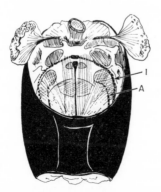

FIG. 13. Dorsal view of the preparation after evisceration and removal of the abdomen. The cardioregulator nerves are indicated by heavy, dashed lines. I, Inhibitory nerve; A, accelerator nerve.

the body cavity and do not come in contact with nerves or heart. Remove the front part of the animal and immediately rinse the body cavity with fresh crayfish solution.

Now flex the "tail" of the animal ventrad until the intersegmental fold between cephalothorax and first abdominal segment is exposed (dorsally). Insert one blade of the scissors and cut through the extensor muscles and on around the entire joint and through all the flexor muscles. This severs the abdomen which should be discarded, unless other experiments are planned which make use of the ventral nerve cord or of the stretch receptors: if in the process of evisceration care is taken to cut the intestine at the boundary between mid- and hindgut before the stomach and appendant organs are removed, the hindgut will remain in position within the abdomen and can then be prepared for a separate experiment.

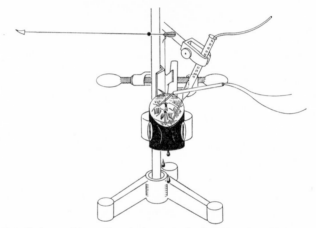

Fig. 14. The relative positions of perfusing cannula, heart hook and electrodes. Diagram of a preparation set up for perfusion, stimulation and recording, showing cannula, heart hook and stimulating electrodes in place. The electrodes stimulate the left inhibitory nerve.

The eviscerated thorax of the animal should be placed in a beaker with aerated crayfish solution as soon as possible. This allows the heart to fill with saline and to expel blood which otherwise would form a clot that prevents proper contact of the perfusion fluids with the heart ganglion.

After 5 min of immersion remove the thorax from the beaker and with the fine, curved forceps pick up any remaining portion of the gonads and remove these. Hold a dissecting needle into the flame of a Bunsen burner and, when red hot, push it down the nerve canal to destroy the thoracic ganglia. If this precaution is not observed, the spontaneous activity of the cardioregulator fibers will obscure the results. The thorax can now be set up as shown in Fig. 14.

Mount the preparation upright in the crayfish clamp, the dorsal side facing you. Immediately lower the medicine dropper so that its tip pierces the pericardium fronto-laterally. Open the stopcock of the funnel and insert the polyethylene tubing in the dropper. This establishes the perfusion of the heart. Now hook the pin into the anterior portion of the heart muscle (you may have to rip the anterior wall of the pericardium to do this) and connect the thread to the lever, pressing it into the wax or plasticene. Carry out this operation while you hold the lever in such a position that the load arm points downward. Now carefully release the lever. If it does not straighten out and does not pull the thread upwards, move the wax or plasticene closer to the fulcrum until the writing arm is just a bit heavier than the pull on the load arm. The effective length ratio of load to writing arm should be at least 1 : 10 and may be as large as 1 : 20. It is imperative that the point of attachment of the thread to the lever is exactly above the heart. When the heart is in diastole the writing arm should be horizontal (see p. 223). Excursions of the writing tip should be at least 1 cm during normal heart activity. Amplitudes of recorded heart beats may easily reach 5 cm, even with crayfish of not more than 10 cm body length.

The origin of the cardioregulator nerves has not yet been described with certainty. Wiersma and Novitski (1942) felt it likely that they are the second and third superior nerves of the subesophageal ganglion, as originally described by Keim (1915) in his monograph of the crayfish nervous system.

The inhibitory and accelerator nerves emerge through openings in the ventral, inner skeleton. The inhibitory nerve of either side runs along the transverse chitinous ridge at the level of the first thoracic ganglion (see Fig. 13). The accelerator nerves run parallel to the inhibitors but emerge one segment posteriorly. They are covered by the flexor muscles shown in Fig. 13 for the first few millimeters but then emerge to run over the extensor muscles (Fig. 13) exposed to the body cavity. For stimulation it is not necessary to expose the accelerator nerves; it is sufficient simply to press the tips of the stimulating electrodes gently against the mid-region of the flexor muscles.

If two pairs of stimulators and electrodes are available, set both stimulators to give repetitive stimulation at 50/sec at 10 V (pulse duration 0·5 msec). Carefully guide the tips of the first pair of electrodes over one inhibitory nerve. As soon as the heart stops beating, turn off the stimulation. Now guide the second pair of electrodes so that the tips come to rest just over the accelerator nerve of one side. As soon as you notice acceleration, turn off the stimulation.

Turn on the "inhibitory" stimulation and gradually reduce the voltage until the heart suddenly starts beating again. Now increase the voltage again to about 1·2 times the threshold voltage. Repeat this procedure with the accelerator stimulation.

If only one stimulator and electrode pair is available, you may begin the experiment by placing the electrode tips over the inhibitory nerve first, and later on change it to the accelerator nerve, or vice versa.

The following is a schedule of exercises that should be performed in order to gain familiarity with the preparation.

1. *Serial stimulation of the inhibitory nerve.* Set stimulator to 1/sec and stimulate for a period of 5 sec. Wait 30 sec during which time you change the setting to 5/sec. Stimulate again for 5 sec. Wait 30 sec during which time you change the setting to 10/sec. Again stimulate for 5 sec. Repeat this performance until you have recorded responses to stimulation with 1, 5, 10, 15, 20, 25, 30, 35, 40, 45 and 50/sec. When you have found a frequency that gives complete inhibition, lower the frequency in steps of 1/sec (keeping the same time schedule) until you have found the threshold for complete inhibition.

2. *Serial stimulation of the accelerator nerve.* Proceed as described under exercise 1, but stimulate with 1, 2, 3, 4, 5, 6, 7, 8, 9, 10, 12, 14, 16, 18, 20, 25, 30, 35, 40, 45 and 50/sec.

3. In order to discover whether there is more than one cardioregulator fiber in each of the nerves stimulated, select a frequency of stimulation that gives an intermediate response and stimulate repetitively while continuously varying the voltage. Note any sudden, stepwise, change in the frequency or amplitude of the heart beat. The number of steps indicates the minimum number of cardioregulator fibers present. It is quite likely that no such steps will be found.

The following exercises require two stimulators and two pairs of electrodes.

4. *Summation.* Place one pair of electrodes over one, the other pair of electrodes over the other inhibitory nerve. Stimulate one nerve with the threshold frequency ascertained under exercise 1, then stimulate the other inhibitory nerve with the same frequency to make sure that the threshold is the same. Differences are more likely due to unequal calibration of the stimulators than to inequality of effectiveness of the two inhibitory nerves. This can, of course, be checked by leaving the electrodes in place and exchanging the stimulators.

Now stimulate the left inhibitory nerve with half the threshold frequency and continue stimulating while, with a delay of a few seconds, the other stimulator, previously set at half threshold frequency, is turned on. The two effects should sum to give threshold inhibition.

Now vary the ratios of stimulation and determine the range over which the frequencies are additive. Be sure to allow 1 min periods of rest between periods of stimulation. Repeat this type of exercise but place the electrodes over the two accelerator nerves.

5. *Adaption.* Stimulate the left inhibitory nerve with threshold frequency and continue stimulation until heart beats resume and reach a steady rate. Now, at one instant turn off the "left" stimulator and turn on the "right" one

(previously set to threshold frequency). If the heart continues to beat, you may conclude that the adaptation to stimulation of the left inhibitory nerve is a post-synaptic phenomenon and not a pre-synaptic one (such as decreasing responsiveness of the inhibitory nerve to stimulation, or decreasing output of transmitter substance from the terminals of the left inhibitory axon(s)).

Place electrodes over the two accelerator nerves. Stimulate the left accelerator at a low frequency, such as 5/sec. Then, while this stimulation continues, add stimulation of the right accelerator nerve, also at 5/sec. Does the result resemble that obtained with stimulation of either accelerator nerve with 10 pulses per sec? Vary the frequencies.

6. *Interaction of accelerator and inhibitory nerve stimulation.* Place one pair of electrodes over one inhibitory nerve, the other over one accelerator nerve. For convenience of expression, we designate the stimulator that activates the inhibitory nerve as the I-stimulator, the other as the A-stimulator.

For the first series of experiments, turn the A-stimulator on, 5 sec later turn the I-stimulator on, 5 sec later turn the I-stimulator off and 5 sec later turn off the A-stimulator. Repeat after 1 min intervals. Set I-stimulator at a subthreshold, threshold and a suprathreshold frequency and vary A-stimulation between 1 and 50/sec in 5/sec steps.

For the second series of experiments turn the I-stimulator on, 5 sec later turn on the A-stimulator, 5 sec later turn off the A-stimulator and 5 sec after that turn off the I-stimulator. Use the same settings as in the first series.

EVALUATION OF THE RECORDS

(a) Plot frequency of stimulation of the inhibitory nerve against heart rate observed during period of maximal effectiveness of the inhibitory nerve at that frequency of stimulation.

(b) Plot frequency of stimulation of inhibitory nerve against percent change in heart rate.

(c) Plot frequency of stimulation of the accelerator nerve against heart rate observed during period of maximal effectiveness of the accelerator nerve at that frequency of stimulation.

(d) Plot frequency of stimulation of the accelerator nerve against percent change in heart rate.

(e) Plot duration of after-effect of "inhibitory stimulation" against frequency of stimulation.

(f) Plot duration of after-effect of "accelerator stimulation" against frequency of stimulation.

(g) Discuss the results evident from plots a–d in relation to the findings obtained in exercises 5 and 6.

(h) Try to interpret the mechanisms underlying the after-effects as described in (e) and (f).

Appendix

Composition of crayfish solution of 10 × stength, to be used as stock solution: NaCl, 120 g; KCl, 4·0 g; $MgCl_2 . 6 H_2O$, 5·0 g; $CaCl_2$ (anhydrous) 15·0 g; H_2O up to 1 000 ml.

Method of preparation: (a) Weigh out NaCl, KCl and $MgCl_2 . 6 H_2O$ and place the powders into a 1 000 ml volumetric flask. Add 700 ml of H_2O and shake until the salts have dissolved. Weigh out the $CaCl_2$ and dissolve this in 100 ml of H_2O in a beaker. Pour the $CaCl_2$ solution into the volumetric flask, mix well and then add H_2O to the 1 000 ml mark. The solution is stable.

(b) Prepare stock solutions of the following: 5 M NaCl (292·2 g/liter); 1 M KCl (74·5 g/liter); 1 M $MgCl_2$ (203·3 g of $MgCl_2 . 6 H_2O$/liter) and 1 M $CaCl_2$ (111 g $CaCl_2$ or 147 g $CaCl_2 . 2 H_2O$/liter). Using clean measuring cylinders and pipettes transfer to a 1 000 ml volumetric flask 41.0 ml of NaCl stock solution, 5.4 ml of KCl stock solution, and 2.6 ml of $MgCl_2$ stock solution. Add 700 ml of H_2O and mix. Now add 13.5 ml of the $CaCl_2$ stock solution, mix and fill with H_2O to the 1 000 ml mark.

To prepare crayfish solution for use in the experiments, add 900 ml of H_2O to 100 ml 10 × stock solution. Buffered crayfish solution of pH 6·5 is is prepared by adding to this 100 ml of 0·2 M Tris-acid maleate buffer, the latter is made up as follows: dissolve 19·6 g of maleic anhydride and 24·2 g of Tris in 1 liter of H_2O. Take 56 ml of this and add 44 ml of a solution of 8·0 g of NaOH/liter. This gives 100 ml of Tris-acid maleate buffer of pH 6·5 of 0·2 M strength.

References

Alexandrowicz, J. S. (1929) Recherches sur l'innervation du coeur de l'écrevisse. *Folia morph.* **1**, 37–67. (In Polish with French summary.)

Alexandrowicz, J. S. (1932). The innervation of the heart of the Crusteacea. I. Decapoda. *Q. Jl microsc. Sci.* **75**, 182–249.

Florey, E. (1960). Studies on the nervous regulation of the heart beat in decapod Crustacea. *J. gen. Physiol.* **43**, 1061–1081.

Hagiwara, S. (1961). Nervous activities of the heart in Crustacea. *Ergebn. Biol.* **24**, 287–311.

Keim, W. (1915). Das Nervensystem von *Astacus fluviatilis* (*Potamobius astacus* L.). Ein Beitrag zur Morphologie der Kekapoden. *Z. wiss. Zool.* **113**, 485–314.

Maynard, D. (1961). Cardiac inhibition in decapod Crustacea. *In* "Nervous Inhibition" (E. Florey, ed.), pp. 144–178. Pergamon Press, Oxford.

Maynard, D. M. (1960) Circulation and heart function. *In* "The Physiology of Crustacea" (T. H. Waterman, ed.), Vol. 1, pp. 161–226. Academic Press, New York and London.

Wiersma, C. A. G. and Novitski, E. (1942). The mechanism of the nervous regulation of the crayfish heart. *J. exp. Biol.* **19**, 255–265.

E. Pharmacology of the Crayfish Heart

The crayfish heart preparation, as described in the preceding exercise, offers an unusual opportunity for neuro-pharmacological experiments. Since the pioneering studies of MacLean and Beznak (1933) many publications have dealt with the excitatory actions of acetylcholine (ACh) on the crustacean heart. There have been many different interpretations of the significance of this, the majority of workers have assumed that ACh acts as the transmitter substance of the cardio-accelerator nerves (Welsh, 1939, 1942; Smith, 1947; Davenport, 1941, 1942; Wiersma and Novitsky, 1942) and of the motoneurons of the heart ganglion (Davenport). More recent evidence indicates, however, that this is not so and that the heart ganglion cells are cholinoceptive even though the cardioregulator nerves are non-cholinergic (Florey, 1963). In the following exercises the student can convince himself of this.

The heart of decapod crustaceans also responds to certain catecholamines (adrenaline, noradrenaline) and indol-alkylamines (5-hydroxytryptamine, 6-hydroxytryptamine) with pronounced excitation. This is an action on ganglion cells (Florey, 1963). While there is no evidence that catecholamines are present in any crustacean tissue, 5-hydroxytryptamine (Maynard and Welsh, 1959), 5,6-hydroxytryptamine (Carlisle and Knowles, 1959) and 6-hydroxytryptamine (Kerkut and Price, 1964) have been detected in crustacean pericardial organs. These neurosecretory structures are presumed to release these compounds into the venous blood that returns to the heart.

γ-Aminobutyric acid mimics the action of the cardio-inhibitory neurons of the crayfish and may, in fact, be the inhibitory transmitter substance responsible for the inhibition of the activity of the heart ganglion (Florey, 1957).

The following exercise involves (1) application of compounds that mimic transmitter substances and neurohormones (for a distinction between these two terms, see Florey, 1962), (2) comparison of their effects with the actions of the cardioregulator nerves, (3) application of drugs that interfere with the transmitter-like compounds, and (4) experiments to discover whether the latter drugs also interfere with the action of the cardioregulator neurons that, presumably, release transmitter substances.

EQUIPMENT AND SUPPLIES

The same equipment is used as in exercise 14 D, p. 247., except that one stimulator is sufficient and that four, instead of one, separatory funnels complete with ring clamps, rubber and polyethylene tubing and screw clamps are required. In addition there is need for one test tube stand, twenty test tubes, seven 1 ml and one 10 ml pipettes. The saline medium is the same solution as that recommended in the preceding exercise. In addition, the following drugs and stock solutions are needed: acetylcholine chloride (acetylcholine bromide is also suitable), γ-aminobutyric acid, eserine (physostigmine salicylate), atropine, picrotoxin, adrenaline (best used in the form of the bitartrate) and 5-hydroxytryptamine (as the creatinine sulfate). Per set-up not more than 1 ml of a solution of 1 mg of each drug in 1 ml of distilled water is required. Of all the drugs listed here, atropine is the most labile; the solutions of others can be stored in the refrigerator for several weeks, provided the distilled water was pure and of a pH of about 5 (due to CO_2). Freshly distilled water should be slightly acidic (pH 5), but distilled water that has been stored in soft glass bottles, may have become slightly alkaline. It is therefore advisable to test the reaction of the distilled water to be used with the aid of a drop of universal indicator, or with indicator paper (the sample containing the indicator, must, of course, be discarded).

Stock solutions are best kept in plastic bottles (50 ml or 100 ml size) with screw caps. Cork stoppers have a habit of turning up in the laboratory's cork supply and once used in contact with a drug solution they can easily confer unwanted pharmacological potencies to other solutions. Do not use spatulas when weighing out drugs: the compounds used here are extremely potent and a small speck of the powder unwittingly transferred to another drug bottle or other container of laboratory chemicals can endanger the future work of an entire laboratory. It is best to gently rotate the opened and inclined bottle that contains the drug until a small quantity of a few milligrams of the drug powder falls onto the preweighed weighing paper. Use an analytical balance and weigh to 0·1 mg. It is preferable to obtain ACh preweighed in ampules (100 mg) since this compound is quite hygroscopic for the preparation of Ach-stock solution see p. 243.

When samples of the different drugs have been weighed, transfer them to the plastic bottle, tapping the weighing paper gently until the last visible granule of the powder has been dislodged. Discard the weighing paper. With an accurate 10 ml pipette, add as many milliliters of distilled water as there were milligrams of the drug weighed out. Do not allow the tip of the pipette to touch the mouth of the plastic bottle because it is quite possible that a bit of drug powder may have got caught there. A contaminated pipette tip should not come in contact with another plastic bottle when the next stock solutions are made up. Now stopper the bottle and shake the contents. Picrotoxin is not very soluble in water and the suspension should be placed in a water bath of at least 70°C. Solution will take place in about 1 h. All stock solutions should be carefully labelled as follows: name of compound, manufacturer, concentration (in this case 10^{-3} g/ml), solvent (in this case distilled water), date, and name of person who prepared the solution.

As a precaution, wash your hands before you continue with the experiment.

SET UP AND PREPARATION

Set-up and preparation are the same as in the preceding exercise, except that three separatory funnels with their accessories should be mounted on one of the ring stands in addition to the one used before.

PRELIMINARY PROCEDURE

Fill one of the separatory funnels with crayfish solution, to each of the other three add 99 ml of crayfish solution. Make sure the stopcock is closed before the saline is added! With the aid of separate 1 ml pipettes add to funnel no. 2 1 ml of eserine 10^{-3}, to funnel no. 3 1 ml of atropine 10^{-3} and to funnel no. 4 1 ml of picrotoxin 10^{-3}. Mix well. Return the stock solutions to the refrigerator.

Now close all the screw clamps on the rubber tubing connected with each funnel, then open the stopcocks. Gradually open the screw clamp of the first funnel until a flow rate of about 2 ml/min is established when the tip of the thin polyethylene tubing is at the level it will occupy when inserted into the positioned intrapericardial cannula (medicine dropper). Repeat the procedure with the other funnels.

Set up serial dilutions of acetylcholine (ACh), γ-aminobutyric acid (GABA), 5-hydroxytryptamine (5-HT), and adrenaline (Adr) as follows. In a test tube rack set up three rows of five, three, five and six test tubes respectively. Add to each 9 ml of crayfish solution. Cover them all with a sheet of paper. Now expose the first tube of the first row and add, with a 1 ml pipette 1 ml of ACh stock solution. Use the same pipette to mix the dilution; insert it all the way into the test tube and gently blow air into the solution so that this rises up in the test tube and rinses both the outside of the pipette and the entire inside of the test tube. Draw some of the solution up into the pipette and release again, repeat five times, then withdraw 1 ml of the mixture, wipe the outside of the pipette with a fresh piece of tissue paper, and transfer to the next test tube. Repeat there the mixing procedure. Always keep all the other test tubes covered. Continue until all the tubes in the first row have been mixed. Carefully label each tube: you now have a series of dilutions ranging from 10^{-4} to 10^{-8} g/ml. Using a new 1 ml pipette, prepare similar dilution series for GABA, 5-HT and Adr. Return the stock solutions to the refrigerator and briefly rinse the pipettes before placing them into the wash-receptacle.

Now dissect a crayfish and mount the heart preparation. Establish perfusion with crayfish solution and record the heart beat. Make all necessary adjustments to obtain good records on the kymograph. Move the stimulating electrodes over the inhibitory nerve of the left or the right side and determine the threshold for complete inhibition, using the experience gained in the

L

preceding exercise. Then change the electrode position so you can stimulate an accelerator nerve. Record the effects of stimulation at 5, 10, 15, 20, 25 and 30 pulses per sec.

EXPERIMENTS

1. Use a 1 ml tuberculin syringe with a fine needle (no. 23 or thinner) and inject a "slug" of 1 ml of ACh 10^{-8} into the rubber tubing of funnel no. 1 (crayfish solution) below the screw clamp. Observe the effect, if any, and record it. Using the same syringe, inject a similar "slug" of ACh 10^{-7} and so forth until strong excitation is obtained. Now open the stopcock of funnel no. 2 (eserine), close stopcock of funnel no. 1 and exchange the polyethylene tubing in the cannula (medicine dropper) that delivers the perfusion fluid to the heart. Allow the eserine solution to flow for 5 min, then repeat the sequence of injections (into the tubing of no. 2 funnel) of increasing concentrations of ACh. (*Note*: rinse the syringe before going from 10^{-4} or 10^{-5} to 10^{-8}!).

When a normal, or near normal heart rate is restored, stimulate the accelerator nerve at the same frequencies that were tried before. Change electrode position and stimulate the inhibitory nerve at the frequency that before gave threshold inhibition and try to find the new threshold frequency, should this have changed.

2. Open stopcock of funnel no. 3 (atropine) and close that of no. 2. Exchange the polyethylene tubing. Allow 5 min perfusion with the atropine solution then inject again increasing concentrations of ACh in 1 ml slugs.

When the heart rate has again become steady, stimulate the inhibitory nerve and find out whether there has been a change in the "inhibitory threshold". Then change electrode positions again and stimulate the accelerator nerve at 5, 10, 15, and so forth.

You should now be in a position to evaluate the action of ACh when you can answer the following questions. (a) Is the action of ACh similar to that of the accelerator nerve? (b) Does eserine enhance both the action of ACh and of the accelerator neurons? (c) Does atropine block both the action of applied ACh and that of the transmitter released by the accelerator nerve?

3. Open stopcock of funnel no. 1 (crayfish solution), close stopcock of funnel no. 3 and exchange the polyethylene tubing in the cannula. After an interval of 10 min inject 1 ml of 5-HT 10^{-9}. Note the effect, if any, then inject 1 ml of 5-HT 10^{-8} and so forth, until strong excitation (acceleration and an increase in amplitude) is obtained.

4. Inject 1 ml of Adr 10^{-8}, observe the effect, if any, and follow this with injections of increasing adrenaline concentrations, until strong excitation is obtained.

You can now determine the relative sensitivity of the heart to the two drugs. Remember, however, that the concentrations are given in g/ml and not as molar concentrations. Evaluate the effects in terms of the interpretation suggested in the introduction to the preceding exercise (14 D, p. 247) and discuss whether the drugs act predominantly on the muscle, or on the ganglion cells.

5. Inject 1 ml of GABA 10^{-7}, note the effect, if any, then inject higher concentrations until complete inhibition is obtained.

6. Place the electrodes over the inhibitory nerve and determine once more the inhibitory threshold. Open stopcock of funnel no. 4 (picrotoxin) and close stopcock of funnel no. 1. Exchange the polyethylene tubing in the cannula. At 1 min intervals stimulate the inhibitory nerve at threshold frequency. As inhibition diminishes, increase the frequency. When substantial blocking of the inhibitory action is obtained, inject 1 ml slugs of increasing concentrations of GABA and determine the new threshold concentration for complete inhibition.

7. Shift the electrode position to the accelerator nerve and stimulate serially. Inject a concentration of ACh and/or 5-HT that was previously found to be effective.

You can now evaluate the results of the last experiments (5–7) by answering the following questions. (a) Does GABA mimic the action of the inhibitory nerves? (b) Does pictotoxin block both the action of GABA and that of the inhibitory nerves? (c) Is the action of picrotoxin specific, or does it also affect excitatory actions? (d) Are the actions of GABA and of picrotoxin restricted to synapses between cardioregulator neurons and ganglion cells, or do they also affect the neuromuscular synapses?

REFERENCES

Bain, W. A. (1929). The action of adrenaline and of certain drugs upon the isolated crustacean heart. *Q. Jl exp. Physiol.* **19**, 297–308.

Carlisle, D. B. and Knowles, F. G. (1959). "Endocrine Control in Crustaceans." Cambridge University Press, Cambridge.

Davenport, D. (1941). The effects of acetylcholine, atropine and nicotine on the isolated heart of the commercial crab, *Cancer magister*, Dana. *Physiol. Zool.* **14**, 178–185.

Davenport, D. (1942) Further studies on the pharmacology of the heart of *Cancer magister*, Dana. *Biol. Bull. mar. Biol. Lab., Woods Hole* **82**, 255–260.

Florey, E. (1957). Further evidence for the transmitter-function of Factor-I. *Naturwissenschaften* **44**, 424–425.

Florey, E. (1962). Neurohormones. *Physiologist, Lond.* **5**, 285–293.

Florey, E. (1963). Acetylcholine in invertebrate nervous systems. *Can. J. Biochem.* **41**, 2619–2626.

Kerkut, G. A. and M. A. Price (1964). Chromatographic separation of cardiac accelerators (6-HT and a mucopeptide) from *Carcinus* heart. *Comp. Biochem. Physiol.* **11**, 45–52.

MacLean M. N. and Beznak, A. B. L. (1933). The effects of sympatheticomimetic *Arb. ung. biol. Forsch. Inst.* **6**, 258–272.

Maynard, D. M. and Welsh J. H. (1959). Neurohormones of the pericardial organs of brachyuran crustaceans. *J. Physiol., Lond.* **149**, 215–227.

Smith, R. I. (1947). The action of electrical stimulation and of certain drugs on cardiac nerves of the crab, *Cancer irroratus. Biol. Bull. mar. Biol. Lab., Woods Hole* **93**, 72–88.

Welsh, J. H. (1939). Chemical mediation in crustaceans. I. The occurrence of acetylcholine in nervous tissue and its action upon the decapod heart. *J. exp. Biol.* **16**, 198–237.

Welsh, J. H. (1942). Chemical mediation in crustaceans. IV. The action of acetylcholine on isolated hearts of *Homarus* and *Carcinides. J. cell. comp. Physiol.* **19**, 271–279.

Wiersma, C. A. G. and Novitski, E. (1942). The mechanism of the nervous regulation of the crayfish heart. *J. exp. Biol.* **19**, 255–265.

F. Spontaneous Activity of the Crayfish Hindgut and its Control by Drugs

The hindgut of the crayfish extends as a straight tube through the dorso-medial hemocoel of the abdomen. When removed from the animal and placed into a muscle chamber (see below) it exhibits frequent spontaneous contractions. There are two muscle layers: an inner layer of longitudinal muscle bands and an outer circular muscle layer. Situated between them is a nerve plexus. There is also an external superficial plexus composed of the terminals of efferent nerve fibers which reach the hindgut through the intestinal nerve from the sixth abdominal ganglion. Associated with the longitudinal muscle bands are numerous bipolar nerve cells. Further nerve cells extend long processes towards the inner muscosal surface of the gut; they are most likely sensory cells. The histology of crayfish hindgut has been described in detail by Alexandrowicz (1909) and by Janisch (1924).

The muscle fibers undergo coordinated contractions which give rise to peristalsis. Although it is difficult to follow the behavior of the ring muscles that of the longitudinal muscles can be recorded easily and is the subject of the following exercise. The contractions of the longitudinal muscles are enhanced by acetylcholine (ACh); the effect is potentiated by anticholinesterases and blocked by atropine (Florey, 1954). Thus the hindgut exhibits the typical response pattern of a cholinoceptive organ. The spontaneous as well as the ACh-induced contractions are inhibited by γ-aminobutyric acid (GABA) and several related amino acids (Tsuchiya, 1960; Florey, 1961). This inhibition can be blocked by picrotoxin. The hindgut thus shows much of the pharmacological behavior of crustacean skeletal muscle. Glutamic acid and some related compounds cause contraction as well as inhibition (Florey, 1961; Jones, 1962), the latter response can be prevented by the application of picrotoxin.

MATERIALS

For the dissection and preparation of the hindgut the following dissecting instruments are recommended. One pair of coarse scissors with one blunt and one pointed blade, two pairs of small forceps with curved tips, one glass plate (microscope slide), fine sewing thread, and one glass beaker (50–100 ml). In addition, each set-up should be provided with a test tube rack, 20 test tubes, six 1 ml pipettes graduated to 0·1 ml, one 10 ml pipette graduated to 1 ml, two 100 ml beakers, one bowl for waste solutions, a bottle with 1 liter of saline, and six 1 ml syringes with No. 22 needles. The basic saline medium should have the following composition: NaCl 200 mM; KCl 5·4 mM; $MgCl_2$ 2·6 mM; and $CaCl_2$ 13·5 mM per liter. To 9 volumes of this add 1 volume of 0·1 M phosphate buffer. The buffer must be prepared from the sodium salts. It is convenient to prepare 0·1 M stock solutions of Na_2HPO_3 and NaH_2PO_3 and to combine equal volumes of the two just before addition to the saline, the pH will be close to 6·5. The stock solutions are stable, particularly when kept under refrigeration, but the mixture is not. Per experimental set-up about 1 liter of buffered saline should be adequate for the exercise outlined here.

The set-up requires a muscle chamber and a recording device. The chamber described for the clam heart bioassay (p. 233) is perfectly adequate for the purposes of this exercise, otherwise a chamber can be made as shown in Fig. 15. It consists of a short length (about 6 cm) of glass tubing of about 1cm inner diameter, closed at one end by a one-hole rubber stopper. A short piece of glass tubing of suitable diameter is inserted into the hole without protruding through the upper surface of the stopper. It serves as an outflow. A 3 cm piece of thin rubber tubing slipped over the lower end of this tubing permits attachment of a pinchcock. A hypodermic needle (No. 23) pushed through the stopper is used for aeration and mixing.

It is best to use a light, well-balanced heart lever for recording on a kymograph (see Section A). The kymograph should provide a drum speed of about 5 cm per min. Laboratories equipped with mechanoelectric transducers and chart recorders can use these to advantage, provided the transducers offer sufficient sensitivity for tensions in the 100 mg range.

Freshwater crayfish of the genera *Astacus, Pacifastacus, Cambarus, Procambarus* and *Orconectes* have been used successfully; other genera are probably equally suitable. The animals should have a minimal body length of 10 cm.

For each set-up 1 ml quantities of the following drug stock solutions (10^{-3} g/ml) should be provided: acetylcholine chloride (bromide, iodide), atropine, eserine (physostigmine salicylate), sodium glutamate, GABA and picrotoxin. Of these only the atropine solution needs to be made fresh, the

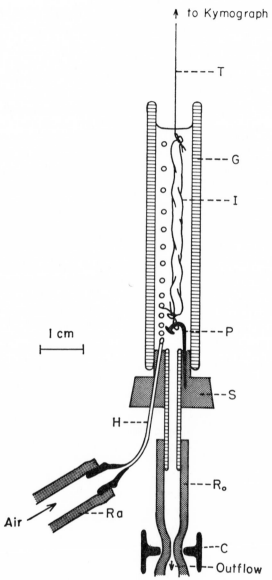

FIG. 15. Diagram to explain the construction of a muscle chamber for the experiment on the crayfish hindgut. The chamber is made of glass tubing (G) and closed off at the bottom by a suitably trimmed rubber stopper (S). The latter is penetrated by a thinner glass tube that serves as an outflow; an attached piece of rubber tubing (R_o) and a pinch clamp (C) serve as outflow valve. Aeration is accomplished by way of a No. 22 hyperdermic needle (H) connected to the air supply with rubber tubing (R_a). A loop of thread attached to the rectal end of the hindgut is slipped over a bent pin (P) inserted in the stopper (S). The anterior end of the hindgut (I) is connected to the writing lever by means of the thread (T).

others are stable for several weeks when kept under refrigeration. Stock solutions are best prepared by weighing out a certain number of milligrams of the particular drug and then adding an equal number of milliliters of distilled water. Picrotoxin will go into solution only when heated. Place the bottle with the suspension into a waterbath of 70–90°C for an hour. It is important that all bottles containing stock solutions be appropriately labelled, indicating name of drug, concentration, solvent, date and name of person responsible for the preparation of the solution.

Prior to the experiment proper, the following solutions should be prepared in test tubes: ACh (salt) 10^{-4}, 10^{-5}, 10^{-6}, 10^{-7} g/ml; atropine 10^{-4} g/ml; eserine 10^{-4} g/ml; sodium glutamate 10^{-4} g/ml; GABA 10^{-4} g/ml, 10^{-5} g/ml; and picrotoxin 10^{-4} g/ml. A fresh 1 ml pipette should be used for each drug. Fill all tubes to be used with 9 ml of saline, then add 1 ml of stock solution of the different drugs to one tube each and label (ACh 10^{-4}; Atr 10^{-4}; Es 10^{-4}; Glu 10^{-4}; GABA 10^{-4}; Pi 10^{-4}). Add 1 ml of the 10^{-4} dilutions of ACh and GABA (using the originally used 1 ml pipettes) and transfer to a tube containing 9 ml of saline. Label ACh 10^{-5} and GABA 10^{-5}. Continue serial dilution of ACh until 10^{-7} is reached.

DISSECTION AND MOUNTING OF THE HINDGUT

Decerebrate the crayfish by piercing the carapace behind one of the eyes with the pointed blade of the scissors. Cut off all the legs at the coxa, then deflect the abdomen downwards until the membrane between cephalothorax and first abdominal segment is exposed. Cut through the extensor musculature immediately below and cut through the exoskeleton of the abdominal segments on both sides keeping the blades of the scissors parallel to the ventral surface of the abdomen and cutting ventral of the segmental joints. The point of the inserted blade should be aimed along the hemocoelic cavity just dorsal of the abdominal artery that lies just over the intestine. During this dissection the transversal flexor muscles of the abdominal segments will be cut. The dorsal part of the exoskeleton can be removed and saved for the preparation of stretch receptors, if desired. The abdominal artery is now to be pulled off the gut and the latter to be sectioned near its exit from the thoracic cavity and close to the anus. The gut can now be removed from the animal and should be laid on a glass plate. By holding the anterior end and gently stroking it with the closed jaws of a second pair of forceps the contents of the intestine can be forced out the posterior opening. A length of thread should now be tied to the anterior end of the organ and a small loop attached to the posterior end. The prepared hindgut can now be transferred to a beaker containing some saline until everything is ready for mounting it.

It is important to rinse the bathing chamber with fresh saline before use and to adjust the airflow so as to achieve a gentle stream of air bubbles when the chamber is filled with saline. The heart lever should be carefully balanced before the intestine is connected to it. When the recording set-up is properly adjusted the hindgut preparation should be mounted as shown in Fig. 15.

PROCEDURE

1. Adjust balance and magnification factor of writing lever until optimal recording is obtained. Allow at least 15 min for the preparation to come to equilibrium performance. Meanwhile note on the record the following information: name of experimenters, date, sex, size and species of crayfish used, length of hindgut, nature of saline, pH, magnification factor of lever, speed of kymograph (or chart speed).

2. Drain the bathing chamber and use the 10 ml pipette to fill the chamber with a measured volume leaving space for an additional 1/9 of this volume. For a chamber that easily holds 2 ml it is most convenient to add 1·8 ml, chambers holding 3 ml should be filled with 2·7 ml, etc. Carefully mark this level. Ideally the entire preparation should be submerged. For convenience this marked level will be referred to as the 9 vol mark.

3. Now add 1 vol of ACh 10^{-7}, using a 1 ml tuberculin syringe and squirting the solution into the bath (previously adjusted to the 9 vol mark). The tip of the needle should be well submerged in the bathing saline and the emerging stream of ACh solution should be directed against the wall of the chamber rather than against the intestine. Observe the effect during 1 min, then drain the bath, fill with saline, drain and fill again to the 9 vol mark.

4. Repeat with the next higher ACh concentration.

5. Add ACh 10^{-5}, and wash as before.

6. Add 1 vol of eserine 10^{-4}. If there is any residual ACh left from the previous applications there will be gradually increasing contractile activity. When this occurs, wash and reapply eserine.

7. After eserine has been allowed to act for 10 min, lower the fluid level in the bath to the 9 vol mark and add 1 vol of ACh 10^{-7}. Observe the effect for 1 min. Then drain the bath, fill with saline, drain and fill again.

8. When the preparation has resumed its normal "resting" activity, add 1 vol of atropine 10^{-4} and allow this to act for 5 min. Lower the bath level to the 9 vol mark.

9. Add 1 vol of ACh 10^{-5}. After 1 min of observation, wash twice, then add 1 vol of atropine.

10. Add 1 vol of ACh 10^{-4}. Observe action for 1 min, then wash twice. Repeat washings 2 min later.

11. Select a concentration of ACh that previously (before atropine) gave an

intermediate response. Add 1 vol to see whether responsiveness to ACh has returned. After 1 min, wash. If necessary repeat this sequence until response returns.

12. Apply 1 vol of GABA 10^{-5}, observe effect (if any) for 1 min, then lower fluid level to 9 vol mark and add 1 vol of ACh of a concentration previously established as being effective (step 11). Observe the effect (if any) for 1 min, then wash twice.

13. Repeat but use GABA 10^{-4}. Wash at least twice.

14. Apply 1 vol of glutamate 10^{-4}. After 1 min lower fluid level to the 9 vol mark and add 1 vol of ACh of the same concentration that was applied in parts 11–13. Observe effect for 1 min, then wash twice. Repeat this sequence.

15. Apply 1 vol of picrotoxin 10^{-4} and allow this to act for 10 min. Lower the fluid level in the bath to the 9 vol mark and apply 1 vol of GABA 10^{-4}. Observe effect (if any) for 1 min, then lower fluid level to 9 vol mark and add 1 vol of ACh as in the previous sections of this exercise. After 1 min wash twice.

16. Apply 1 vol of picrotoxin 10^{-4} and 1 min later after adjusting the fluid level add 1 vol of glutamate 10^{-4}. One minute later adjust fluid level to the 9 vol mark and add 1 vol of ACh. One minute later wash twice.

EVALUATION OF RESULTS

The records should be carefully inspected, particularly with regard to the following.

1. Does eserine potentiate the effect of applied ACh?

2. Does eserine enhance the spontaneous contractions (both in frequency and amplitude)?

3. Does atropine depress the response to ACh?

4. Does atropine depress the spontaneous contractions?

5. Does GABA inhibit spontaneous contractions and cause relaxation? Does it cause initial contraction?

6. Does GABA depress the response to ACh?

7. Does glutamate enhance or depress the spontaneous contractions?

8. Does glutamate interfere with the action of ACh?

9. Does picrotoxin prevent the action of GABA?

10. Does picrotoxin interfere with the action of ACh?

11. Does picrotoxin interfere with the excitatory or inhibitory actions of glutamate?

The evaluation of the results should permit at least preliminary answers to the following questions. Is it likely that ACh is involved in the generation of spontaneous contractile activity, perhaps as a transmitter substance released

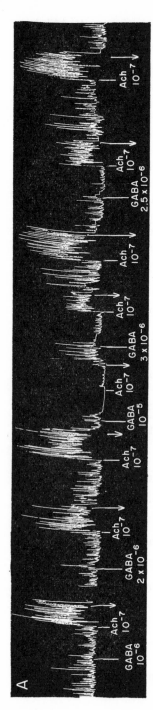
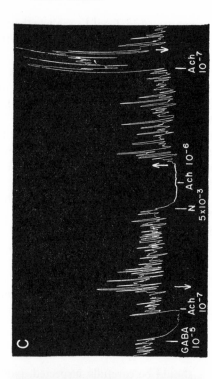
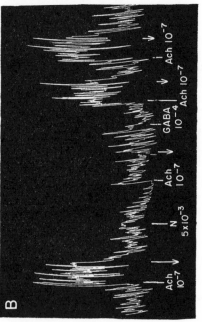

Fig. 16. Sample records obtained from an isolated hindgut of the crayfish, *Pacifastacus leniusculus*, to show the depression of spontaneous contractions and of the effect of applied acetylcholine (ACh) by γ-aminobutyric acid (GABA) and by GABA containing nerve extract, and the blocking of GABA action by picrotoxin. The nerve extract was prepared by boiling a piece of crab peripheral nerve in a tenfold volume of saline. A. Interaction of GABA and ACh; note the graded response. B. Onset of the action of picrotoxin which is maintained at a concentration of 10^{-5} g/ml; note that GABA even in high concentration is unable to prevent the action of ACh; the inhibitory action of a nerve extract (N) is partially blocked. C. After 15 min washing the inhibitory actions of GABA and N are restored. The A was obtained from

by neurons of the intrinsic nervous system of the hindgut? Does the action of picrotoxin indicate that inhibitory elements are involved in the spontaneous coordination of muscular activity of the gut? If GABA and glutamate act on subsynaptic membranes of either nerve or muscle cells do they act on both excitatory and inhibitory synapses?

Discuss the results in relation to the innervation of the hindgut from the sixth abdominal segment and the possibility that ACh, glutamate and GABA might be transmitter substances of regulatory exciting or inhibiting efferent nerve fibers. Consider also that ACh might be a transmitter substance of sensory neurons (Florey and Biederman, 1960).

REFERENCES

Alexandrowicz, J. S. (1909). Zur Kenntnis des sympathischen Nervensystems der Crustaceen. *Jena. Z. Naturw.* **45**, 395–444

Florey, E. (1954). Ueber die Wirkung von Acetylcholin, Adrenalin, Nor-adrenalin, Factor I und anderen Substanzen auf den isolierten des Flusskrebses *Cambarus clarkii* Girard. *Z. vergl. Physiol.* **36**, 1–8.

Florey, E. (1961). A new test preparation for bio-assay of Factor I and gamma-amino-butyric acid. *J. Physiol., Lond.* **156**, 1–7.

Florey, E. and Biederman, M. A. (1960). Studies on the distribution of factor I and acetylcholine in crustacean peripheral nerve. *J. gen. Physiol.* **43**, 509–522.

Janisch, E. (1924). Der Bau des Enddarms von Astacus fluviatilis (*Potamobius astacus* L.). *Z. wiss. Zool.* **121**, 1–63.

Jones, H. C. (1962). The action of L-glutamic acid and of structurally related compounds on the hindgut of the crayfish. *J. Physiol., Lond.* **164**, 295–300.

Tsuchiya, K. (1960). Studies on some inhibitory agents to the contraction of the isolated intestine. I. On the effects of some ω-amino acids on the isolated intestine of crayfish, rabbit and guinea-pig. *Kobe J. med. Sci.* **6**, 35–51.

15

A. Facilitation and Other Properties of Nervous Systems of Sea Anemones

B. Autorhythmic Organs

C. Peripheral Inhibition in Crustacea

D. Slow and Fast Axon Control of Contraction in Insects

E. Properties of Some Insect Sense Organs

F. "Catch" Mechanisms of Molluscs

G. HOYLE

Department of Biology, University of Oregon, Eugene, Oregon, U.S.A.

A. Facilitation and Other Properties of Nervous Systems of Sea Anemones

Time: 1–2 laboratory periods.

Animals required: small sea anemones, *Metridium senile* (preferred) or *Calliactis parasitica*; other species may not give comparable results.

The coelenterate animals have the lowest level of structural organization at which a nervous system exists. It is present in the form of a two-dimensional network of neurones lacking concentration in ganglia, or "brains". Consequently the coelenterates are of special interest relevant to the problems of evolution of nervous systems since they represent the most primitive level of neural organization.

Unfortunately, the nerve cells are very small, and detailed analyses are not yet possible, but in the hands of the brilliant analytical minds of G. J. Romanes, G. H. Parker, C. F. A. Pantin and others, using simple techniques, sea anemones have yielded a good deal of information about the functional properties of nerve nets.

Although it was believed by earlier workers that the network is a syncitium, it is now known to comprise discrete neurones and synapses. The neurones are primitive, in that they are only multi- or bipolar, and transmit equally in all directions. Perhaps even the synapses between them are relatively nonpolarized. The net therefore conducts outwards from a point of stimulation in a circle, but with a decrement, presumably dependent on properties of the synapses. This determines that the extent of a response depends on the intensity and on the duration of the stimulus, stronger and longer stimuli giving effects travelling farther from the excited point.

Two principle means have been adopted in order to differentiate function. Firstly, the provision of well-developed anatomical tracts within the network having relatively elongated neurons with few interposed synapses and therefore selective and faster conduction. These are *through-conducting* paths. Secondly, the extreme development of facilitation mechanisms at certain synapses. Facilitation is dependent on the building up of excitatory states at certain neuro-neural and myo-neural junctions which decay slowly, enabling impulses following closely behind to jump across otherwise "refractory" synapses.

PRELIMINARY INVESTIGATIONS

Some days before starting the experiments, place individual anemones on glass plates (old photographic plates are suitable) and let the animals settle on them. A few hours before the experiment pass hooks made from bent entomological pins through the margin of the oral disk.

A graded, local behavioral response is produced by touching the tip of a tentacle, which bends towards the mouth. Continued or stronger stimulation of the same point leads to a bending of neighbouring tentacles, accompanied by a localized raising of the edge of the dish. This is the *edge-raising reaction*. If the stimulation is yet further continued, the edge-raising reaction extends for some distance around the disk until finally the disk is drawn down by the longitudinal mesenteric muscle and covered over by contractions of the sphincter muscles.

A general response, possessing all-or-none characteristics, involving the whole body-wall, is produced by applying a quick prod to the pedal disk with a glass rod. The longitudinal mesenteric retractor (*Metridium*) or marginal sphincter (*Calliactis*) muscles (see Fig. 1) give a series of three or four distinct responses which take place nearly simultaneously throughout the musculature, leading to disk-withdrawal or sphincter-closure, respectively.

Note visually the latency on touching various parts of the body, namely tentacles, oral disk, lips, top and sides of the column and the edge of the pedal disk. You may make these observations quantitatively by using a kymograph drum at a fast speed. Quickly pass a hook made from a bent entomological pin through the margin of the oral disk and connect it via a thread to a light spring lever. Leave the anemone for some time to recover. Arrange a stimulus marker to write immediately above the writing point of

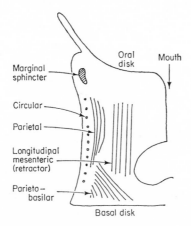

FIG. 1. Diagram of section through half a sea anemone in the plane of a perfect mesentery to show location of musculature.

the lever. Depress the key in the marker circuit at the moment of touching.

The anemone can survive brutal surgery, so that conduction along various parts of the network can be investigated by cutting strips from various parts, longitudinally or circularly, with only one end still attached. The free end is stimulated. Not all parts of the net conduct at equal speeds. Make a map showing conduction times in various regions. It is even possible to isolate both halves except for a narrow bridge of tissue.

EXPERIMENTS WITH CONTROLLED ELECTRICAL STIMULATION

APPARATUS

Kymograph; fresh sea water; two pairs of sea water/agar/chlorided silver electrodes in glass tubes; ball-and-socket clamp; stimulus marker/stimulator combination.

Set the glass plate on which the animal has settled obliquely in a jar of fresh sea water and connect the pin to a weak spring (semi-isometric) lever. Do not connect the animal directly to a simple isotonic lever, since it will not give a steady baseline owing to natural spontaneous movements. Place against the side of the animal, close to its basal disk, the smooth lips of a pair of electrodes made by enclosing chlorided silver wire in 5 mm diameter glass tubes filled with sea water/agar (see Fig. 2). Connect the electrodes to a stimulator coupled with a stimulus marker, for example the Grass SM 5. Alternatively, a simple mercury cup operated by an electromagnet may be

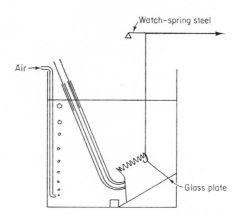

Fɪɢ. 2. Arrangement for stimulating and recording from a sea anemone which has settled on a glass plate.

used to discharge a condenser through the animal, recharging in the rest position (Fig. 3).

Note that widely spaced single shocks (give 5 msec pulses or equivalent condenser shocks) do not give a response, no matter how strong, except on extremely rare occasions. Return to a small strength and give a pair of identical shocks at a 1 sec interval. Repeat, gradually increasing the strength until a contraction occurs. This is either a quick withdrawal (*Metridium*) or a quick closing response (*Calliactis*). Using the same interval, increase the strength and repeat. Allow about 2 min between each test for recovery. There is no change in the size of the response. How do you interpret this? The answer is that the response is of the all-or-none kind.

Set the stimulus strength 20% above threshold and apply pairs at 6, 4, 3, 2, 1, 0·5, 0·3 sec intervals (see examples in Fig. 4A). Plot the height of the

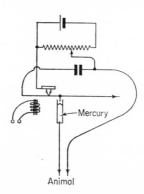

Fɪɢ. 3. Simple apparatus for simultaneously stimulating and marking on a kymograph.

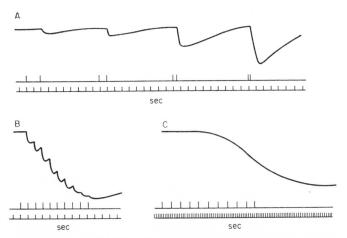

FIG. 4. Typical results of sea anemone experiments. A. Responses of retractor (or oral sphincter) muscles to pairs of shocks with decreasing interval. Note marked facilitation. B. "Staircase", summation of contractions showing initial facilitation. C. Slow, delayed contraction elicited by widely spaced (5 sec) shocks.

response as a function of interval between pulses. Note that a state of facilitation is set up by the first shock in an interval of about 0·5 sec and that this declines slowly.

Now study the summation of responses to ten shocks applied at progressively decreasing intervals between shocks (Fig. 4B).

Place a second pair of similar electrodes on another part of the column. Deliver one suprathreshold shock through the first pair and then give a second one of similar strength through the second electrode. Compare the record with that obtained by passing both shocks through the same electrode. Replace the electrodes in another place and repeat. Place both electrodes in new sites and repeat. All the responses are essentially identical. The nerve net of the column acts as if it were a single, unified excitatory element.

Compare your results with those obtained by Pantin (1935).

SLOW RESPONSES

Stimulate the mid-column at an interval of 1 every 5 sec. After three or four stimuli, note that a very slow contraction occurs (Fig. 4C).

TROUBLE-SHOOTING

A major source of trouble lies with the animals, which may simply shut down and stay that way. Two tricks may be used. First try the effect of feeding the anemone a few drops of juice obtained from a crushed clam. If this fails to alert the specimen, add $MgCl_2.6H_2O$ to the sea water, about 10 g/liter. This relaxes the nervous system, but is not quite strong enough to cause synaptic block.

SWIMMING SEA ANEMONE

Should an anemone of the genus *Stomphia* be available, and a *Dermasterias* or *Hippasterias*, note the reaction of *Stompia* to touching by the starfish. In a set of complex sequential acts the anemone first fills itself with sea water, extends and closes its mouth. It then contracts its circular muscles and at the same time releases its adhesion to substrate whilst relaxing the circular muscles of the basal disk. A bulge appears in the basis which causes the anemone to "pop" off the substratum. Meanwhile the oral disk expands, the anemone, now suspended in the sea water, coming to resemble a medusa in appearance. There follows a remarkable series of quick contractions of individual parieto-basilar muscles, first on one side, then on the other, next on the first side but in an adjacent muscle and back to the second until all the muscles have responded. The movements are powerful and the anemone "swims" away in an ever increasing spiral.

Take a settled *Stomphia* and attach it to a kymograph. Apply electrodes to its column and stimulate it with a single shock. There is a small response. Increase the strength and repeat. The response is stronger. This response is due to contraction in the parieto-basilar muscles which are well developed in *Stomphia* in association with swimming.

Apply a series of four or five strong shocks at 1 per sec. There is a strong retraction, due to excitation of the longitudinal retractors, which respond, like those of *Metridium*, only to the second of a close pair of shocks. In many cases the response will be quite different, and identical to that shown by the animal when touched by *Dermasterias*.

The sequence of contractions may be recorded kymographically. The total sequence lasts up to about 4 min.

BIBLIOGRAPHY

Hoyle, G. (1960). Neuromuscular activity in the swimming sea anemone, *Stomphia coccinea* (Müller). *J. exp. Biol.* **37**, 671–688.
Pantin, C. F. A. (1935). The nerve-net of the Actinozoa. I. Facilitation. *J. exp. Biol.* **12**, 119–138.
Parker, G. H. (1918). "The Elementary Nervous System." Lippincott, Philadelphia.
Romanes, G. J. (1876). "Jellyfish, Starfish, and Sea Urchins, Being a Research on Primitive Nervous Systems." Appleton, N.Y.

B. Autorhythmic Organs

Time: 2–3 laboratory periods.

Animals required: Large lugworm (*Arenicola* sp.); large earthworm (*Lumbricus* sp. or *Allolobophora* sp.).

Rhythmicity in heart muscle is very familiar; automatic regular activity of gut and associated organs and locomotory appendages of some animals is less well known. Nevertheless it plays an important role in behavior. It may be contrasted with reflexly determined activity and likened to an electrically driven alarm clock, giving rise to periodic motor output in the presence only

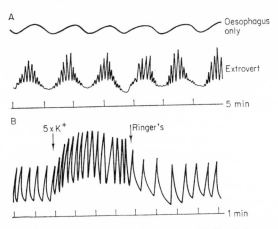

FIG. 5. Examples of rhythms. A, *Arenicola* extrovert; B, *Lumbricus* crop-gizzard.

of continuous input. In its simplest form, autorhythmicity may be generated in the muscles themselves. More commonly, it is determined by a plexus of nerves within the muscle. The detailed mechanisms involved in causing the rhythmicity are in no cases understood. (Fig. 5.)

Two preparations will be studied, both associated with feeding behavior of annelids.

APPARATUS

Kymograph, levers, at least four 400 ml beakers, dissecting dish, pins, silk or nylon thread (medium fine). Bent glass rod, air supply and aerator.

CHEMICAL SOLUTIONS

Arenicola   Make up to:

0·6 M NaCl	140	g	4 liters
0·6 M KCl	44·7	g	1 liter
0·4 M CaCl$_2$.2H$_2$O	29·4	g	500 ml
0·4 M MgCl$_2$.6H$_2$O	41	g	500 ml
0·6 M NaHCO$_3$	25·2	g	500 ml
0·6 M NaH$_2$PO$_4$.7H$_2$O	80	g	500 ml

Earthworm

First: Make up 4 liters of 0·0025 M NaHCO$_3$ = 0·84 g NaHCO$_3$ in 4 liters distilled water.

0·11 M NaCl	12·91 g	2 liters 0·0028 M
0·11 M KCl	4·1 g	500 ml
0·08 M CaCl$_2$.2H$_2$O	5·9 g	500 ml
0·08 M MgCl$_2$.6H$_2$O	8·1 g	500 ml
0·11 M NaHCO$_4$	0·92 g	100 ml distilled water.
0·11 M NaH$_2$PO$_4$.7H$_2$O	2·05 g	100 ml

Artificial sea water

For each 100 ml take 1·8 ml of the 0·6 M KCl, 2·8 ml 0·6 M CaCl$_2$, and 14·5 ml 0·6 M MgCl$_2$ and make up to 100 ml with 0·6 M NaCl.

EXPERIMENT. 1. THE *Arenicola* EXTROVERT PREPARATION

"Lugworms" (various species of the genus *Arenicola*) are obtainable by digging in estuarine and shoreline mud all over the world. They feed by taking in particles of sand, obtaining it by everting the proboscis which is inflated by body-fluid under pressure. It is then withdrawn into the body after its lumen has become filled with particles. The process occurs in a series of "bursts", gradually increasing in amplitude to a peak and then subsiding. A dual rhythm is involved. The slower rhythm probably represents the gulps as food is slowly passed into the alimentary canal; the faster one represents each food-procuring cycle. The rhythms can be suppressed by the intact animal, but they are "built-in" to the neuromotor complex of the anterior part of the gut and movements recur at remarkably regular intervals.

DISSECTION

Take a lugworm in your hand and locate the gills and the lighter, flatter ventral surface. With a pair of fine, pointed, *sharp* scissors which cut well, snip somewhere in the mid-line between the gills in the long axis, with the points of the scissors towards the head. Do not be afraid. Snip rapidly forwards, following the ventral groove as closely as possible. This cut should finish exactly at the point where the ventral groove crosses the first chaetigerous annulus, and should just divide that annulus.

Pin out on the dissecting dish, with the main body well pinned sideways and that of the head turned inside out. Avoid pulling on, or stretching, the esophagus. Free the esophagus by dividing the septa with a scalpel (No. 11 blade) and mesenteries. Tie it about 1 mm posterior to the septal pouches (which are just behind the first chaetigerous annulus), and leave about 8 in. of thread from this ligature.

You must next carry out the most crucial part of the dissection, the division of the retractor muscle sheath, which is deep red in color. Start vertically, where there is a natural opening in the sheath, and work round until the sheath is completely divided. At this stage you should be able to see a small papilla, the nuchal pouch, lying dorsally, and the metastomial muscles, which mark the line of the esophageal connective nerve branches. Tie a second ligature at about the level of the metastomial muscles and use the threads to form a loop of a few millimeters' diameter. Cut just beyond the ligature. The isolated preparation is known as the "extrovert" preparation.

EXPERIMENTS

The preparation is mounted vertically by attaching the posterior loop to a glass arm and the anterior one to a kymograph arm (see Fig. 6). Leave sufficient space below the preparation to easily remove a beaker containing solutions by first lowering a supporting stand under the beaker. The first solution should be artificial sea water. Bubble air through the bath to keep it stirred and blow out CO_2 formed by the tissue. Record on a slowly moving drum the periodic outbursts. Leave for several hours, perhaps overnight, for the preparation to settle down, to give best results. Some preparations will, however, give good results immediately.

Note the slow "driving" rhythm of the esophagus leading to very slow oscillations in total tone. A quicker oscillation in the extroverted anterior part of the gut, the feeding cycle, is superimposed, increasing in amplitude to a peak coinciding with peak esophageal tone. Perhaps this activity is suppressed during the relaxed phase of the esophageal cycle. Whilst you are waiting for the preparation to relax, prepare a number of solutions with different ionic concentrations, pH, etc. With your standard "cocktail bar" solutions for marine animals you may simply take more, or less, of a given cation by substitution. For example, to make 100 ml of solution with 5 × potassium, take 9·0 ml (5 × 1·8) 0·6 M KCl, 2·8 ml 0·6 M $CaCl_2$ and 14·5 ml 0·6 M $MgCl_2$ and make up to 100 ml with 0·6 M NaCl.

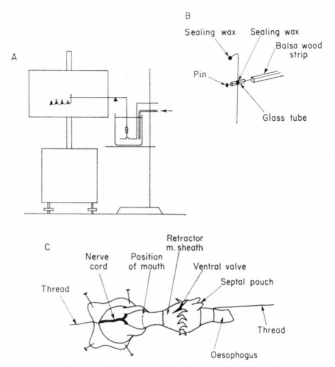

FIG. 6A. Apparatus for *Arenicola* extrovert and earthworm crop-gizzard experiments. B. Detail of scribing point for kymograph. C. Details of *Arenicola* extrovert (× 5) before transfer from dissecting dish.

To raise the pH (more alkaline) add $NaHCO_3$ (in place of NaCl) and to lower it add NaH_2PO_4.

Make a point of studying the effect of excess K^+ up to 10 ×, excess of Ca^{++} up to 4 ×, Mg excess up to 4 × and also the absence of these ions. Study also increases and decreases of pH.

Always return to artificial sea water between experiments, and wait until the normal rhythm is restored.

If you have pharmacological interests, examine the effects of physiological $(10^{-5}-10^{-7})$ concentrations of acetylcholine, adrenaline and other drugs on the preparation.

Make sure you remember to add your name, date, room temperature and other details to your records. The points of changing solutions, as well as the details of the kind of change, should be included. For example, if you change to 5 × K^+ place an arrow exactly under the recording point and write: "To 5 × K^+." On returning to the normal solution place an arrow and write: "To S. W. Ringer's."

This is a simple experiment and little can go wrong. The two main sources of error are solutions incorrectly made up and incorrect loading of the kymograph lever. If there are no contractions, or if there is a persistent contracture with, perhaps, rather frequent small contractions, you have probably added too much potassium or insufficient magnesium. With regard to loading, bear in mind that the extrovert has to work against a force, and load the lever somewhat; not sufficiently to stretch the extrovert beyond body-length but just so as to extend it if it has contracted. Make sure the lever arm is horizontal, that the preparation is exactly below the point of attachment to the lever and so forth. The pressure of the writing tip on the drum should be very light, to prevent frictional forces interfering with the movements. An excellent form of writing point which can be adjusted by means of a small bead of wax to give very delicate pressure, but which will compensate for lack of perfect alignment in the lever arm is shown in Fig. 6B.

You may learn more about the preparation and both its physiological and behavioral implications from papers by Professor G. P. Wells, some examples of which are given on p. 280.

EXPERIMENT 2. EARTHWORM "CROP-GIZZARD" PREPARATION

It is a relief to come to this preparation after attempting the extrovert. The rhythm, although less complex, and therefore not quite so interesting, is much faster, and the tissues respond sooner, so you have a better chance of getting home in time for supper. This is also one of the most reliable preparations extant; if it does not work it is *your fault*! Dissect carefully, do not pinch, pull or stretch the delicate living machinery it is your privilege to handle.

Locate the darker, smooth dorsal surface, lacking prickly setae and hold the living unanesthetized worm in your hand with the ventral surface downwards. Do not flinch as you make a quick snip along the mid-line dorsally, about 1 in. back from the anterior end, cutting rapidly forwards. At this point you may pin the worm down by its body-wall and complete the longitudinal cut, if necessary. There is no need to extend the cut beyond the 21st or 10th segments. Locate the bulging gizzard most posteriorly and tie a thread round the gut just beyond it. The crop is immediately anterior to the gizzard. Make a loop and tie this round the esophagus just in front of the crop. You may now very carefully cut the preparation free.

Mount it as for the *Arenicola* preparation, but be careful what solution you bathe it in. The earthworm, being terrestrial, has blood whose osmotic pressure is only about one-fifth that of a marine animal.

Use an earthworm Ringer's solution containing: 1·5 ml 0·11 KCl, 1·5 ml 0·08 M CaCl₂, made up to 100 ml with 0·11 M NaCl, all solutions made up with 0·0025 M NaHCO₃ (see stock solutions).

EXPERIMENT

The preparation will show a simple series of contractions and relaxations occurring once every 10–60 sec in the Ringer's solution. Whilst it is settling down, make up a series of solutions with different proportions of ions. Choose the same proportions as you used in the *Arenicola* experiments so that you may compare them. These are absence of potassium, magnesium, calcium; excess of potassium (up to 10 ×), magnesium, calcium (up to 6 ×); high pH, low pH. Note that several parameters of the simple rhythm may be affected. These are frequency (of contractions), amplitude, contraction rate, relaxation rate, general tonus.

Make a chart in which you note the actions of each ionic change upon each of these parameters.

At the end of the experiment, compare the results with the *Arenicola* results and any others you may have done. Similar studies may be carried out on isolated vertebrate and invertebrate hearts, strips of gut, crops of molluscs, etc.

BIBLIOGRAPHY

Wells, G. P. (1937). Studies on the physiology of *Arenicola marina* L. 1. The pacemaker role of the oesophagus, and the action of adrenaline and acetylcholine. *J. exp. Biol.* **14**, 117–157.

Wells, G. P. (1950). Spontaneous activity cycles in polychaete worms. *Symp. Soc. exp. Biol.* **4**, 127–142.

Wells, G. P. (1952). The proboscis apparatus of *Arenicola*. *J. mar. Biol. Ass. U.K.* **31**, 128.

C. Peripheral Inhibition in Crustacea

Time: 1–3 laboratory periods.
Animals required: large crayfish (any species).

Crustaceans can regulate muscular contractions not only by varying the frequency of impulses in motor axons, but also by discharging a different kind of motor axon, which itself does not cause a contraction, at the same time as the excitatory one. These axons act at the level of the neuromuscular junction, interfering with the electrical activity associated with excitatory junctional potentials.

They do this in each of two ways.

1. *Pre-synaptic inhibition*. Recently discovered, but now fully substantiated, it is possible that an interaction between the inhibitory and excitatory axons occurs before the neuromuscular synapse is reached. The mode of action is not known, but the effect is to reduce the output of transmitter substance from the excitatory terminal (see Dudel and Kuffler, 1961).

2. *Post-synaptic inhibition*. A well-known phenomenon, this consists of an independent action of the inhibitory transmitter on subsynaptic membrane. This is probably in the nature of a specific conductance increase to chloride ions. The equilibrium potential for chloride is higher than the potential level towards which the membrane falls during excitatory transmitter action alone. The net result of inhibitory transmitter action occurring at the same time as excitatory, is to reduce the effective excitatory depolarization. Since the tension developed is proportional to the depolarization, less tension is developed during inhibition.

The inhibitory action is enhanced in each of two ways.

1. *Frequency*. The inhibitory action, like the excitatory, increases with increasing frequency. The effective parameter is therefore the ratio of inhibitory to excitatory frequencies.

2. *Timing*. Inhibitory action is more effective when it just precedes excitatory action. The relative effectiveness of timing differs in different preparations. In some muscles maximum inhibitory action is slight, but in others it can result in a 100% fall in tension.

APPARATUS

Kymograph, levers, two micromanipulators, two pairs of fine *platinum* electrodes (silver will not do as it kills the axons!), nylon thread, dish with wax, two electronic stimulators, small clamp with ball-joint base.

SOLUTION

Van Harreveld's crayfish solution

	g
NaCl	12·0
$CaCl_2.2H_2O$	1·5
KCl	0·4
$MgCl_2.6H_2O$	0·25
$NaHCO_3$	0·2

Make up to 1 liter.

AIM

The aim of the present experiments is to study the action of the inhibitory axon which counteracts the single excitatory axon innervating the abductor of the dactylopodite (= opener of the claw). The primary goal is to demonstrate the mechanical occurrence of peripheral inhibition. Depending on the apparatus available, students may use kymographic or oscillographic means of recording. The associated electrical activity may also be studied, by extracellular methods. The advanced student may wish to study the excitatory and inhibitory junctional potentials by direct intracellular recording.

PREPARATION

Use an isolated claw of the crayfish. To obtain it, gently but firmly twist the claw about the ischiopodite joint until it autotomizes. Do not cut it across! Very carefully snip away the inner surface of the meropodite until the muscles are exposed. Cut out the tendon of the main flexor and then rip out the whole muscle with a single, strong movement. You will now see the nerve running above the extensor muscle. Cut across the tendon of the extensor and carefully cut it all away (much harder than removing the flexor).

Clamp the preparation at the carpopodite, using the small clamp provided. Locate the closer tendon through the thin cuticle at the articulation with the dactylopodite. Cut into and through the closer tendon. A light weight may be applied to the tip of the dactyl (in order to return it to the closed position after contraction of the opener) (Fig. 7).

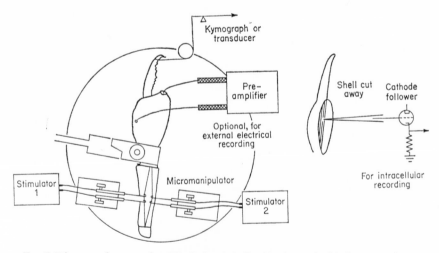

FIG. 7. Diagram of preparation. The isolated cheliped is clamped with the exposed nerves bathed in crayfish Ringer's solution. The micromanipulators should preferably have independent control for each electrode of the pair.

Locate the meropodite in a shallow dish of crayfish Ringer and observe the nerve. The nerve can often be seen under the binocular dissecting microscope to be divided into three principal bundles.

Take a very fine mounted needle and use it to split the three bundles apart. Operate the needle in the same manner as you would a pen, making a 30° angle with the horizontal. Use a gentle stroking motion, with the point moving backwards and forwards parallel to, but between, the bundles (Fig. 8).

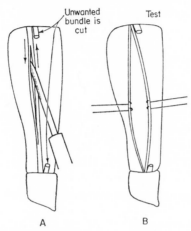

FIG. 8. Mode of separating small bundles of axons, and eventually single axons. The whole bundle is split into two (A) and each bundle is engaged by a pair of micromanipulated stimulator hooks (B). Unwanted bundles or axons are cut right out.

Usually one of these contains the single opener axon, a second the specific opener inhibitor axon (see below) and the third no axons of interest. Remove the latter. If your claw does not yield bundles containing the two axons required it is easier to take a fresh claw than to seek the axons by further splitting.

EXPERIMENT

Always start by placing the stimulating electrodes as far back (proximal to the body of the animal) as possible. If the nerve deteriorates later at the stimulating electrodes you can then move them forwards and continue the experiment. First investigate the action of the excitor alone. This axon seldom evokes a twitch for it is a "slow" axon giving rise to only small, facilitating junctional potentials which in turn barely surpass the threshold for contraction coupling in the muscle. At higher frequencies of excitation the junctional responses increase in height (facilitation) and also summate, leading to much greater contraction (Fig. 9A).

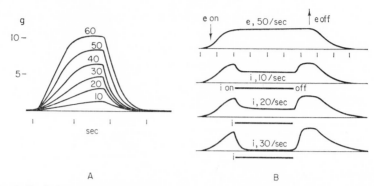

FIG. 9. Typical mechanical responses. A. To excitor axon alone stimulated at frequencies (per sec) shown. B. Peripheral inhibition: effect of stimulating inhibitory axon at frequencies stated during continued stimulation of excitatory axon at 50/sec.

Plot a graph showing the relationship between maximum extent of contraction (either force or contraction height under moderate load) as a function of frequency of excitation.

To test the inhibitor, stimulate the excitor-containing bundle at 30 per sec until a good contraction is obtained and then stimulate the inhibitor bundle at the same frequency in brief bursts. The contraction should decline fairly dramatically with each burst. On cessation of inhibition a large contraction returns. Investigate first the effect of different frequencies of stimulation of the excitor axon using a light isotonic lever.

Starting with an excitor frequency of 20 per sec, find the minimum frequency of stimulation of the inhibitor which just causes complete inhibition. Increase the frequency in 10 per sec steps and repeat. Note the ratio of i/e for just complete inhibition at each e frequency (Fig. 9B).

Use a fixed e frequency and study the effect of i frequency on the rate of inhibitory relaxation.

Study the effect of the duration of bursts of i stimulation on the size of the e contraction ensuing on cessation.

If two stimulators are available, couple them so as to drive both axons at the same frequency from one stimulator but at different times (by using the variable delay control).

By varying the delay the i impulses may be timed to arrive just after, at the same time as, or just before, the excitory. Can you detect any differences in the efficiency of inhibition at different phasings?

ASSOCIATED ELECTRICAL ACTIVITY

Should electrical recording apparatus be available the student should study the electrical concomitants of the excitatory and inhibitory activity.

APPARATUS

Cathode ray oscilloscope or pen oscillograph with a frequency response better than 50 counts/sec with capacity-coupled pre-amplifier giving a total amplification of at least 200 μ V/cm deflection; two fine platinum or chlorided silver wire electrodes attached to shielded input cables of the pre-amplifier. A balanced, push-pull amplifier is better than a direct-coupled one.

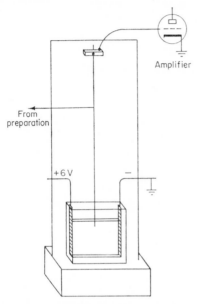

Amplifier

From preparation

+6 V   —

FIG. 10. Simple form of mechano-electrical transducer suitable for crayfish experiment when using cathode ray oscilloscope or pen oscillograph.

Note: if a double-channel oscilloscope or oscillograph is available it is probable that a movement transducer will also be at hand. This may then be used in place of the kymograph, and electrical and mechanical records displayed simultaneously. A simple form of transducer, suitable for the present experiment, may be made as shown (Fig. 10).

RECORDING: EXTRACELLULAR

Drill a small hole through the shell lying above the opener and snip off the non-movable propodite of the claw. Insert one electrode into the drilled hole and the other into the cut end of the propodite. Turn on the amplifier and oscilloscope. It will now be desirable to have the stimulator isolated from ground by isolation units. Simple units may be made by winding air core transformers having a few hundred turns of laquered copper wire for both primary and secondary.

It will be necessary to first cut away the shell on the inner margin of the shell, exposing the closer muscle. Now remove this muscle completely, taking care not to damage the opener muscle which lies beneath. Also, the motor axons enter along the inner face of the opener muscle and they are delicate. Observe the muscle fibers running parallel to the cut margin, with the aid of a binocular dissecting microscope. Submerge the fibers in crayfish Ringer's

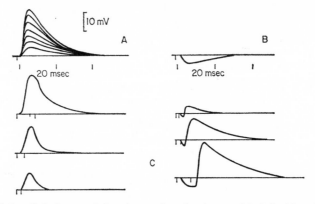

FIG. 11. Intracellularly recorded excitatory junctional potentials (e.j.p.'s) and inhibitory junctional potentials (i.j.p.'s). A. Progressive growth of e.j.p. by facilitation during repetitive stimulation at 30/sec. B. Same as A, but i.j.p. C. Interaction of e.j.p. and i.j.p. at various intervals between arrival times of e and i at junction.

solution and micromanipulate a glass capillary microelectrode into position with its lip poised ready to penetrate a muscle fiber. Lower the tip slowly, whilst observing the oscilloscope beam, until a sharp deflection is observed as the tip enters the fiber and the resting potential is encountered.

Now you are in a position to observe the junctional potentials. Turn up the stimulator strengths; first to the excitatory axon, then to the inhibitory, using the pulse generator of one stimulator to trigger the other at the same frequency. Note the effect of increasing frequency of stimulation on the magnitude of the j.p.'s (Fig. 11A). The e.j.p. grows greatly in height with repetition, i.e. facilitates. Plot a graph of the extent of facilitation (ratio of final height of e.j.p. to initial height) as a function of frequency. Facilitation is slight for the i.j.p.'s (Fig. 11B).

Vary the delay between the stimuli and observe the effect on the height of the excitatory junctional potential (e.j.p.) (Fig. 11C). Plot a graph of the height of the e.j.p. as a function of interval between the stimuli.

NOTE ON INHIBITORY JUNCTIONAL POTENTIALS

The electrical events associated with inhibitory transmitter action are commonly hyperpolarizing, compared with the depolarizing ones of excitation. However, they may be very small, or even zero, in the crayfish, and they are sometimes of opposite sign, namely depolarizing. This is particularly the case in the spring. Fibers lying together and having exactly similar resting potentials may have inhibitory junctional potentials of opposite sign. There is no inconsistency in these findings. The junctional potential results from a specific conductance increase to chloride ions, so its size and polarity depend on the chloride equilibrium potential (ECl), which may be above, or below, resting potential. ECl is, however, almost invariably greater than the threshold for contraction, so stimulation of i counteracts effectively the depolarization given by e.

TROUBLE-SHOOTING

If the muscle fails to contract when the excitatory axon is stimulated, this is probably due to deterioration at the region of the stimulating electrodes resulting from the accumulation there of hydrogen ions. Move the electrodes distally by the smallest possible amount required to recover the response. Likewise with the inhibitor.

BIBLIOGRAPHY

Dudel, J. and Kuffler, S. W. (1961). Presynaptic inhibition at the crayfish neuro-muscular junction. *J. Physiol., Lond.* **155**, 543–562.

Hoyle, G. and Wiersma, C. A. G. (1958). Inhibition at neuromuscular junctions in crustacea. *J. Physiol., Lond.,* **143**, 426–440.

Marmont, G. and Wiersma, C. A. G. (1938). On the mechanism of inhibition and excitation of crayfish muscle. *J. Physiol., Lond.,* **93**, 173–193.

van Harreveld, A. and Wiersma, C. A. G. (1937). The triple innervation of crayfish muscle and its function in contraction and inhibition. *J. exp. Biol.,* **14**, 448–461.

D. Slow and Fast Axon Control of Contraction in Insects

Time: 1 laboratory period.

Animals required: large locust or grasshopper (e.g. *Schistocerca*, any species; *Locusta migratoria*; *Romalea microptera*; *Melanoplus*, any species).

Many insects and crustaceans are extremely small and a functionally important muscle may comprise but a single fiber. The arthropods have made use of the fact that the intrinsic fundamental unit of muscular contraction is an infinitely small amount of tension or shortening. The familiar twitch of fast vertebrate muscle fibers is superimposed upon the basic contractile response by the propagated all-or-none action potential. The latter, when present, as in fast vertebrate muscles, is elicited by electrical depolarization at an electrical threshold below that required to initiate contraction, which is also activated electrically. By contrast, the membrane of arthropod muscles is not all-or-none, but instead gives only graded responses whose magnitude is directly related to the magnitude of depolarization past a threshold. Such responses propagate with a decrement and soon die out along the length of a fiber.

The problem of propagating the depolarization along the muscle fiber has been taken care of by having several motor nerve terminals, which are distributed to all parts of the fiber. The neuromuscular junctional potentials are fundamentally small, but subject to growth during repetition by a facilitation process. The greater the repetition rate, the greater the rate of rise. Consequently the rate and extent of depolarization of the muscle membrane, and in turn the contraction, are dependent upon the frequency of excitation of the motor nerve. At low frequencies the contraction is very slow, at high frequencies it can be quite vast. Many arthropod muscles have a single such axon supplying a whole muscle, or there may be three or four supplying separate bundles of muscle fibers. Other muscles, especially those which are sometimes required in nature to provide very vigorous, fast contractions, such as the jumping muscles, also have a second axon supplying the same muscle fibers. This axon gives rise to very much larger junctional potentials which in turn give rise to large graded responses of the fiber membrane, and fast twitch contractions. There is little, if any, facilitation. To distinguish between the two kinds of axon, the former are termed "slow", since they give rise to slow contractions, and the latter "fast".

AIM

The aim of the exercise is to study the "slow" and "fast" axon control of movement in the jumping leg of an orthopteran.

PRELIMINARY OBSERVATIONS

Watch the jumping leg in action during pottering and walking. Note the smooth, slow, well-controlled extensions of the tibia. The "slow" axon is exclusively concerned with these movements. Now touch the anal cerci and observe the jump. This takes only 1/30 sec and so is not perceptible to the eye. A "fast" axon supplying the extensor tibiae is exclusively concerned with the act of jumping.

APPARATUS

Kymograph (or transducer and oscillograph), dish with plasticene or dental wax, weak "isometric" lever, two pairs of fine tapered silver electrodes or micromanipulators. Advanced students may use glass capillary micro-electrodes to record intracellularly from the muscle fibers, or extracellular leads to record from the whole muscle.

SOLUTIONS

Prepare 1 liter of Hoyle's locust saline (Hoyle, 1953) containing:

	g
NaCl	8·2
KCl	0·7
$MgCl_26H_2O$	0·8
$CaCl_22H_2O$	0·3
$NaHCO_3$	0·3
NaH_2PO_4	0·8

Add the calcium chloride last, after making up to almost 1 liter with distilled water. Stir constantly whilst adding slowly. Make up to exactly 1 liter.

DISSECTION

First behead the insect. This operation is not strictly necessary, but the preparation is just as good headless and therefore seems more humane. Lay the insect on its back in a bed of soft wax, with the legs spreadeagled. The hind legs should make a 90° angle with each other, and be perfectly horizontal. This will require some padding with wax. It is especially important to build up around the coxa and trochanter with wax to prevent them from moving. This minimizes the risk of losing the legs by autotomy. The forelegs may be buried completely. See that the tibia are free to move.

Now take a scalpel with a No. 11 blade and cut around the meso- and metathoracic sternal plates until a section can be lifted off cleanly, after cutting through the muscles attached below and the endophragmal skeleton. This leaves the metathoracic ganglion and its attached nerves fully exposed (Fig. 12). Very little further dissection should be needed. Locate the largest nerve leaving the ganglion and entering the jumping leg. This is the crural nerve. Gently crush the nerve as close to the ganglion as possible. This is better than severing.

EXPERIMENT

Note that spontaneous extensions occur from time to time. Extensions should be evoked reflexly. These are all relatively slow. The "fast" axon

M

travels in the crural nerve, the "slow" axon in another trunk, the two coming together in the trochanteral joint.

Micromanipulate a pair of fine tapered silver-wire hooked electrodes under the crural nerve. These may be made by attaching the wires to the anode of a 6 V dry battery and dipping them into a bath containing a lead attached to the cathode and a 2% silver nitrate solution. Make a number of repeated dips, washing in between. The silver wire (basic diameter = 0·007 in.) is corroded

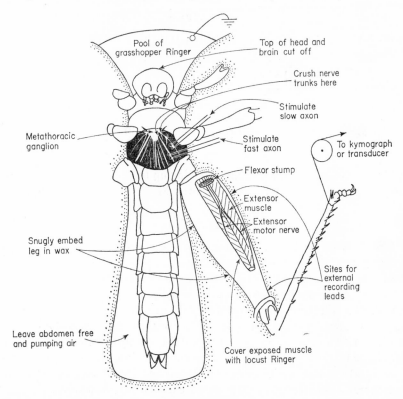

Fig. 12. Drawing to show locust/grasshopper preparation after dissection to expose nerves containing slow and fast axons.

away as soluble silver nitrate is formed. Stop the process when the right diameter tips (about equal to the nerve diameter) are reached, and bend into hook shape by pressing the blunt back of the No. 11 blade against the tips. Solder the wire to leads attached to the manipulator. If you are in a hurry, simply make electrodes from entomological pins and push these into the preparation, up against the nerve trunk. With a little practice the nerve, as well as that containing the "slow" axon, may be located by pushing two pins through the undissected cuticle and stimulating with respect to an indifferent lead in the anterior thorax.

Now pass a single 1 msec pulse across the electrodes on the crural nerve, at a rate of 1/sec, and gradually increase the strength. Note that a violent extensor thrust occurs at a sharp threshold. This may be preceded by flexion, if the flexor "fast" motor axons have a lower threshold. The much greater strength of the extensor overcomes this response, but it may be desirable to locate the flexor tendon near the "knee" and cut it.

Connect the distal end of the tibia by a stout thread to an isometric lever and a kymograph, or to a force transducer and oscillograph. Continue to raise the stimulus strength. Note that only one size of response occurs—there is but a single "fast" axon to the muscle. Stimulate repetitively at higher frequencies until a smooth tetanus is obtained, recording the genesis of tetanus (Fig. 14D). Calibrate your lever or transducer and plot a curve of tension against frequency. Note that the full tetanic force is maintained but briefly, and that tension falls off rapidly during maintained stimulation.

You should now turn your attention to the "slow" axon. This runs in the middle branch of the triple-branched third nerve. Locate the nerve and trace it into the leg. Place fine hook electrodes under the nerve. Stimulate with 1 msec pulses at 20/sec, raising the strength until a contraction just occurs. Now raise the stimulus strength. There is no further increase in tension— again one axon. There will in some preparations be a slight decrease in tension. This is because the nerve also contains a third axon innervating the jumping muscle, and it can cause a weak inhibition of the "slow" axon response. It does not inhibit the "fast" axon response.

Using 20% suprathreshold strength, reduce the frequency of stimulation to 1/sec and observe the response. Some preparations will give a minute, barely detectable, twitch. Gradually increase the frequency of stimulation and record the contractions at 5, 10, 15, 20, 25, 30, 40, 50, 60, 100, 150, 200 pulses per sec (see examples in Fig. 13A). Note that the maximum tension is maintained during prolonged stimulation, perhaps for hours. Note: the nerve containing the "slow" axon also contains the homologue of a crustacean peripheral inhibitory axon. If your stimulus pulse is strong this axon will be stimulated, in addition to the excitor. It gives very weak inhibition, however, so will not greatly influence your results.

COMBINATION OF "SLOW" AND "FAST" AXON EFFECTS

Stimulate the "slow" axon at various frequencies and superimpose single, or pairs of "fast" responses. During locomotion many insect muscles (weaker than the extensor tibiae) use occasional "fast" axon responses to supplement "slow" axon discharges (Fig. 14C).

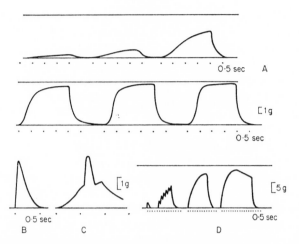

FIG. 13. Mechanical responses of extensor tibiae (results from locust). A. Force developed by slow axon stimulation at various frequencies stated. Time = 0·5 sec. B. Single twitch (F response). Time = 0·5 sec. C. Slow axon response elicited at 50/sec with single F axon response superimposed. Time = 0·5 sec. D. Fast axon responses to show fusion of twitches and tetanus: single twitch, then bursts at 2/sec.; 10/sec.; 50/sec.

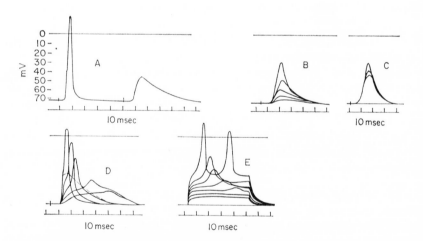

FIG. 14. Examples of intracellularly recorded slow and fast axon electrical responses A. Single excitations of first F axon, then S axon (this fiber gave a large S axon response) Time = 10 msec. B. Facilitation of small S axon response. Time = 10 sec. C. Facilitation of large S axon response. Time = 10 msec. D. Progressive decline of response in 20 mM/liter magnesium. Time = 10 msec. E. Initiation of typical graded electrical responses by intra- cellularly applied depolarizing pulses. Time = 10 msec.

Electrical recording

Advanced students will wish to record the electrical activity associated with the two motor axon responses.

Extracellular. Best results will be obtained by drilling small holes through the cuticle with an entomological pin, one in the "knee" and the other about one-third along the leg, proximally. Insert fine platinum or chlorided silver wires, insulated to their tips, into the holes and connect to a pre-amplifier. It will be necessary to use stimulus isolation devices. Record the small, facilitating "slow" axon junctional potentials (s.j.p.'s) and the larger, non-facilitating "fast" (f.j.p.'s) (Fig. 14).

Intracellular. Cut away the cuticle surrounding the flexor muscle and remove the flexor and retractor unguis (claw) muscles completely. Take great care, for the three efferent axons lie on the surface of the extensor tibiae. Micromanipulate a glass capillary microelectrode into place above the muscle and advance the tip until a resting potential is obtained. Stimulate the axons and note the responses. Only about one-third of the fibers receive the S axon, though almost all receive the F. The V-shaped bundle of fibers located most proximally has a relatively high proportion of dually innervated fibers.

After facilitation, the s.j.p.'s may give rise to small graded responses.

BIBLIOGRAPHY

Hoyle, G. (1953). Potassium ions and insect nerve muscle. *J. exp. Biol.* **30**, 121–135.
Hoyle, G. (1955a). The anatomy and innervation of locust skeletal muscle. *Proc. R. Soc.* B, **143**, 281–292.
Hoyle, G. (1955b). Neuromuscular mechanisms of locust skeletal muscle. *Proc. R. Soc.* B, **143**, 343–367.
Hoyle, G. (1958). The leap of the grasshopper. *Sci. Am.*
Usherwood, P. N. R. and Grundfest, H. (1965). Peripheral inhibition in skeletal muscle of insects. *J. Neurophysiol.* **28**, 497–518.

E.   Properties of Some Insect Sense Organs

Time: 2 laboratory periods.

Animals required: cockroach (*Periplaneta americana*); large grasshopper or locust.

The different kinds of sensory mode—photic, mechanical, chemical, phonic, etc.—are all transduced by the sense organ into electrical signals which excite all-or-none propagated impulses in sensory axons. The pattern of impulses is quantitatively related to the stimulus and thereby transmits *information* concerning the environment inwards to the central nervous system.

Insects provide many excellent preparations with which to study the sensory responses electrophysiologically. A serious study of the properties of sense organs requires careful control over stimulation parameters, but important features may be observed with simple methods.

AIM

The aim of the present work is to study sensory discharges associated with simple photic, phonic and mechanical stimulation.

APPARATUS

Recording electrodes: these may simply be very small silver entomological pins. Solder them to flexible shielded cables and dip them in a plastic insulating material, or in a solution of shellac. Allow the insulation to dry. Then make a fine nick in the insulation about one-third from the point. Fine hook electrodes of tapered platinum or silver wire, attached to micromanipulated shielded cables are better.

Amplifier/oscilloscope combination with loud-speaker monitor. A tape-recorder and a variable-frequency sine-wave oscillator are desirable accessories.

SOLUTION

Prepare Hoyle's (1953) locust saline containing:

	g
NaCl	8·2
KCl	0·7
$MgCl_2 6H_2O$	0·8
$CaCl_2 2H_2O$	0·3
$NaHCO_3$	0·3
NaH_2PO_4	0·8

Make up to 1 liter in distilled water.

EXPERIMENT 1. CERCAL NERVE DISCHARGE AND GIANT AXON FIRING IN COCKROACH

When a resting cockroach is disturbed it runs vigorously. This reflex reaction is mediated via large axons in the ventral nerve cord, three in each half, plus three smaller ones, which run uninterruptedly from the last abdominal ganglion through to the metathoracic ganglion. There they synapse with interneurones which in turn cause locomotion.

It is particularly easy to record the large action currents given by these fibers. Pin a cockroach on its back on to a cork board so as to immobilize its abdomen. Next take two insect-pin electrodes and push them through the abdomen in the mid-line, about 1 cm apart. Connect the electrodes to an amplifier/oscilloscope combination with loud-speaker monitor. Balance the amplifier and note any spontaneous nervous activity in the form of hiss or clicks on the loudspeaker, depending on the frequency and magnitude of impulses.

Now gently blow on the anal cerci with short puffs—a medicine dropper may be used to provide the puffs. Note brief bursts of large spikes due to impulses in the giant axons.

Increase the strength of the puffs. The bursts last a little longer and the impulses fire at a higher frequency. Note the general disturbance of the animal, which struggles to escape, and that twitches occur in leg muscles, each following the stimulus after a barely perceptible delay. These reactions together constitute the "startle" response. Further progress may be made if micro-manipulated hook electrodes are available.

DISSECTION

Starting in the mid-abdomen, make cuts near the margin of the ventral sclerites on both sides and continue them, first forwards, then backwards, to the last segment. The latter cuts should be made very carefully to avoid cutting underlying nerves. Cut across the sclerites anteriorly and gently lift up the medial portion. Cut away muscles attached to the sclerite, working backwards until the whole piece can be removed. You may now observe the paired ventral nerve cord without further dissection. Should the insect be very fatty, it is easier to try another one than to remove the fat unless you are very skillful at dissection. Locate the chain of ganglia and the associated nerves. In particular, note the larger last abdominal ganglion and the two stout cercal nerves coming into it from the cerci (Fig. 15).

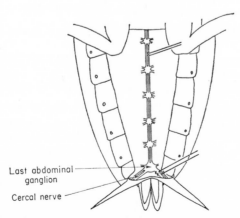

Last abdominal ganglion

Cercal nerve

FIG. 15. Dissection of cockroach last abdominal ganglion, cercal nerves and ventral nerve cord, with certain electrode locations used in the experiments.

Place the hook electrodes under the cord between the last (6th) and 5th ganglia. Apply an air puff and observe, or better record, if a camera is available for use with the oscilloscope, the burst of impulses. Now shift the electrodes to a position near the metathoracic ganglion. Apply a similar puff and record. Note that there appear to be more action potentials. This is because the giant fibers do not each conduct at the same speed. After passing along the cord, the slower ones lag behind. At the start they merely summate with the faster ones and cannot be seen individually.

PRE-SYNAPTIC RECORDING

Since there is a synaptic relay in the ganglion, with integrative properties, it is of interest to compare the giant fiber bursts with the input. The latter should be observed by shifting the electrodes to the cercal nerve. Here the axons are tiny and the action currents small. It may be necessary to raise the nerve on hook electrodes and suck away the bathing fluid with a fine pipette until the nerve is in air, before you can observe the impulses.

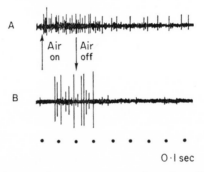

FIG. 16. Copy of oscillographic responses to an air puff applied between arrows. A. Recorded from the cercal nerve. B. Recorded from the nerve cord. Time = 0·1 sec.

There are many more cercal nerve fibers than there are giant axons in the cord. Consequently a burst of impulses contains a very large number of spikes and sounds like a hiss, rather than clicks, on the loudspeaker. Measure the duration of the discharge in the cercal nerve following a brief air puff and compare it with the burst of giant fiber activity occurring in response to a similar stimulus. Note that the input burst is a few times longer than the output, and contains very many more units. There is a scaling down of both numbers and frequency during integration in the ganglion (Fig. 16).

What is the weakest air movement which can just cause a response? Does the nerve respond to sounds? Over what frequency range? Do you think a cockroach can "hear" through its cerci?

There will probably be an electronic stimulator available to the advanced student. This should be connected to stimulating electrodes placed under a cercal nerve. Place the recording electrodes at a distant point, under one half of the cord, first on the heterolateral side, then on the homolateral. You may stimulate the cercal nerve with a single shock. Remember that this produces an unnatural input to the ganglion in the form of a large synchronous volley of impulses. At threshold, two or three small spikes occur in the heterolateral connective, and some six to eight in the homolateral, of which three are giants. Now study the effects of giving bursts of excitation, singly at first, then repetitively. Can you cause a "startle" response to occur?

EXPERIMENT 2. AUDITORY NERVE OF GRASSHOPPER

Insects have evolved a variety of auditory organs, often with a tympanum (eardrum). In locusts and other large grasshoppers these form a pair located on the ventral margin of the dorsal sclerites of the first abdominal segment and should be observed by rotating the hindlegs anteriorly.

AIM

The experiment is concerned with recording electrical activity in the auditory nerve and studying the hearing capabilities of the grasshopper.

APPARATUS

One pair of fine silver hook electrodes, micromanipulator, amplifier with loudspeaker monitor and cathode ray oscilloscope. Sine wave oscillator. The experiment will also be helped by a recording camera and a tape recorder.

DISSECTION

Behead the insect and press the thorax and fore and middle limbs firmly into plasticene to immobilize the animal. Stretch out the hind limbs so that the tympanae are exposed and unimpeded and embed their femora.

Next remove the ventral sclerite of the third thoracic segment, exposing the nervous system from the margin of the abdomen as far as the metathoracic ganglion. The dissection should be minimal. When cutting through the metasternal apophysis, make the cut as ventral as possible.

Locate the paired ventral nerve cord and several fine nerves running almost parallel to it. Running over the triangular apophysis is a slightly thicker nerve. This nerve is the auditory or tympanal nerve, and contains sensory fibers from the "ear" (Fig. 17). Micromanipulate a pair of fine hook electrodes under the nerve on one side and gently raise the electrode assembly. Turn on the amplifier/loudspeaker/oscilloscope combination, allow for warm-up time and balance. You should now see and hear continuous nerve impulse traffic, with occasionally an added burst. Take a small medicine dropper and suck away hemolymph from under the nerve. The spikes are now much larger, the sounds louder. This situation is best for observing and recording, but the nerve will rather quickly dry out. Avoid stretching or pinching the nerve. At intervals of not more than 2 min, moisten the nerve with a drop of locust saline and suck it away again for recording.

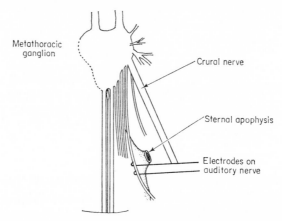

FIG. 17. Metathoracic ganglion of grasshopper or locust showing location of auditory nerve and recommended site for placing recording electrodes.

Make a number of simple natural sounds, jangle keys, make vocal sounds, clicks and taps and observe the response in the auditory nerve. Note that the hearing organ is especially sensitive to sibilants (hissing).

Next take the oscillator and make pulses of sounds at different frequencies. Gradually increase the frequency, starting at 50 counts/sec and note the frequency range over which the organ is sensitive. If the oscillator has a graduated power output scale, or better, if a sound meter is available, find for each frequency, in 100 counts/sec steps, over the entire sensitive range, the minimum sound intensity at which a nervous response is just produced. Plot a graph showing the minimum loudness as a function of frequency. If you have a quiet corridor, move the loudspeaker progressively farther away from the preparation and compare the sensitivity with your own ear.

Repeat the experiment on your own hearing, using your subjective judgement for "just hearing", at the various frequencies, and compare the two curves. Note the similarity; man can hear in the range from 30 to 14 000 counts/sec, whilst the insect auditory apparatus responds in the range from about 100 to 10 000 counts/sec. Both are most sensitive in the region of 1 000 counts/sec—a major component of the sibilant.

TROUBLE-SHOOTING

This preparation is surprisingly easy to make and is excellent for the demonstration of recording of a simple, easily understood sensory process. It is not likely to go wrong, unless either the wrong nerve is located, or the nerve is stretched or allowed to become dry. An average preparation will live for several hours in locust saline. Should the nerve be difficult to locate because of excessive fat, it is better to take another insect. It may be necessary to starve the insects for a week before study.

EXPERIMENT 3. OCELLAR NERVE

The ocellus is structurally a relatively simple visual receptor, yet illustrates the complexity of light transduction processes and functioning. The organ gives a continuous nervous discharge in the dark, which ceases upon illumination. The ocellus probably functions only as a form of photocell, indicating total light intensity.

AIM

To record the electroretinogram (ERG) associated with the ocellus transducer action and impulses in the ocellar nerve.

APPARATUS

Pair of extremely fine hook electrodes, micromanipulator, amplifier, focusable light spot, oscilloscope. A gear-driven rotating semicircular disk for interrupting the light beam is desirable.

PREPARATION

Take an isolated head of a large locust or grasshopper and embed it, jaws downwards, in a wax dish. Locate the three ocelli. Dissect away one side of the head until you have exposed the medium ocellar nerve and cleaned the surrounding area sufficiently to be able to place the electrodes under it (Fig. 18).

EXPERIMENT

Note that no nerve impulses are obtained from the nerve. Now turn off all room lights and focus the spotlight on the ocellus. Slowly interrupt the beam of light. Note that there is a potential change at "light off", with a relatively slow rate of decline. It takes about 1 sec to return completely to the baseline if you are using a direct-coupled amplifier. A capacity-coupled amplifier will distort the change, depending on its own time-constant. Use the longest available input time-constant if you have an a.c. amplifier only. Now return the light. Note that there is a larger potential change at "light on". This is of opposite electrical sign and has a similar time course. The potential changes constitute the electroretinograms of the ocellus. Study the relationship between the magnitude of the ERG and the intensity of the light beam.

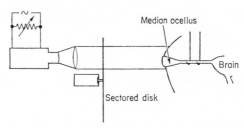

Fig. 18. Diagram of set-up for recording impulses in ocellar nerve.

Now sever the connection between the nerve and the brain. This reduces current flow associated with the ERG. With the ocellus in the dark, increase the gain of the amplifier to its maximum. Note the continuous discharge of small nerve impulses. Turn on the light. The discharge stops immediately. At the moment of switching the light on a single large nerve impulse passes along the nerve. Equally suddenly turn off the light. Two or three medium-large impulses occur, accompanied by resumption of the firing of small impulses.

TROUBLE-SHOOTING

Nothing stands in the way of success in this experiment except lack of dissection skill in the operator.

BIBLIOGRAPHY

Hoyle, G. (1953). Potassium ions and insect nerve muscle. *J. exp. Biol.* **30**, 121–135.

COCKROACH CERCAL NERVE—GIANT AXON

Roeder, K. D. (1948). Organization of the ascending giant fiber system in the cockroach (*Periplaneta americana*). *J. exp. Biol.* **108**, 243–261.

LOCUST/GRASSHOPPER AUDITORY NERVE

Pumphrey, R. K. and Rawdon-Smith, A. F. (1936). Synaptic transmission of nervous impulses through the last abdominal ganglion of the cockroach. *Proc. R. Soc.* B, **121**, 18–27.

OCELLAR NERVE

Hoyle, G. (1955). Functioning of the insect ocellar nerve. *J. exp. Biol.* **32**, 397–407.

F.   "Catch" Mechanisms of Molluscs

Time: 2 laboratory periods.
Animals required: mussels (*Mytilus*, any species).

Several muscles of molluscs are capable of maintaining a state of contraction for many hours or even for days continuously, without intermittent relaxation and with very little energy expenditure. Functionally, this capability enables intertidal marine molluscs to withstand prolonged exposure and wave buffeting. This kind of extended strong contraction is apparently impossible for vertebrates.

A very high resistance to stretch, up to 40 kg/cm^2 (about 10 × maximum tetanic force of a vertebrate striated muscle) is developed. These molluscan muscles are chemically unique in that they contain large quantities of paramyosin. They are physiologically unique in that they maintain the contraction with the expenditure of extremely small amounts of energy. This led Jordan (1918) to propose that they have a "Sperrung" or "catch" mechanism which is set following shortening, maintaining the shortened state. Relaxation requires an unlocking of the catch.

The exact ways in which molluscan muscles achieve these functions are still unknown, but their intrinsic interest is greatly enhanced by the presence of the unique mechanisms found nowhere else in the animal kingdom.

A favourite preparation for the study of the "catch" mechanism is the isolated anterior byssus retractor muscle (ABRM) of *Mytilus*. The muscles are long (up to 8 cm depending on the specimen), composed of parallel fibers, and can be made to go into a "catch" state simply by passing direct current (d.c.) through them. The catch is relaxed by passing alternating current (a.c.).

AIM

The aim of the present experiments is to demonstrate the "catch" mechanism in an isolated muscle, and to show how it may be relaxed by direct electrical, neural or chemical action.

APPARATUS

Kymograph, dry battery with potentiometer or electronic stimulator giving d.c., Variac a.c. transformer, muscle chamber with slotted bridge, two non-polarizable electrodes, one pair fine platinum electrodes on manipulator, electronic pulse generator.

SOLUTIONS

Sea water, acetylcholine, 5-hydroxytryptamine (10^{-4}).

DISSECTION

Open a mussel carefully by inserting a large, strong knife in the opening
on the concave ventral border. Place the cutting edge towards the "blunt"
end of the shell and cut downwards through the posterior adductor muscle.
The shell halves can then be pried open. Lay the animal on its back with
both halves exposed and note the two cream-colored ABRMs running
from their common insertion on the byssus (see byssal threads which have

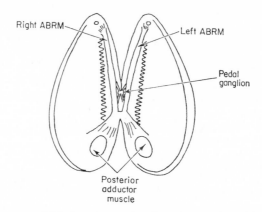

FIG. 19. Appearance of *Mytilus* after cutting through posterior adductor and opening.
The paired anterior byssus retractor muscles (ABRM) will be removed.

been secreted by it) to insert one on each pointed end of the shell halves
(Fig. 19). Seize hold of the orange/black foot and pull it away completely,
but be careful not to tear away the byssus. Using the byssal threads as a
holding point, carefully clean away the connective tissue surrounding the
ABRMs. Note the pedal ganglia and remove them. (In a later experiment
on a fresh animal they will be left in place.)

Now snip away the shell so as to leave only two small pieces round the
points of attachment of the muscles. Free the muscles as far as the byssus
and attach threads, one on each side of the ABRM/byssus attachments.
Carefully divide the byssus centrally and then cut away the attachments of
the posterior byssus retractor muscles (PBRMs), which are fan-shaped.
You now have two ABRM preparations. Soak them in ice-cooled sea water
at about 10°C.

EXPERIMENT

Mount the ABRM in the muscle chamber and make the byssal end the
fixed point (Fig. 20). Attach a thread to the shell and connect it to an isometric
lever. Now pass under the ABRM a slotted partition and place the ABRM

in the slot. Fill the bath with sea water or artificial sea water, to just cover the muscle. Place massive non-polarizable electrodes on either side of the partition and connect in parallel to both the stimulators.

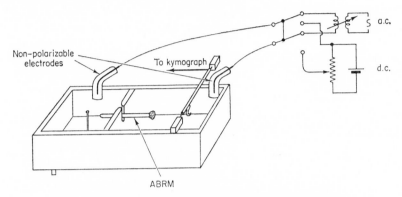

FIG. 20. Preparation and modes of stimulation and recording.

DIRECT CURRENT

Apply a brief (5 msec) d.c. pulse of about 10 V amplitude. Note that there is no contraction. Repeat the stimulus at 1/sec. How many stimuli do you need to obtain a response? The relaxation, as well as the contraction, will be much slower than you have previously experienced, for example, with the frog gastrocnemius, but the relaxation is not particularly slow. Brief pulses of direct current do not bring in the "catch" mechanism. Next stimulate the ABRM by passing continuous direct current (Fig. 21A), but for not more than about 2 sec, just sufficient to obtain a good contraction. You may now go and have a cup of coffee. It will take many minutes, or even more than an hour, for relaxation to be complete. Do not forget to apply a time marker trace to your record.

After relaxation has occurred change the sea water. Next make a record showing the effect of summating successive d.c. stimulations given at intervals of about 1 min. Note the small cumulative effect.

ALTERNATING CURRENT

Leave the first preparation to rest and recover and replace it with its partner. Gradually raise the a.c. stimulus strength until contraction starts, then give a 1 sec stimulus. Note that the contraction is a little quicker than after d.c., but reaches about the same maximum force. If the contraction is not isometric it may appear greater than with d.c. The relaxation is dramatically

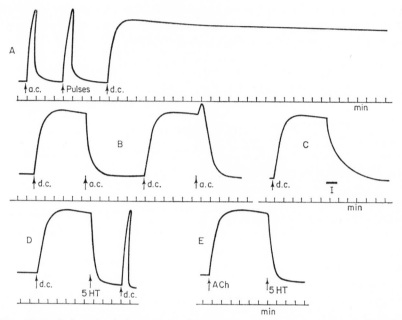

FIG. 21. Typical mechanical responses of ABRM. A. Responses to brief short bursts of alternating current, brief (10 msec) direct current pulses and continued (10 sec). Time in min. B. Relaxation of tonic contraction following applied d.c. by, first, weak a.c., which does not itself lead to contraction, then stronger a.c. which gives a contraction but is followed by a rapid rate of relaxation. C. Relaxation of tonic contraction by stimulating visceral ganglion weakly (showing presence of relaxing or inhibitory nerves). D. Relaxation of established contractural response and abolition of cability of "catch" response by 5-hydroxytryptamine. E. Initiation of "catch" contraction by acetylcholine and antagonization by 5-hydroxytryptamine.

faster than that following a long d.c. pulse. Repeat the experiment, stimulating about five times at intervals of 1 min. There is no summation of contractions.

COMBINATION OF DIRECT AND ALTERNATING CURRENT—
RELAXATION OF THE "CATCH" CONTRACTION

Arrange the leads so that you can give d.c. and a.c. alternately through the same electrodes. Start by passing direct current until a prolonged contraction has been evoked. This should be done by passing weak current for a longer time rather than by a very strong current, which may cause irreversible local damage to the preparation. Now interpose a burst of a.c. If this is weak enough, but not too weak, the muscle will not show any additional contraction but will immediately relax, even whilst passing the current (Fig. 21B).

The relaxation will not stop upon cessation of current passage, but continue at the same rate until full relaxation is reached. Again elicit a "catch" contraction by d.c. and apply a stronger a.c. stimulus. A small additional contraction will occur, but upon turning of the a.c. relaxation will occur at the fast rate associated with the normal a.c. response. Thus a.c. has unlocked the catch set by the d.c. stimulus.

THEORIES

There are three favourite hypotheses among many which have been put forward to explain the phenomena you have observed. One proposes that d.c. acts upon a molecular mechanism associated with paramyosin. There are two versions of this notion, one calling for the formation of special bridges between actomyosin and paramyosin, which have a very slow rate of breakage. The second requires a pH change followed by crystallization of the paramyosin. On this theory relaxation by a.c. may be due either to direct molecular action or indirect, via "relaxing" nerve elements. A second general theory suggests that d.c. acts indirectly, by causing intramuscular neural elements to fire prolonged bursts of impulses which excite the muscle to a slowly decaying tetanus. a.c. is supposed to lead to a termination of the discharge. A third theory proposes that there are two sets of nerve elements, one excitatory, leading only to the "catch" state when stimulated alone, the other releasing a relaxing (but not inhibitory) substance. Direct current excites only the former nerves, whilst brief pulses excite both nerves.

EXPERIMENTS ON NATURAL RELAXATION

Make a new preparation, keeping both muscles together and do not remove the pedal ganglia. Put one muscle in place in the chamber under the partition and manipulate a pair of platinum electrodes astride the pedal ganglia. First elicit a "catch" response with d.c. Now stimulate the pedal ganglia weakly with 3 msec pulses at a frequency of 50/sec. In favourable preparations quick relaxation of the "catch" contraction occurs, with a very brief latency. The experiment proves that some efferent neurones release a substance which either inhibits excitatory neural elements or unlocks the "catch" by direct chemical action.

PHARMACOLOGY

Take a relaxed ABRM in the sea water bath and a drop of acetylcholine chloride, sufficient to bring the concentration to about 10^{-6} M. The muscle goes into contracture similar to the d.c. "catch". After a few minutes, in which there is no relaxation, remove the bathing solution and replace with fresh sea water. The contraction remains. Add 5-hydroxytryptamine (5-HT = serotonin) to the bath, to make 10^{-7} concentration. Note rapid onset of relaxation (Fig. 21D). With another preparation, activate a d.c. "catch" contraction and then add 10^{-7} 5-HT. Again relaxation. The molluscan ganglia contain 5-HT and the muscle contains an enzyme which can destroy it, so it could be a transmitter substance, or relaxing agent.

Now take an ABRM relaxed in the 5-HT sea water and stimulate it with d.c. It gives a strong contraction, probably much faster than in sea water alone, and then relaxes immediately.

The natural excitatory transmitter substance is not known, but the preparation as a whole is cholinergic. Add a drop of 10^{-4} acetylcholine to the sea water bath and note the contraction which occurs. It closely resembles the response to d.c. Add 10^{-5} 5-HT during the contraction. There is rapid relaxation (Fig. 21E).

BIBLIOGRAPHY

Winton, F. R. (1937). The changes in viscosity of an unstriated muscle (*Mytilus edulis*) during and after stimulation with alternating, interrupted and uninterrupted direct currents. *J. Physiol.* **88**, 492–511.

Twarog, B. M. (1954) Responses of a molluscan smooth muscle to acetylcholine and 5-hydroxytryptamine. *J. cell. comp. Physiol.* **44**, 141–164.

Hoyle, G. and Lowy, J. (1956). The paradox of *Mytilus* muscle: a new interpretation. *J. exp. Biol.* **33**, 295–310.

Jordan, H. (1918). Über die Physiologie der Muskulatur und des Zentralen Nerven systems bei holorganartigen Wirbellosen; insbesondere bei Schnecken. *Ergebn. Physiol.* **16**, 87–227.

Lowy, J. and Millman, B. M. (1963). The contractile mechanism of the anterior byssus retractor muscle (ABRM) of *Mytilus edulis*. *Phil. Trans. R. Soc.* B, **246**, 105–148.

Takahashi, K. (1960). Nervous control of contraction and relaxation in the anterior byssal retractor muscle of *Mytilus edulis*. *Annotnes zool. Jap.* **33**, 67–84.

16 | Recording from the Crayfish Abdominal Extensor Muscle Preparation with Microelectrodes

H. L. ATWOOD

Department of Zoology, University of Toronto, Toronto, Canada

and

I. PARNAS

Department of Zoology, Hebrew University, Jerusalem, Israel

ANIMALS AND APPARATUS

For this experiment freshwater crayfish (e.g. *Procambarus clarki* (Girard), *Orconectes virilis* (Hagen), or other available species) should be obtained. The larger specimens are preferable. They can be maintained in fresh water (preferably chlorine-free) with occasional feeding (small pieces of liver or meat). A holding temperature of 10–15°C will generally be satisfactory.

To perform the experiments it is necessary to have equipment for manufacture and use of glass capillary microelectrodes as follows: a microelectrode puller; glass tubing of suitable diameter; a vacuum desiccator or side-arm vacuum flask; two micromanipulators; an electrode holder for microelectrode manipulation; a cathode follower input probe; and an oscilloscope.

Other items of equipment used in the experiments include: a binocular dissecting microscope and lamp; a compound microscope; a few slides and coverslips; an electronic stimulator, preferably with stimulus isolator included; stimulating electrodes; oscillograph camera with recording paper or film; developing tank and photographic solutions; a chamber (with wax bottom) to hold the preparation.

In order to put the equipment requirements into more concrete terms, some of the specific items used by students at the University of Toronto to perform this experiment are noted below. For most of the items many satisfactory alternatives are available; the list is given merely to serve as a frame of reference.

For pulling microelectrodes, the Micro-pipette Puller M I (Industrial Science Associates, New York) was used. (Electrodes can be pulled by hand or with various "home-made" pullers; see Donaldson (1958) or Nastuk

(1964).) The electrodes were pulled from Pyrex tubing of 2 mm outside diameter and 1 mm inside diameter, and had resistances when filled of 4–12 MΩ. For filling, a side-arm vacuum flask attached to a water suction pump with high-pressure rubber tubing was used (see Experimental details, p. 311).

The electrodes were used in conjunction with a Zeiss Jena sliding micromanipulator; others which could be used include those made by Prior and by Brinkman. The manipulation requirements of this experiment are less stringent than in many other microelectrode experiments. Electrode holders of the type shown in Fig. 1 were used. A Tektronix Type 502 A oscilloscope was used for electrical measurements, and records were made by means of a Cossor Model 1428 oscillograph camera and Ilford HP3 film (Tri-X film or photographic paper would also be suitable). Dissections and manipulations were viewed with the aid of a Zeiss Operation Microscope (working distance, 120 mm). For nerve stimulation, a Grass SD5 stimulator was employed.

There are a number of commercially available high-impedance input probes for use with microelectrodes (for example, the Negative Capacity Electrometer Amplifier, Model A-35, Medistor, Seattle, Washington, or the HF1 Neutralized Capacity Amplifier, Bioelectric Instruments, New York). It is also possible to construct "home-made" probes from electrometer vacuum tubes or field effect transistors (e.g. Donaldson, 1958).

CHEMICAL SOLUTIONS

1. For filling microelectrodes, a solution of 3 M potassium chloride (220·5 g/l) is required. This should be filtered into a clean bottle before use, to avoid introducing dirt into the microelectrodes.

2. The normal crayfish solution (after van Harreveld, 1936) has the following composition:

NaCl	12·0 g/litre
KCl (5·4 mM)	0·4 g/litre
CaCl$_2$	1·5 g/litre
MgCl$_2 \cdot 6H_2O$	0·5 g/litre
NaHCO$_3$	0·17 g/litre

In making up the solution, the first four substances should be added first, then enough distilled water to bring the volume up close to its final level, and lastly the NaHCO$_3$ and the necessary additional distilled water. After aeration and thorough mixing of the solution, the pH should be checked. If necessary, a few drops of dilute HCl or a small additional amount of NaHCO$_3$ may be added to bring the pH of the solution to 7·4. Another commonly adopted method is to buffer the solution at pH 7·4 by including

200 ml of 0·05 M Tris-maleate buffer as part of the volume of 1 litre of solution. The buffer is made as follows:

Tris acid maleate	50 ml
(24·2 g/l Tris and	
23·2 g/l maleic acid)	
0·2 M NaOH ·	54 ml
(8·002 g/l NaOH)	
Distilled water	96 ml

3. For study of the effect of potassium ion on the muscle membrane potential, a solution containing high potassium is required:

NaCl (153 mM)	8·87 g/litre
KCl (60 mM)	4·42 g/litre

(Other ingredients as in the normal crayfish solution.)

4. For staining axons in the preparation, a solution of 1% methylene blue in normal crayfish solution should be prepared (1 g solid methylene blue in 100 ml crayfish solution).

5. For fixation of muscle fibres in the preparation, a mixture of formalin in crayfish solution is required (1 part commercial formalin, 40% HCHO, and 7 parts crayfish solution).

6. For the study of drug effects on muscle potentials, solutions containing γ-aminobutyric acid (GABA), picrotoxin and strychnine are required. Stock solutions from which suitable dilutions can be made are given below. It is suggested that 100 ml of each is probably adequate.

γ-Aminobutyric acid: 1·0 g per litre of crayfish solution, or 0·1 g/100 ml.
Strychnine nitrate: 5 g per litre of crayfish solution, or 0·5 g/100 ml.
Picrotoxin: 1·2 g per litre of crayfish solution or 0·12 g/100 ml.

All drug solutions should be stored in the dark in a refrigerator when not in use. Remember that they are *poisonous* and should be handled with due respect and caution.

IDEA AND PRINCIPLE

The crayfish abdominal extensor muscle preparation is easier to make than most other muscle preparations, and is thus a convenient one for application of microelectrode technique for the first time. Microelectrodes can be used to measure muscle membrane resting potentials and nerve-evoked muscle potentials. They can be used to investigate the effects of ions and drugs on muscle fibre membrane properties and neuromuscular transmission.

Crustacean muscle has become fairly popular material among electro-physiologists, partly because of the relatively large sizes of the muscle fibres and motor axons. The abdominal extensor muscle preparation introduces many of the physiological and histological features of crustacean material, including polyaxonal and multiterminal innervation of muscle fibres (Hoyle, 1957), differentiation of muscle fibres into fast and slow-contracting types (Atwood and Dorai Raj, 1964; Kennedy and Takeda, 1965a, b), excitatory and inhibitory innervation (Wiersma, 1961), and variability of excitatory post-junctional events (Hoyle and Wiersma, 1958). The axons supplying the extensor muscles have a rather complicated pattern of distribution, which can be investigated by methylene blue staining and by microelectrode recording.

Several laboratory periods of 3 or 4 h can be alloted to this preparation.

Period 1. Preparation and testing of microelectrodes.

Period 2. Examination of the anatomy, innervation, and histology of the preparation.

Period 3. Study of the resting membrane potentials of muscle fibres, and effects of potassium ion.

Period 4. Study of nerve-evoked muscle potentials, including the distribution of those associated with individual axons.

Period 5. Effects of drugs (GABA, picrotoxin) on nerve-evoked potentials.

Period 6. Effects of drugs (strychnine) on nerve-evoked potentials.

EXPERIMENTAL DETAILS

MICROELECTRODES

The manufacture and testing of glass capillary microelectrodes has been described in several references (e.g. Donaldson, 1958; Nastuk, 1964). A brief outline of procedure is included here for convenience.

The first step is to pull the electrodes on the pipette-pulling machine from glass tubing. It may be found convenient to cut the tubing into lengths of about 9 cm (thus yielding, for each machine pull, two electrodes of about 5 cm). As a precaution against blockage of electrode tips by dirt, the tubing may be washed with chromic acid, then with distilled water, and oven-dried.

In most pipette-pulling machines, the degree of heating of the coil, and the parameters of the force applied to pull the glass tubing, can be adjusted, and after a few trial pulls it should be possible to obtain electrodes of about the right shape (Fig. 1). These should be examined under the compound microscope to make sure that they taper smoothly to a sharp point with no break or ball at the end. Once the right setting for the machine has been determined, a large number of electrodes can be rapidly pulled.

To fill the electrodes, mount them tip downwards in filling solution (3 M KCl). As a rough-and-ready expedient, the electrodes can be mounted on a slice of rubber stopper with slits cut in the edges to accept the stems (Fig. 1). The filling solution and electrodes are then heated close to the boiling

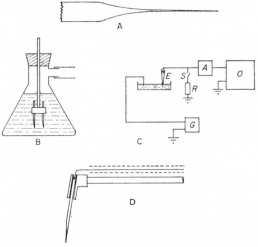

Fig. 1. Details of microelectrode technique. A. Sketch of microelectrode tip, showing the general shape. B. Arrangement for filling microelectrodes. The electrodes are mounted on a piece of rubber stopper attached to a glass rod. C. Arrangement for testing electrode resistance. Electrode (E) makes contact with saline in a dish, to which a signal is led from a generator (G). Pre- amplifier (A) is led to the oscilloscope (O). Resistor of known value (R) can be switched in (S) to shunt the input to earth. D. A holder for microelectrodes, made from plastic. Dotted line indicates cathodal screening of the input lead.

point (making sure that the container holding the electrodes is not sealed, otherwise an explosion could result). Then connect the desiccator or flask containing the electrodes to a water vacuum pump and allow bubble formation to occur. During this stage the air in the electrodes will be replaced by water vapour. After about 10 min of boiling under reduced pressure, reduce the vacuum and gradually readmit air to the container. (It is good policy to install a second flask as a trap between the water vacuum pump and the electrode container to prevent water being sucked into the latter). Hopefully, the vacuum treatment will have removed the air from the microelectrodes, leaving them filled with 3 M KCl after reduction of the vacuum. If air is obviously still present in the electrodes, the process should be repeated in an attempt to remove the last vestiges of air.

After filling, the electrodes should be removed and stored, for example in a Petri dish containing 3 M KCl and along the bottom a strip of plasticene grooved to hold the microelectrodes. Stored electrodes remain usable for about 2 weeks.

It is not possible to determine with certainty whether an electrode is usable by inspection under the light microscope. Instead, the suitability of an electrode is judged by the less direct method of measuring its electrical resistance. Usable electrodes (for this experiment) will generally be of 4–20 MΩ resistance. Very high resistance usually indicates a blocked or incompletely filled electrode tip; low resistance, a broken tip. Such electrodes should be discarded.

To measure electrode resistance, a chlorided silver wire, borne by a manipulator, is first inserted into the open end of the electrode. The free end of the wire is connected to the input of the cathode follower or neutralized capacity pre-amplifier, which in turn is connected to the oscilloscope. The tip of the electrode is lowered into saline in a dish. A calibrated square-wave signal is introduced into the saline through a chlorided silver wire (e.g. from the square wave calibration source of the 502 oscilloscope).

At the input of the cathode follower, one or more resistors of known value (Fig. 1, R) can be arranged to shunt the input to earth (switch S). With S open, the full amplitude (V) of the square wave appears on the scope (with some "rounding off" at the corners due to loss of high frequency components of the signal). When S is closed, R forms a potential divider with the micro-electrode resistance (E).

The proportion (V_1) of the original square wave, which now appears across R and on the oscilloscope, is:

$$V_1 = V.R/(R + E)$$

from which

$$E = R.(V - V_1)/V_1$$

Thus if R is 10 MΩ, and E is 10 MΩ the amplitude of V will be halved when S is closed. If E is very small (broken-tipped electrode), closing S will reduce V by a negligible amount; but if E is very large, V will be greatly reduced. Incompletely filled electrodes can usually be identified by instability of the scope trace or gross distortion of the square wave even before resistance is tested.

There are other ways to measure electrode resistance (see, for example, Donaldson, 1958), but the above method is widely used and easily arranged.

Ideally, the rise time of a square wave recorded through a usable micro-electrode should be less than 100 μsec, to preserve the true characteristics of rapid bioelectric potentials. With a neutralized capacity pre-amplifier, the rise time can be made very much less than 100 μsec. In the case of conventional or "home-made" cathode followers, the input lead must be cathodally screened (Donaldson, 1958). The rise time of the signal will depend largely on the length of the input lead, which should be kept as short as conveniently possible to obtain a reasonable signal rise-time.

DISSECTION OF THE ABDOMINAL EXTENSOR MUSCLES

Remove head and abdomen from a crayfish. Cut through the shell along the lower lateral border of the abdomen on each side, along the series of small indentations (Fig. 2). When the shell has been separated into two parts, pry

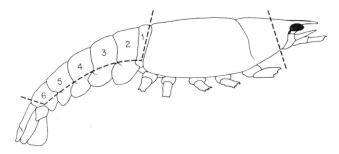

FIG. 2. Dissection of the abdominal extensor muscles. Dotted lines indicate the position of the cuts to be made. Numbers indicate segments of the abdomen.

them apart, starting at the anterior end. The lower half of the abdomen, together with the flexor musculature, will separate readily from the upper half of the abdomen and the extensor musculature. Sometimes it may be necessary to sever some of the flexor muscle connexions to the upper shell, but for the most part careful pulling will suffice to break the flexor connexions.

The extensor musculature comprises a relatively small mass of white muscle attached along the upper half shell. The preparation can be anchored (ventral, or muscle, side up) by pushing a straight pin through the shell at each end into a wax-bottom dish (Fig. 3). The preparation should be kept in crayfish solution, and will remain in good condition for several hours if the solution is periodically replaced, and provided the temperature of the solution is less

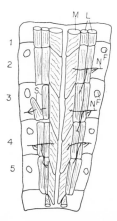

FIG. 3. A dissected preparation, viewed from the open (ventral) side. Segments are numbered from the front. M, L, medial and lateral deep extensor series; N, segmental nerves; F, attachment to flexor muscle; S, superficial extensor muscle (deep extensors removed in this segment).

than 20°C. For this purpose the replacement saline can be pre-cooled. At higher temperatures the preparations "age" more rapidly, but will still respond for at least an hour or two.

ANATOMY OF THE EXTENSOR MUSCULATURE

A careful preliminary study of the anatomy of the preparation should be made, as the subsequent physiological work largely depends on this knowledge.

The anatomy has been described in several papers (e.g. Pilgrim and Wiersma, 1963; Parnas and Atwood, 1966). Each abdominal segment has its own set of muscles, with a nerve supplying them on each side (Fig. 3). The larger *deep extensor muscles* are uppermost in the preparation. In these can be distinguished a *medial* muscle, with fibres twisted in a helix, and a *lateral* muscle (subdivided into L_1 and L_2) with straight-running fibres (Fig. 4). The attachments and delimitations of each muscle should be observed and studied. Are the muscles in all segments similar? How does contraction and shortening of these muscles make the tail extend?

Underneath the deep extensors are the smaller *superficial extensor muscles*; parts of them can often be discerned while the deep extensors are still in

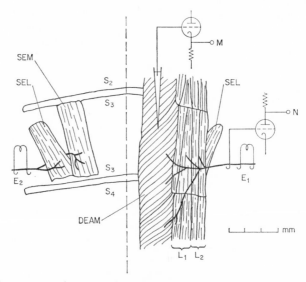

FIG. 4. Extensor muscle preparation showing positions of recording and stimulating electrodes. *DEAM*, medial deep extensor muscle; L_1, L_2, divisions of the lateral deep extensors; *SEM*, *SEL*, superficial extensor, medial and lateral heads; S_{2-4}, the abdominal segments; *M*, intracellular recording from medial deep muscle; *N*, recording of nerve potentials; E_1, E_2, stimulation of axons of the deep and superficial muscles respectively.

place, but they are fully revealed only by dissecting away the latter muscles (more particularly L_1 and L_2). Most of the present exercise will be concerned with the more accessible deep extensors, hence this further dissection will not usually be required.

Drawings should be made to illustrate the anatomical features of these muscles. It is worth bearing in mind that only a few species of crayfish (especially *Procambarus clarki*) have been studied in detail. In other species there may be some features which are not exactly the same as in *Procambarus*.

INNERVATION

A visual study of the innervation can be conducted by staining the axons in the nerve and on the muscle's surface with methylene blue. In relatively undamaged preparations good staining is readily achieved using the straight-forward methylene blue solution. It is not necessary to use reduced methylene blue. Apply a few drops of methylene blue solution to the surface of the preparation while the latter is still covered by a shallow layer of saline. After 5–10 min, wash the stain away and examine the preparation under the microscope. If the axons are still faintly stained, repeat the staining procedure.

In well-stained preparations the axons will stain dark blue while the muscle remains light. The axons can be followed as they run on to the surface of the muscle and branch. Note that each segmental nerve divides into a branch supplying the deep extensors, a branch supplying the superficial extensors (and stretch receptors), and a sensory branch (Fig. 3). Study particularly the innervation of the deep extensors, noting that more than one segment of the musculature is innervated by each nerve, and that different axons supply different parts of the musculature; they do not all branch together, as in the classical description of the innervation of crustacean leg muscles (van Harreveld, 1939). Also, the pattern of branching is not the same in all segments.

Make drawings of the innervation, and attempt to determine the parts of the musculature (medial, L_1, or L_2; segment number) supplied by individual axons. The innervation scheme for certain segments of the abdomen of *Procambarus* is given under Results (p. 320), but this scheme does not neces-sarily apply to all segments or to all species. Be on the look-out for differences.

HISTOLOGY OF THE MUSCLE FIBRES

When observations on gross anatomy and innervation have been com-pleted, the preparation may be fixed in formalin solution (24 h) for histo-logical examination of fixed muscle fibres. (During fixation, the muscles should be held at rest length or even slightly stretched.) If preferred, muscle fibres from a specimen prepared previous to the laboratory period may be used.

Dissect a few fibres, or parts of them, from the various parts of the deep muscles (medial, L_1, and L_2) and also from the superficial muscles; tease them with needles into fine, longitudinally separated shreds, mount them on a slide under a coverslip, and examine them under the compound microscope. Focus on the muscle fibre striations, and measure or estimate the sarcomere length (distance between recurring striations) in various fibres. Is there any marked difference in sarcomere length in fibres from various parts of the deep muscles, or in fibres from the superficial muscles as compared with those from the deep muscles? What significance can be assigned to these observations?

MEASUREMENT OF MUSCLE FIBRE MEMBRANE POTENTIALS

Set up a fresh preparation of the abdominal extensor muscles in normal crayfish solution. Pin it securely to the wax bottom of the preparation dish.

Mount a tested microelectrode in the electrode holder and make a connexion to the wire connected to the cathode follower input. Lower the electrode until the tip enters the solution above the preparation. Bring the beam of the oscilloscope to a known position on the tube face. Make sure that recording is d.c., at a vertical sensitivity of about 10–20 mV/cm. Then, under microscopic examination, lower the electrode towards one of the medial or lateral deep extensor muscles, in a region free of connective tissue or other obstacles. Carefully bring the electrode tip to the surface of the muscle. As the tip touches a muscle fibre, a slight movement of the oscilloscope beam will occur. A small further advance of the electrode will then usually effect penetration of the cell. The beam of the oscilloscope will indicate a negative potential (the membrane resting potential) of 60–75 mV. Ideally the resting potential should appear very abruptly without slow drift to the final level. Sometimes difficulty in penetration will be encountered; in this case, try another location, and/or small up and down excursions of the electrode tip, or a sharp tap to the table or support under the preparation dish. The electrode should not be forced too deeply into the muscle: the tip may break, or pass out of the cell, or cause damage. After a few penetrations have been made with success, sample membrane potentials of fibres in (a) the medial deep extensor, (b) the lateral deep extensors. Be sure to select fibres in undamaged regions of the muscle. Is there any statistical difference between the resting potentials in the medial and lateral muscles? What range of values is present?

Investigate the effect of raised potassium ion concentration on the resting potential, using several solutions made up by mixing various amounts of the high potassium solution with small amounts of the normal crayfish solution. (For example, 2 vol of the normal solution and 1 vol of the high potassium solution give 3 vol of a solution containing 23·5 mM potassium ion.) Apply the solutions in order of increasing potassium content. After replacing one solution by the next in the series, let the preparation soak in it for 5–10 min, then measure the resting potentials of several cells in a selected region of the muscle. Make all measurements in the same region.

Make a graph of the results, plotting resting potential against log potassium ion concentration. According to the Nernst equation, the resting potential is related to the potassium ion concentration, roughly as follows (at 20°C):

$$\text{Resting potential} = 58 \log (K_{in}/K_{out}) \text{ mV}$$

where K_{in} is the potassium ion concentration inside the membrane, and K_{out} is the potassium ion concentration outside the membrane.

Check your plot to see how closely it follows this relationship. Is it a straight line? Does it have a slope of 58 mV per tenfold change in external potassium ion concentration? Draw through the average resting potential at 5 mM potassium ion, a line having the expected 58 mV/decade slope; compare with your plot. How would you deduce from this type of plot the potassium ion concentration inside the muscle fibres?

STIMULATION OF THE AXONS

The nerve supplying the deep extensor muscles in each segment contains a number of axons. These cannot readily be separated for individual stimulation, but it is possible to stimulate individual axons by careful adjustment of the stimulating pulse, and thus to determine which parts of the muscles are supplied by the stimulated axon.

For stimulation, use a thin (0·10–0·005 in.) platinum wire, insulated with varnish except at the very tip (through which current will flow to stimulate the axon). Position this by micromanipulator on the nerve, and connect or solder the end furthest from the preparation to a wire led from the negative side of the stimulator output. Return the positive side of the stimulator output to the bath (using a platinum or silver wire terminal). Setting the stimulating pulse duration to 0·05–0·1 msec, and the repetition frequency to 1/sec (or single shock mode), slowly increase the stimulating voltage, while watching the muscles through the dissecting microscope. If the preparation is reasonably fresh, and the equipment is working, parts of the musculature will give twitch contractions (often rather weak) at a fairly low voltage (0·5–3 V).

Penetrate the responding part of the musculature with a microelectrode (see Fig. 4 for a diagram of the general layout). Trigger the oscilloscope sweep with the stimulator; set the time base to 10 msec/cm. As the stimulation voltage is increased a point will be reached at which a muscle potential will appear:

this may be excitatory, in the form of a spike, graded response, or "pure" post-synaptic potential (see Results, p. 323), or it may be inhibitory, in the form of a small, relatively long-lasting, hyperpolarizing or depolarizing potential. Once a potential has been seen, at a low threshold, attempt to establish which parts of the musculature are responding, by several penetrations. Then try altering the stimulating voltage to see what changes in the potential can be induced. Changes may be related either to input from additional excitatory axons, or to input from inhibitory axons (see Results, p. 324, and Kennedy and Takeda, 1965a). Try altering frequency of stimulation (up to about 20/sec) to see if the potential appearing at the lowest threshold exhibits facilitation, or lack of it. When the above observations have been made, the position of the stimulating electrode on the nerve can be changed in an attempt to bring in a different axon at the lowest threshold. Other nerves in the preparation can also be tried. Obtain photographic records of the muscle potentials: be sure to note the oscilloscope calibrations associated with each record. In photographing spike-shaped responses, establish whether or not these overshoot the level of zero membrane potential, by withdrawing the microelectrode and photographing a sweep of the oscilloscope beam on the frame bearing the record of the muscle potential.

If time permits, try to penetrate fibres in the superficial extensor muscle (Fig. 4) and study the effects of stimulating the nerve supplying this muscle. Muscle potentials will be of the "pure" post-synaptic type, and rather small. The innervation pattern of individual axons is too complex to be worked out by the methods suggested in this exercise.

There are two difficulties which should be borne in mind when the above exercise is attempted. First, the microelectrode can be dislodged by muscle movement. In slightly aged or fatigued preparations the movement is much less vigorous and the difficulty not as serious as in fresh preparations. By suspending the microelectrode on a flexible wire, rather than placing it in a holder, more movement of the electrode is possible without withdrawal. Secondly, it is possible sometimes to stimulate two excitatory axons at about the same threshold, thus obtaining an incorrect distribution for a supposed "single axon". This difficulty can be coped with only by careful adjustment of the stimulation, careful attention to what is going on in the preparation and by repetition of the observations in other segments or other preparations.

APPLICATION OF DRUGS

Crustacean muscle differs from vertebrate striated muscle in its responsiveness to pharmacological agents. Some of the substances which affect the crustacean muscle fibres and neuromuscular transmission can be readily studied in the crayfish extensor muscle preparation.

Set up a preparation in the normal crayfish solution, and make a photographic record of muscle potentials evoked by one of the axons. Then replace the normal crayfish solution with one containing 10^{-5} g/ml GABA (1 vol of the original GABA solution to 99 vol of normal crayfish solution). Observe, and photograph, the effects on single muscle potentials (1/sec or single shock stimulation). Note also any effects on muscle contraction. After a few minutes, or when it appears that the full effect has occurred, replace the solution with normal saline, and note whether any recovery occurs. Repeat the experiment with other doses of GABA (e.g. 2×10^{-5} g/ml, 10^{-4} g/ml, 2×10^{-6} g/ml); are any differences in the rapidity or extent of the effect observed? If possible, study effects of GABA both on the excitatory post-synaptic potentials and on the spike-shaped or graded membrane responses.

After familiarity with effects of GABA has been obtained, try adding 6×10^{-4} g/ml picrotoxin (1 vol of the original picrotoxin solution to 1 vol of normal crayfish solution), and then a solution containing 10^{-5} g/ml GABA together with 6×10^{-4} g/ml picrotoxin (1 vol of the original GABA solution, 50 vol of the original picrotoxin solution, and 49 vol normal crayfish solution). How does the inclusion of picrotoxin affect the responsiveness to GABA?

Recently it has been found that strychnine, long known for its action on the vertebrate central nervous system has also an effect on neuromuscular transmission in the crayfish deep extensor muscle preparation (Parnas and Atwood, unpublished). Study the effects of strychnine by adding a solution containing 10^{-3} g/ml (1 vol of the original strychnine solution to 4 vol normal crayfish solution) to a preparation in which excitatory muscle potentials have been recorded. Observe and photograph the effects, which may develop slowly (allow about 10 min after addition of the drug). Determine whether or not the effect can be reversed by restoring the normal crayfish solution. If time permits, try other dosages of the drug (e.g. double and half).

Other drugs may also be tested on the preparation (see below).

RESULTS

HISTOLOGY

In *Procambarus clarki*, the histological features of the deep and superficial extensors are very different. Sarcomeres of 2 to 5 μ are encountered in the deep extensors, the shortest sarcomeres being found in the medial deep extensors (Abbott and Parnas, 1965). In the superficial extensors, much longer sarcomeres of 8–12 μ are always found. When cross sections are cut through the muscles, marked differences again appear: the fibres in the deep extensors are tightly bound together in a compact mass, whereas those in the superficial extensors are separated; within the fibres the contractile elements are differently arranged (Parnas and Atwood, 1966). A similar situation has been established in the deep and superficial flexor muscles of the abdomen (Kennedy and Takeda, 1965a,b). In both extensors and flexors, the superficial muscles are slow-contracting tonic ones, used in postural activity; the deep muscles are fast-contracting phasic ones, used in the tail flick (for escape or swimming). Physiological differences between the two muscle groups parallel the morphological differences.

INNERVATION

The innervation of the deep extensor muscles in middle abdominal segments (3 and 4) of *Procambarus clarki* has been worked out by the methods of methylene blue staining and selective stimulation of single axons, as outlined above. In each segmental nerve, five excitatory axons and one inhibitory

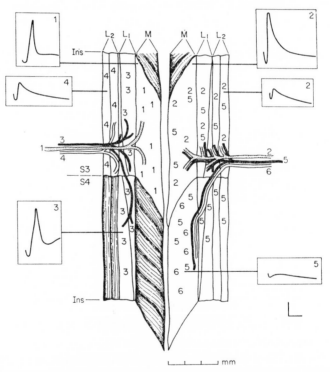

FIG. 5. Innervation of the deep extensors (segments 3 and 4, *Procambarus clarki*), showing the main branches of axons entering segment 3. Each axon is numbered, together with the parts of the musculature which it supplies. Tracings of representative electrical responses are shown for each axon. Calibration for the electrical responses: time, 20 msec; voltage, 1, 3, 4, 2 (top), 20 mV; 2 (bottom), 10 mV; 5, 4 mV. Note that both post-synaptic potentials and spike-shaped responses occur. (After Parnas and Atwood, 1966.)

axon appear. The distributions of the individual axons, and some of the muscle potentials evoked by them, are illustrated in Fig. 5 (after Parnas and Atwood, 1966).

Individual axons supply specific regions of the musculature, and some of them supply parts of two segments. The muscle potentials, even those evoked in different fibres by the same axon, are rather variable.

RESTING POTENTIALS

Table I provides an example of resting potential measurements from the medial and lateral deep extensors in normal saline. Use of the t test shows that there is no significant difference between the two muscles in this respect.

TABLE I

Resting potentials in lateral and medial deep extensor muscles
in normal crayfish solution

	Lateral muscle resting potentials (mV)		Medial muscle resting potentials (mV)
Fibre 1	76·5	Fibre 1	70·5
2	84·5	2	70·5
3	78·0	3	70·5
4	76·0	4	67·5
5	62·0	5	70·5
6	73·5	6	73·5
7	73·5	7	73·5
8	76·0	8	73·5
9	73·5	9	74·5
10	76·0	10	70·5
Mean	75·0 ± 1·8 (S.E.)	Mean	71·5 ± 0·7 (S.E.)

t test: $t = 1.94$.
(No difference between means at $P = 0.05$).

Note. The values were taken from a student experiment. It is evident that the standard error is less for the second series than for the first; this may reflect the fact that more experience in making penetrations had been gained by the time the second series of measurements was made.

In Table II and in Fig. 6 results are presented from an experiment in which potassium ion concentration was increased to study the effect on membrane potential measurements. The plot is not a perfectly straight line; in particular, the slope decreases at lower potassium ion concentrations, perhaps due to decreased permeability to potassium ions (Hoyle, 1957; Hodgkin, 1964).

N

TABLE II

Variation in resting potential with external potassium ion
concentration in medial deep extensor fibres

Potassium ion (mM/l)	Resting potentials (mV)	Mean (mV)
5·0	74, 76, 76, 72, 74, 76	74·7
8·9	68, 68, 64, 66, 66, 68	66·7
12·9	60, 60, 62, 64, 58, 64	61·3
20·7	52, 48, 52, 52, 50, 52	51·0
25·6	44, 46, 44, 46, 44, 42	44·3
32·5	36, 40, 40, 38, 40, 40	39·0
38·0	34, 38, 36, 36, 32, 34	35·0
60·0	28, 26, 28, 28, 30, 30	28·3

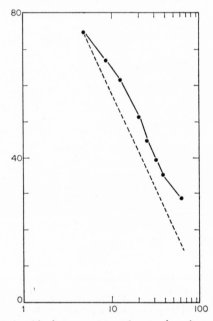

FIG. 6. Plot of relationship between external potassium ion concentration (abscissa, log scale) and membrane potential, for medial deep extensor muscle fibres. The dotted line indicates a slope of 58 mV per ten-fold change in potassium ion.

The slope of the plot in its linear region is not much different from the theoretically expected 58 mV per decade change in K_{out}.

NERVE STIMULATION

Single excitatory muscle potentials recorded from the deep extensors of *Procambarus clarki* are of three general types: "pure" post-synaptic potentials, post-synaptic potentials with superimposed graded membrane responses, and large spike-shaped responses which may approach or overshoot the zero membrane potential level (Figs 5 and 7). It should be noted that the graded

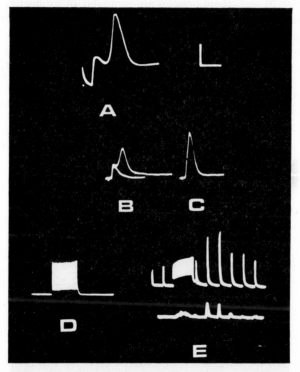

FIG. 7. Excitatory potentials from deep extensor muscles. A. Post-synaptic potential with a delayed secondary response appearing during the decay phase. The response occurred in the medial muscle with a stimulus to axon 1. B. Record from L_1 responding to axon 3. Two stimuli were given; the first elicited a post-synaptic potential, the second a delayed secondary response. C. A spike-shaped response occurred in the same location after a short burst of stimuli at 20/sec (facilitation). D. Lack of facilitation of the post-synaptic potential generated in L_2 by stimulation of axon 2 at 30/sec (note slower time base for this record). E. Post-tetanic potentiation in L_2 with stimulation of axon 4. The lower trace shows the tension responses of the muscle. After a short train of closely spaced stimuli, the electrical and mechanical responses increase in size. Calibration: time, (A) 10 msec, (B, C) 20 msec, (D, E) 1 sec; voltage, (A) 10 mV, (B, C, E) 20 mV, (D) 5 mV.

membrane responses and spike-shaped responses are all excited by post-synaptic potentials set up by the chemical activity of the transmitter substance. These post-synaptic potentials are distributed along the length of the muscle fibre (Fatt and Katz, 1953b). If the post-synaptic potentials are large enough they can initiate an additional "electrically excited" membrane response.

Some of the axons (e.g. axon 2, Fig. 5) typically give spike-shaped responses in one part of the innervation field, and post-synaptic potentials in other parts. With fatigue or ageing of the preparation, the number of spike-shaped responses decreases, as does the vigour of the muscular contraction. In fact, fatigue can be induced by a short period of continuous repetitive stimulation (at, say, 10 or 20/sec); these muscles are incapable of supporting prolonged, uninterrupted contractions. Normally, in the tail flick, the contractions are intermittent.

The post-synaptic potentials of the deep extensor muscles show moderate facilitation, or sometimes none, with repetitive stimulation (Fig. 7). However,

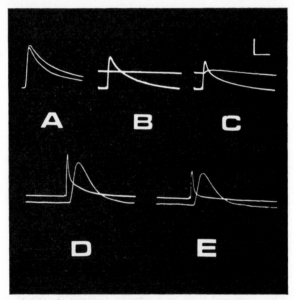

FIG. 8. Manifestations of inhibitory activity in the deep extensor muscles. A. Post-synaptic potential (L_2, axon 4), with (bottom trace) and without (top trace) a simultaneous inhibitory stimulus. Note increased decay rate of the potential with inhibition. B and C. Simultaneous records made from the medial muscle (top) and L_2 (bottom). A stimulus to axon 4 produces a post-synaptic potential in L_2 (B). Simultaneous stimulation of axon 5 gives rise to an inhibitory potential in the medial muscle and to increased rate of decay of the excitatory potential in L_2 (C). D and E. Electrical record (top) and tension record (bottom) of activity in the medial muscle. In D, axon 1 was stimulated; in E, axon 5 was also stimulated, and the responses produced by axon 1 show attenuation. Calibration: time, (A) 10 msec, (B, C) 20 msec, (D, E) 40 msec; voltage, (A, B, C) 10 mV, (D, E) 20 mV.

post-tetanic potentiation (increase in amplitude of the response to a single shock following a burst of closely spaced stimuli) can be quite pronounced (Fig. 7).

Activation of inhibitory axons may give rise to inhibitory post-synaptic potentials, if the inhibitor is active at the lowest threshold, which is usually not the case. More often, the inhibitor acts to reduce the amplitude of excitatory potentials, when it is stimulated at the same time as a lower-threshold excitatory axon (Fig. 8). Spike-shaped responses are often reduced to graded responses with simultaneous inhibitory input; graded responses tend to disappear entirely. Excitatory post-synaptic potentials characteristically show an increased rate of decay when the inhibitor is simultaneously activated, even though the amplitude of the excitatory response may be little reduced.

In the superficial extensor muscles there are five motor axons and one inhibitor supplying each muscle, but fibres within the muscle receive a variable number of the total available axons. The excitatory post-synaptic potentials are smaller than in the deep muscles, and for the most part show more pronounced facilitation with repetitive stimulation (Fig. 9). Graded responses

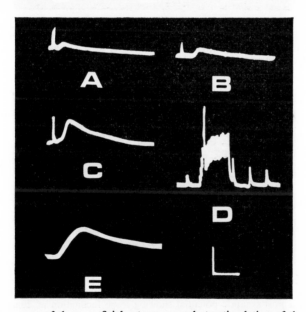

FIG. 9. Responses of the superficial extensor muscle to stimulation of the nerve. A–C. Single post-synaptic potentials produced in a muscle fibre by three different axons. D. Responses to stimulation of the third axon at 20/sec, showing facilitation of the post-synaptic potentials and a single graded response. E. Tension development with stimulation of the nerve at 20/sec. Note slow increase and relaxation. Calibration: time, A–C, 20 msec; D, 1 sec: E, 4 sec; voltage, A–C, 10 mV; D, 20 mV. (After Parnas and Atwood, 1966.)

are occasionally seen with repetitive stimulation in some fibres, but not with single stimuli. No twitch-like contractions occur in these muscles; instead, the contraction develops and relaxes very slowly, and its speed and magnitude increase with increasing frequency of the indirect stimulation.

EFFECTS OF DRUGS

GABA acts to reduce the amplitude of the excitatory muscle potentials and to increase their rate of decay. The associated muscle contraction is also reduced (Fig. 10).

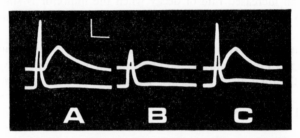

FIG. 10. Effect of GABA on spike (lower trace) and twitch tension (upper trace) produced by axon 1, in the medial deep extensor of a rock lobster. A. Control in normal saline. B. Soon after addition of 10^{-5} g/ml GABA. C. Recovery after restoration of normal saline. Calibration: time, 20 msec; voltage, 20 mV.

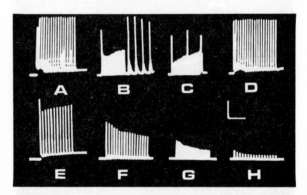

FIG. 11. Effect of stimulation of axon 1 on normal (A–D) and strychnine-treated (E–H) deep extensor preparations. A. Spike-shaped responses at 3/sec stimulation. B and C. After fatigue, a post-synaptic potential showing some facilitation at 20/sec stimulation (B), was obtained; occasional graded responses occurred. C. Persistence at 20/sec stimulation. D. Recovery of the spike-shaped response after a period of rest. E. Spike-shaped responses in another preparation. F. Response after 2 min exposure to 1 mg/ml strychnine nitrate, showing antifacilitation of the electrical responses. G. Persistence of antifacilitation during stimulation at 20/sec. H. After a rest period of 1·5 min the response continued to decline; complete block occurred at 5 min. Calibration: 20 mV, 2 sec.

At 10^{-5} g/ml GABA these effects are usually quite well marked, and are even more pronounced at higher doses. The preparation recovers in normal saline, at least from 10^{-5} g/ml GABA (Fig. 10). Picrotoxin antagonizes the action of GABA and prevents reduction of the excitatory muscle potentials. It is thought that this effect is attributable to inactivation of the inhibitory receptor areas on the muscle, which are normally activated by GABA (Grundfest et al., 1959).

Strychnine also reduces the excitatory muscle potentials, but more slowly and less reversibly (Fig. 11). The mechanism of action is very likely on the pre-synaptic nerve terminals rather than on the receptor areas of the muscle. Glutamic acid stimulates contraction in a strychnine-blocked preparation, as it does in the normal muscle (cf. Van Harreveld and Mendelson, 1959). The peculiar antifacilitation of the muscle potentials during repetitive stimulation also suggests a pre-synaptic action.

Trouble-shooting

The most common sources of trouble are associated with the microelectrode technique itself. Failure to penetrate a cell, or low resting potential values, may be due to a broken electrode (check electrode resistance). Instability of the trace may be caused by lack of contact of the saline in the electrode with the wire leading to the cathode follower, or to blockage of the electrode tip (check electrode resistance, and discard the electrode if the resistance is unduly high), or to lack of contact of the bath with the grounding wire.

Another source of trouble is 60 or 50 c/s interference from the mains. This may be hard to eliminate. Attention should be given to correct grounding procedures, arrangement of equipment, etc. Sometimes higher frequency interference comes from fluorescent overhead lights, which may have to be turned off.

The preparation, if poorly made, or too old, or allowed to heat up too much, may fail to respond to stimulation of the nerves. Efforts should be made to get clean, undamaged preparations and to maintain them below 20°C.

Pulling out of the microelectrode during a muscle contraction is common. Since the muscle potential occurs before the contraction, most of it can be recorded even when the electrode pulls out. Some parts of the muscles contract or are displaced less than others, and there is an advantage in attempting to place the electrode there. With fatigue of the preparation there is less contraction but of course fewer of the spike-shaped responses are then recorded.

Conclusions

The main points which the above experiments serve to illustrate, are as follows.

(1) In the abdominal extensor muscles, there is separation of the contractile elements into the *deep* muscles and the *superficial* muscles. These differ in structure, innervation, and electrical and contractile properties.

(2) In the deep muscles, the individual axons entering from a segmental nerve supply discrete areas of the musculature, in some cases in two segments.

(3) The excitatory axons, when stimulated, typically evoke large post-synaptic potentials, graded responses, or spike-shaped responses in the areas of the musculature which they innervate. Impulses in the inhibitory axons reduce the amplitude of the excitatory responses, and increase the rate of decay of excitatory post-synaptic potentials.

(4) In the superficial extensors, the post-synaptic potentials are smaller, and graded membrane responses uncommon. Facilitation of excitatory post-synaptic potentials is usually more pronounced than in the deep extensors.

(5) GABA activates the inhibitory areas of the muscle membrane, which are blocked by picrotoxin.

(6) Strychnine blocks neuromuscular transmission, probably by an effect on the pre-synaptic terminals of the excitor axons.

(7) The membrane potential of fibres in the deep extensor muscle is sensitive to potassium ion concentration, in approximate agreement with the Nernst equation.

(8) The abdominal muscles are different from the more usually studied leg muscles in many ways.

Further Ideas

Other experiments which could be attempted on this preparation include the following.

(1) Simultaneous recording of tension and electrical events in the deep extensors. This requires a strain gauge or mechano-electronic transducer of suitable sensitivity, fitted with a probe to make contact with the transverse segmental ligaments associated with the deep extensors.

(2) Effects of other drugs and ions on the muscle potentials; for example, acetylcholine (10^{-5} g/ml), strontium or barium chloride (20–50 mM, replacing osmotically equivalent sodium chloride), choline chloride (replacing sodium chloride).

(3) Further analysis of the effects of strychnine in the deep extensors, for example, by recording the nerve potential in the strychnine-treated preparation (Fig. 4).

(4) Effects of strychnine on the potentials of the superficial extensors. The effect is much less pronounced than in the case of the deep extensors.

(5) More thorough study of the effects of ions on the resting potential; for example, by replacement of sodium chloride by potassium in conjunction with a non-penetrating anion (acetate or propionate) rather than chloride.

Cleaning Up

All equipment, both mains and battery operated, should be switched off at the end of the experiment. Carefully wipe up any spilled saline and KCl solution, especially from equipment. Unused microelectrodes should be stored in a safe place. Remains of preparations and animals should be wrapped up in paper towels and deposited in the appropriate disposal bag or container. Wash out preparation dishes with fresh water, and leave them to dry for the next laboratory period.

Bibliography

Abbott, B. C. and Parnas, I. (1965). Electrical and mechanical responses in deep abdominal extensor muscles of crayfish and lobster. *J. gen. Physiol.* **48**, 919–931. [An account of propagated spikes in deep extensor muscle fibres; see Parnas and Atwood (1966) for further information.]

Atwood, H. L. and Dorai Raj, B. S. (1964). Tension development and membrane responses in phasic and tonic muscle fibres of a crab. *J. cell. comp. Physiol.* **64**, 55–72. [A study of the different kinds of muscle fibre encountered in a crab muscle. Note that in this muscle, unlike the case of the abdominal muscles, diverse types of fibre occur in the same muscle.]

Donaldson, P. E. K. (1958). "Electronic Apparatus for Biological Research." Butterworths, London. [A very useful description of microelectrode technique is included in this book, together with much information on apparatus of various types.]

Fatt, P. and Katz, B. (1953a). The electrical properties of crustacean muscle fibres. *J. Physiol., Lond.* **120**, 171–204. [Effects of certain ions on directly-evoked crustacean muscle potentials: effect of potassium ion on the resting potential; much information on the electrical properties of the muscle fibres.]

Fatt, P. and Katz, B. (1953b). Distributed "end-plate potentials" of crustacean muscle fibres. *J. exp. Biol.* **30**, 433–439. [Demonstration of the fact that post-synaptic potentials occur at multiple sites along crustacean muscle fibres, instead of at one point as in many vertebrate muscle fibres.]

Grundfest, H., Reuben, J. P. and Rickles, W. H. (1959). The electrophysiology and pharmacology of lobster neuromuscular synapses. *J. gen. Physiol.* **42**, 1301–1323. [An account of the effects of GABA, picrotoxin, and other substances on crustacean muscle fibres.]

Hodgkin, A. L. (1964). "The Conduction of the Nervous Impulse." Thomas, Springfield. [A readable review of information relating to resting and action potentials of nerve; some of the findings apply also to muscle.]

Hoyle, G. (1957). "Comparative Physiology of the Nervous Control of Muscular Contraction." Cambridge University Press. [Although some of the material is now out-dated, this book contains a good account of the resting and action potentials, and of the earlier work on arthropod muscles.]

Hoyle, G. and Wiersma, C. A. G. (1958). Excitation at neuromuscular junctions in Crustacea. J. Physiol., Lond., 143, 402–425. [Illustration of the variability of nerve-evoked potentials in crustacean muscle fibres.]

Kennedy, D. and Takeda, K. (1965a). Reflex control of abdominal extensor muscles in the crayfish. I. The twitch system. J. exp. Biol. 43, 211–227. [A description of the fast abdominal flexor muscles, which are similar in many respects to the deep extensor muscles.]

Kennedy, D. and Takeda, K. (1965b). Reflex control of abdominal flexor muscles in the crayfish. II. The tonic system. J. exp. Biol. 43, 229–246. [A description of the innervation and certain other properties of the superficial flexor muscles, which are similar to the superficial extensors.]

Nastuk, W. L. (Ed.) (1964). "Physical Techniques in Biological Research," Vol. 5. Electrophysiological methods, Part A. Academic Press, New York and London. [Contains a chapter on the microelectrode techniques of value as a reference.]

Parnas, I. and Atwood, H. L. (1966). Phasic and tonic neuromuscular systems in the abdominal extensor muscles of the crayfish and rock lobster. Comp. Biochem. Physiol. 18, 701–723. [An account of the innervation and physiology of the abdominal extensor muscles in Procambarus and Panulirus; of particular relevance to the present experiments.]

Pilgrim, R. L. C. and Wiersma, C. A. G. (1963). Observations on the skeleton and somatic musculature of the abdomen and thorax of Procambarus clarkii (Girard), with notes on the thorax of Panulirus interruptus (Randall), and Astacus. J. Morph. 113, 453–587. [Contains further details of the anatomy of the abdominal extensor muscles.]

Van Harreveld, A. (1936). A physiological solution for freshwater crustaceans. Proc. Soc. exp. Biol. Med. 34, 428–432. [The original recipe for crayfish solution.]

Van Harreveld, A. (1939). The nerve supply of doubly-and-triply-innervated crayfish muscles related to their function. J. comp. Neurol. 70, 267–284. [A description of the pattern of innervation in crustacean leg muscles.]

Van Harreveld, A. and Mendelson, M. (1959). Glutamate-induced contractions in crustacean muscle. J. cell. comp. Physiol. 54, 85–94. [Description of the stimulating effect of glutamate on crustacean muscle fibres.]

Wiersma, C. A. G. (1961). The neuromuscular system. In "The Physiology of Crustacea" (T. H. Waterman, ed.), Vol. 2. Academic Press, New York and London. [A review of earlier work on crustacean neuromuscular physiology.]

17

A. Isolated and *in situ* Heart Preparation of the Snail *Helix aspersa*

B. Intracellular Microelectrode Recording from the Brain of *Helix*

R. J. WALKER

Department of Physiology and Biochemistry, University of Southampton, England

A. Isolated and *in situ* Heart Preparation of the Snail *Helix aspersa*

ISOLATED HEART OF *Helix aspersa*

The animal used in this experiment is the common garden snail, *Helix aspersa*. Mature specimens in their second year are ideal, smaller younger snails are more difficult to cannulate and the heart tears more readily. The apparatus for recording the heart beat consists of a straw lever system arranged for amplification of the beat and a smoked kymograph drum for recording the beat. Such a system is outlined in Fig. 1. The writing portion is shown in more detail. It consists of a glass tube, inner bore being slightly larger than a normal pin, to which a bent length of glass tubing is fixed by means of sealing wax. The system can be attached to the end of the straw lever by means of a pin. The lever is best balanced prior to the attachment of the heart.

There are several salines which have been used for perfusion through snail hearts. The two that are recommended are after Meng (1960) and from Rozsa and Graul (1964), the latter being taken from a saline suggested by Jullien. The composition of Meng's Ringer is as follows:

NaCl	3·45 g/litre
KCl	0·43
$CaCl_2$	1·17
$NaHCO_3$	1·10
$MgCl_2 . 6H_2O$	3·31

One problem with this Ringer is the tendency of the calcium to precipitate. This can to some extent be avoided by dissolving all the salts save for calcium chloride in about 900 ml, then adding the calcium chloride and making the volume up to 1 litre.

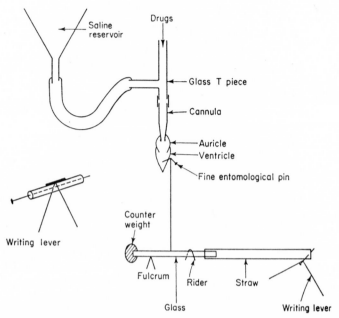

FIG. 1. The perfusion and recording system for the isolated snail heart preparation. Inset is an enlargement of the writing lever.

The composition of Jullien's Ringer is as follows:

NaCl	6·5 g/litre
KCl	0·14
CaCl$_2$	0·12
NaHCO$_3$	0·02
NaH$_2$PO$_4$	0·01

THE DISSECTION

Removal of the shell

The snail is held in the left hand and a cut is made following the spiral of the shell as shown in Fig. 2. Remove the broken pieces of the shell as you proceed, taking care not to penetrate the visceral mass. The position of the heart can now be seen, firstly because the mantle tissue immediately over the pericardium is darkly pigmented and secondly because the heart is usually beating and this can clearly be observed (Fig. 3).

Exposure of the heart

Now identify the pneumostome and insert one blade of a pair of scissors through it and cut the mantle away from the body-wall, now cut in the opposite direction to free the rest of the collar (Fig. 4). Make the cut in such

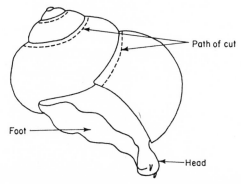

FIG. 2. The snail is held in the left hand and the shell removed by cutting along the path indicated by the dotted line.

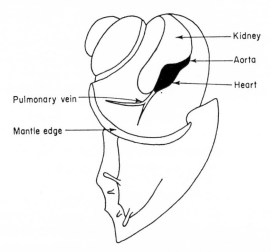

FIG. 3. Snail with shell removed to show the position of the heart, pulmonary vein, aorta, and kidney. Note the darkly pigmented mantle tissue immediately over the pericardium.

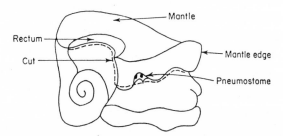

FIG. 4. Snail with shell removed to show the position of the cut for exposure of the heart.

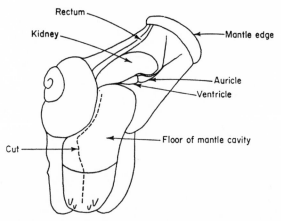

FIG. 5. The mantle edge is pinned back to expose the heart. The dotted line indicates the line along which to cut to expose the viscera.

a position that the rectum remains attached to the freed portion. This part of the dissection may be performed with the snail pinned to a wax block or held in the hand. However, the snail must now be pinned to a wax block, pins being inserted through its foot and head and through the cut mantle edge (Fig. 5).

Cannulation of the heart

The tips of a pair of fine forceps are passed under the main pulmonary vein just before it enters the pericardium and a thread is drawn through. A slit is now made in the vein distal to the thread and the cannula (filled with Ringer) is inserted and gently worked forwards and into the apex of the auricle. The cannula is then tied in place. A slit is made in the pericardium to allow the heart to bulge outwards and cuts are made around the heart to free it from the surrounding tissue (Fig. 6). The cannula is then inserted into the end of the glass T-piece and Ringer perfused through the heart (Fig. 1). It is important to try and avoid the entry of bubbles of air into the heart. By this means both the auricle and ventricle are perfused and seen to contract. An alternative method is to tie a loose ligature between the auricle and ventricle and insert the cannula as before, but this time continue pushing it forward until it enters the ventricle and then tie it in place using the ligature loosely tied between the auricle and ventricle. This method gives only the ventricular beat. A bent entomological pin, no. 20, is hooked into the ventricle and attached via a length of cotton to the lever system. The contractions of the heart can now be recorded on a lightly smoked drum. Figure 7A–C shows the effect of perfusing 5-hydroxytryptamine and acetylcholine respectively through the heart, the substances being added through the open top of the

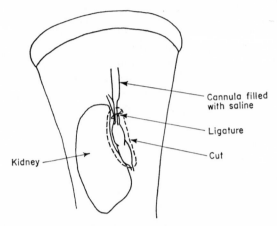

FIG. 6. The cannula filled with saline is inserted through a slit in the pulmonary vein and pushed into the apex of the aorta and tied in place by means of a ligature. The dotted line indicates the line of cutting for removal of the heart from the surrounding tissue.

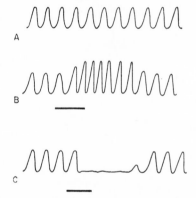

FIG. 7. Contractions from an isolated snail heart recorded on a smoked drum using a system outlined in Fig. 1. A, normal heart beat; B, effect of 5-hydroxytryptamine on the heart beat; C, effect of acetylcholine on the heart beat.

T-piece. Should the heart fail to beat of its own accord, then 1 ml of 10^{-6} g/ml 5-hydroxytryptamine can be perfused through it. This usually starts the heart beating. A heart will continue to beat if perfused for more than 24 h.

THE ISOLATED HEART-NERVE-BRAIN PREPARATION

The isolated heart preparation can be extended to include the visceral nerve and the supra- and suboesophageal ganglionic mass. This will then give one a very useful heart-nerve-brain preparation. In this case the dissection is taken to the stage outlined in Fig. 5. Now cut along the line indicated in Fig. 5 to expose the visceral mass. Carefully turn the contents exposed to either the right or left of the animal. Identify the long narrow band of white muscular tissue, the pharyngeal retractor muscle, which runs from the pharynx to the columella of the shell. Identify the oesophagus, the region of the gut connecting the pharynx to the crop. Cut through both the pharyngeal retractor muscle and the oesophagus, the suboesophageal ganglionic mass

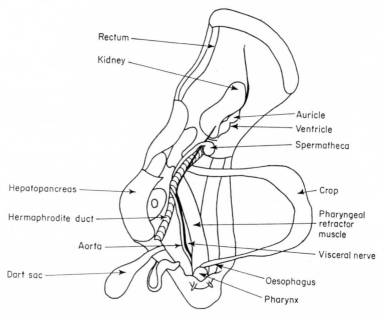

FIG. 8. This shows the path of the visceral nerve. The contents of the rostral region of the body have been displaced to the left and right of the animal. Note the path of the visceral nerve in relation to the hermaphrodite duct.

will now be exposed (Fig. 9). Slip the pharynx through the circumoesophageal commissure. Identify the visceral nerve and the cephalic aorta. The aorta passes between the ganglia which make up the suboesophageal mass and extends to the pharynx Running along the side of the aorta and often closely applied to it is the visceral or intestinal nerve. The aorta and nerve run together as far as the hermaphrodite duct. At this juncture, the aorta passes over the duct while the nerve runs along the edge of the duct in a caudal direction. The nerve runs along the edge of the hermaphrodite duct until it reaches the spermatheca, when it passes beneath the duct from the spermatheca and continues caudally until it reaches the kidney. Just before it reaches the kidney, it bifurcates to form the auricular and ventricular branches of the visceral nerve. The preparation can be lightly stained with methylene blue to assist in its identification. This nerve also innervates parts of the reproductive system, the gut and kidney. For an experiment the nerve is usually traced as far as the spermatheca, and all tissue rostral to this can be cut away. The pulmonary vein is then cannulated as before and any remaining tissue can be cleared away, so leaving the brain, nerve, heart, and a little hepatopancreatic and kidney tissue. The whole can be mounted on a piece of

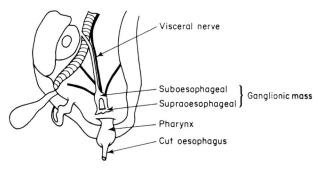

FIG. 9. This shows the position of the sub- and supraoesophageal ganglionic mass following the removal of the pharyngeal retractor muscle and crop. The pharynx has been slipped through the circumoesophageal commissures and pulled forwards.

wax with a hole in it. The heart can be suspended above the hole, allowing the cotton to the lever to pass through it. The brain can sit in a hollow depression in the wax which is filled with Ringer. Vaseline can be smeared over the nerve to prevent desiccation. The nerve or brain can now be stimulated and the effect noted on the smoked drum.

In situ SNAIL HEART

In these experiments, either *pomatia* or *aspersa* can be used, though the heart of *pomatia* gives a more even beat. The dissection is the same as for the isolated nerve-heart preparation up to Fig. 9. Following cannulation of the pulmonary vein the beginning of the aorta is carefully exposed and cut. A second cannula is now inserted into the aorta and tip of the ventricle and tied in place with cotton. A slit is made in the pericardium to allow the heart to protrude from the pericardial cavity. A small heart clip is attached to the ventricle and connected via cotton to a lever and the contractions recorded as before on a smoked drum. The foot and part of the visceral mass can be cleared away, leaving a preparation which is similar to the isolated heart-nerve-muscle preparation (Fig. 10). Stimulation of the visceral nerve may either inhibit or accelerate the heart beat depending on the parameters of stimulation (Fig. 11). Alternative methods to that of a smoked drum may be employed for recording the heart beat. One method is to use two fine

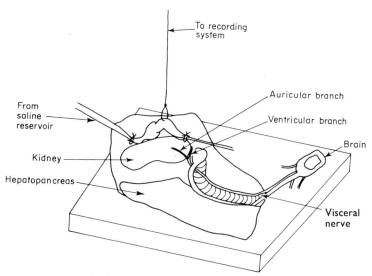

FIG. 10. The complete brain-nerve-heart preparation can be seen in this figure. The whole is pinned to a wax block. The heart clip from the ventricle passes to the recording system.

silver electrodes which are then connected via pre-amplifiers to an oscilloscope; a type of electrocardiogram can then be recorded.* The shape of the electrocardiogram varies greatly depending on the positions of the two electrodes (Fig. 12). This method is useful if one wishes to record nervous

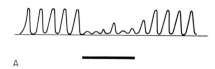

A

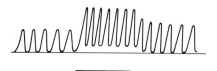

B

FIG. 11. Stimulation of the visceral nerve may result in either inhibition (A) or excitation (B) of the heart beat. This response depends on the voltage and frequency of stimulus and also on the time of year.

* In this the pericardium is not slit.

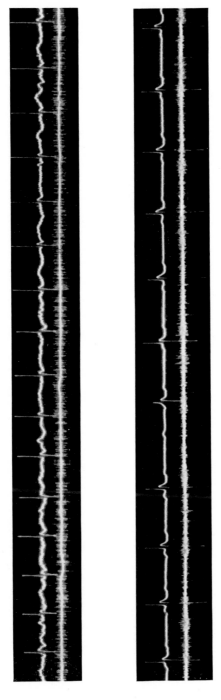

Fig. 12. Two records are shown. The upper trace of each record shows the shape of the heat beat when recorded by means of two silver external recording electrodes placed over the pericardium. The lower trace in each record shows spontaneous activity recorded from the visceral nerve with external silver electrodes.

activity from the nerve which necessitates the use of an oscilloscope. The major disadvantage of this method of recording is that as the heart dries slightly, so the shape of the recording changes and may disappear. Also it often requires much searching over the surface of the pericardium to obtain a satisfactory record. An alternative and more reliable and reproducible method makes use of a semi-conductor strain gauge which is incorporated into a Wheatstone bridge circuit (Fig. 13). In this case the pericardium is slit to expose the ventricle and a heart clip and cotton connects the ventricle to the strain gauge. In the figure, two balancing potentiometers are employed,

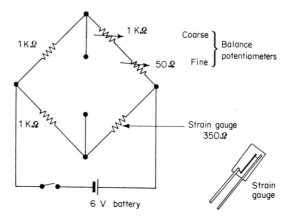

FIG. 13. A diagram of the Wheatstone bridge circuit for the strain gauge. Either a 6 V or 9 V battery may be used. More accurate balancing can be achieved by having both a fine and course potentiometer but this is not essential. Inset is a diagram of the strain gauge showing the most suitable form of terminal. The input can be fed straight onto the oscilloscope.

one a course adjuster and one for fine adjustment. These p type of semi-conductor strain gauges can be obtained from Ether Ltd, Caxton Way, Stevenage, Herts, England; the style of termination shown in the figure is the best to use. Contractions recorded via the strain gauge can be amplified and displayed on an oscilloscope and/or pen recorder (Fig. 14). This type of recording can be used in conjunction with intracellular single cell recording from neurones in the brain. Using this preparation, saline perfused through the heart can be collected via the aortic cannula and analysed for material released from, for example, the nerve terminations of the visceral nerve in response to nerve or brain stimulation. Such a method is of great value in investigating the presence of and in collecting possible cardioregulatory substances. This method has been used to demonstrate the release of 5-hydroxytryptamine from the visceral nerve on stimulation which led to excitation of the heart (Rozsa, 1966). It would also be a convenient preparation

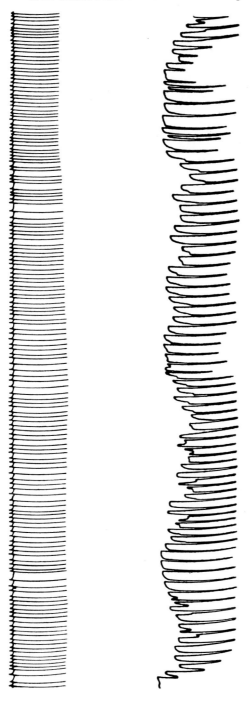

FIG. 14. The lower trace shows heart beats recorded using the strain gauge. The upper trace shows simultaneous intracellular recording from a neurone in the visceral ganglion of the brain.

for soaking the brain in labelled compounds and studying the release of these or related compounds from the heart following stimulation of the nerve.

BIBLIOGRAPHY

Korn, M. E. (1964). Some problems of neuromuscular mediation in the higher invertebrates. Thesis. Oxford University.

Koshtoiants, Kh. S., Smirnova, N. A. and Popkova, R. (1959). The cerebral and abdominal ganglia and the regulation of cardiac activity in *Helix pomatia*. *Sechenov physiol. J. USSR*, **45**, 70–76. (Trans.).

Meng, K. (1960). Untersuchungen zur Störung der Herztätigkeit beim *Helix pomatia*. *Zool. Jber.* **68**, 539–566.

Ripplinger, J. (1957). Contribution a l'étude de la physiologie du coeur et de son innervation extrinseque chez l'Escargot (*Helix pomatia*). *Annls scient. Univ. Besancon* (2) Zool. Physiol. **8**, 3–179.

Rozsa, K. S. and Perenyi, L. (1966). Chemical identification of the excitatory substance released in *Helix* heart during stimulation of the extra cardial nerve. *Comp. Biochem. Physiol.* **19**, 105–113.

Rozsa, K. S. and Graul, C. (1964). Is serotonin responsible for the stimulative effect of the extracardiac nerve in *Helix pomatia*? *Annls Biol. Tihany* **31**, 85–96.

B. Intracellular Microelectrode Recording from the Brain of *Helix*

The gastropod molluscs are ideal animals for intracellular recordings from brain cells; they have large diameter neurones, 100–150 μ, which are located on the surface of the ganglion. This means that on removal of the connective tissue sheath from over the ganglion the cells can clearly be seen. In addition there can be no doubt that drugs and ions perfused over the preparation are reaching the membrane of these cells. They are also ideal for iontophoretic injection, since the electrode filled with the compound to be tested can be brought into position over the impaled cell.

THE PREPARATION

The snail is prepared as for the heart experiment, except that there is no need to cut initially round the mantle edge to expose the heart. The shell is simply removed (Fig. 2), and the animal pinned, fully extended, to a wax block. A cut can now be made, as indicated in Fig. 5, to expose the body contents (Fig. 8). The oesophagus and pharyngeal retractor muscle are now cut and the pharynx slipped through the circumoesophageal commissure (Fig. 15). The thick upper layer of connective tissue can now be removed, either with the brain *in situ* or after the brain has been removed from the animal. The advantage of the former method is that the nerves and muscles attached to the brain can be pinned in a stretched position, so holding the brain in a rigid position. This makes it easier to remove the connective tissue without damaging the underlying surface cells. In either case the outer connective tissue is carefully picked up with a fine pair of forceps and an incision

made at point X (Fig. 15). (This is best performed under a binocular microscope.) The cut connective tissue is now gently pulled upwards and the cut
extended in both directions, finally encircling the suboesophageal ganglionic
mass, as indicated in Fig. 15. The outlines of the three major ganglia should
now be visible (Fig. 16). If the procedure has been followed correctly, the
cells should now be clearly visible, with the aid of a dissecting binocular, but
should be held firmly in position because of the presence of the fine inner

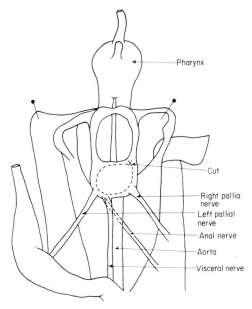

FIG. 15. The pharyngeal retractor muscle and the oesophagus have been cut and the
pharynx slipped through the circumoesophageal commissures to reveal the entire brain.
The dotted line indicates the path for cutting for removal of the thick outer connective
tissue.

connective tissue layer. If this has been damaged, then the cells in the damaged
area will "ballon" out and may be seen to be floating freely when the preparation is placed in the Ringer solution. Cells in this state are very difficult to
penetrate successfully with a microelectrode. The next stage in the dissection is
to remove a small area of this fine inner connective tissue layer from over a few
cells. This fine inner layer acts as a barrier to penetration by the electrode and
often results in the loss of the electrode tip. This next stage is the most
difficult one to perform successfully. A glass hook (see inset in Fig. 16) is
carefully and gently pushed into and under the thin connective tissue layer,
then moved along a little way under the connective tissue and the tip pushed
out through the tissue again. The glass rod is now pulled upwards gently,

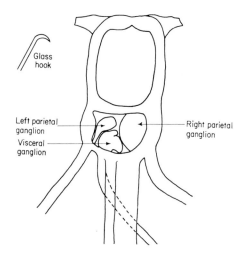

FIG. 16. On removal of the thick outer connective tissue, the three major dorsal ganglia in the suboesophageal ganglionic mass can be seen. Inset is the pointed glass rod for the removal of the inner thin connective tissue layer.

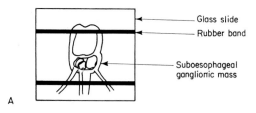

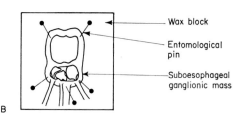

FIG. 17. Two methods for holding the brain firm are shown. A. The brain is mounted on a piece of glass slide under a rubber band. B. The brain is pinned onto a wax block using fine entomological pins (no. 20).

causing a small tear in the connective tissue. This should partially expose a small group of cells, without allowing them to "ballon" out. The brain is cut away from the surrounding tissue to leave a preparation as shown in Fig. 16. It can now be placed on a slide, held in position by rubber bands (Fig. 17A) or pinned out on a piece of wax (Fig. 17B). The brain is now placed in the chamber and viewed with the binocular microscope which is held horizontally. Lighting is best from the back and above, focusing onto the preparation with a convex lens for maximum intensity over the preparation.

The Apparatus

The recording electrodes are the normal glass capillary microelectrodes filled with 3 M KCl. Electrodes with a resistance of between 5 and 10 MΩ are ideal for this preparation. Electrodes with these relatively high resistances have to be connected to a cathode follower before being connected to the oscilloscope. The valve is in a probe unit separated from the main chassis

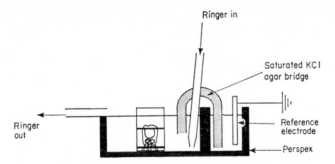

FIG. 18. The complete bath set-up with a brain in position is shown. The bath is partially filled with wax and the slide plus brain rests on this wax at an angle of about 60°. The preparation is illuminated from above and behind and viewed from in front with the binocular microscope held horizontally. The front of the bath is made of glass.

and can be mounted above the electrode. A bridge system is very useful for depolarizing or hyperpolarizing a cell. When changing the ionic composition of the Ringer it is advisable to insert an agar bridge between the reference electrode and the preparation (Fig. 18). When testing the response to drugs it is advisable to use electrodes filled with 1 M K acetate, since chloride ions leaking from the electrode into the cell may alter the response of the cell to the drug.

18 | Chromatographic Demonstration of Dopamine in the Brain of *Helix aspersa*

C. B. SEDDEN

Department of Physiology and Biochemistry, University of Southampton, England

ANIMALS AND APPARATUS

Fifty brains of *Helix aspersa* (garden snail) (see p. 335 for dissection).
Descending chromatography tank.
Strips of Whatman paper No. 1, size approx. 6 in. $\times$ 17 in.
Pasteur pipette with fine tip.
Hamilton microsyringe, 10 μl.
Hair dryer.
Shandon spray.
Separating funnel, 500 ml.
Hanoveria ultraviolet lamp.

CHEMICALS

N HCl (102 ml conc. HCl made up to 1 litre with distilled water).
95% Acid ethanol (95 ml absolute ethanol + 5 ml N HCl).
n-Butanol.
Ammoniacal ethylenediamine (36 ml water + 4 ml NH_3 + 10 ml ethylene-diamine).
10^{-3} Standard solutions (0·1 g/100 ml N HCl) of:

> Adrenaline
> Noradrenaline
> Dopamine (3-hydroxytyramine)
> Dopa (3,4-dihydroxyphenylalanine)

PRINCIPLE

The brains are "killed" immediately by immersion in N HCl. The dopamine is extracted into HCl and ethanol is added to precipitate the proteins. These are removed by centrifugation. The extract is spotted in a line on the paper to prevent overloading. Standard dopamine is added to half the extract to ensure that other substances are not interfering with the R_F.

METHOD

SENSITIVITY OF THE SPRAY

To find out how much catecholamine is detected using ethylenediamine, quantities of 3·0–0·01 μg are spotted onto filter paper, dried and sprayed with the prepared ethylenediamine. The paper is then dried in a fume cupboard and examined under the u.v. light. The catecholamines fluoresce yellow.

At least 0·05 μg should be detected.

PREPARATION OF THE SOLVENT (n-BUTANOL SATURATED WITH N HCl)

200 ml n-butanol is shaken with 50 ml N HCl in a separating funnel and left to stand for 24 h. The lower layer is then run off and discarded. Some of the butanol is run into the bottom of the tank and left to saturate the atmosphere.

CHROMATOGRAPHY OF THE STANDARDS

A line is drawn 4 in. from one end of the strip of chromatography paper and the position of the standards marked on it (see Fig. 1). A total of 2 μl of each standard is spotted on the paper in 1 μl aliquots using the Hamilton microsyringe. The spots are dried with the hair drier. The opposite end of the paper is cut as shown in Fig. 2.

The end of the chromatography paper with the line is placed in the trough in the prepared chromatography tank. It is secured in place with a glass rod; 100 ml of the solvent is then poured into the trough and the tank closed with the glass lid. The chromatogram is left to develop for 50 h.

The paper is removed from the tank and hung in a fume cupboard to dry, if it is aided with a hair drier this stage takes about 30 min. The paper is

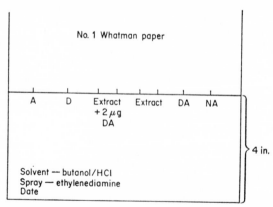

FIG. 1. Key: DA, Dopamine; NA, noradrenaline; D, dopa; A, adrenaline.

This end of paper placed in
chromatography trough

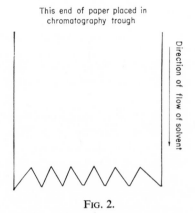

Direction of flow of solvent

FIG. 2.

then sprayed with the ammoniacal ethylenediamine solution using a Shandon spray. The paper is again dried with the hair drier. It is examined for the catecholamines under the ultraviolet light (see Fig. 3).

As the chromatograms are left for such a long time the solvent front disappears off the end of the paper. In order that the solvent will continue to flow straight down the paper and not over to one side the end is cut as in Fig. 2. The R_F, that is the position on the chromatogram of the compound with relation to the solvent front, cannot be measured. The distance they have moved is therefore quoted with respect to the fastest moving compound, in this case dopamine.

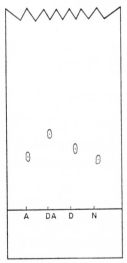

FIG. 3.

PREPARATION OF THE EXTRACT

The brains are removed from the snail, wiped quickly on tissue to remove any mucus and placed in N HCl which is in a 25 ml beaker standing in ice. When all the brains have been removed, they are dried on a piece of tissue and weighed. They are then added to 0·5 ml acid ethanol and sliced as finely as possible with a pair of scissors. The extract is left for 10 min at 0°C. The contents of the beaker are then transferred to a 10 ml centrifuge tube and spun in a refrigerated MSE centrifuge at 38 000 × g for 10 min at 4°C. The supernatant is removed and divided into two.

Two μl dopamine standard are added to one half of the extract. This and the other half of the extract are then spotted onto the chromatogram using the Pasteur pipette. The extracts are put on in a small strip ½ in. long keeping it as thin as possible (see Fig. 1). The standards are then added as before and the spots dried with the hair drier.

The chromatogram is developed and sprayed as described under Chromatography of the standards (p. 348). The R_D values are again noted.

RESULTS

	R_D Values × 100
Dopamine	100
Dopa	74
Noradrenaline	51
Adrenaline	57
Extract + dopamine	104
Extract	104

It is seen that in this solvent the fluorescent spot in the extract runs the same distance as dopamine added to the extract.

TROUBLES

It may be found that the supernatant from the extract after centrifugation is very thick, if so re-centrifuge and next time cut the brains up more coarsely.

If the solvent front does not run down the paper in a horizontal line check that the tank and troughs are not sloping.

CONCLUSIONS

From the fact that the R_D values are the same one can conclude that the substance which fluoresces in the extract could be dopamine. However, to be certain it is necessary to repeat the experiment using other solvents.

OTHER EXPERIMENTS

To verify the results from the first experiment it can be repeated using the following solvent systems.

1. n-Butanol/acetic acid/water. Mix together in the proportions 60 : 15 : 25. Develop overnight. (It should not run off the end of the paper.)

	$R_F \times 100$
Dopamine	39
Adrenaline	32
Noradrenaline	28
Dopa	20

2. n-Butanol/ethanol/water; 2 : 1 : 1. Develop overnight. (It should not run off the end of the paper.)

	$R_F \times 100$
Dopamine	55
Adrenaline	45
Noradrenaline	42
Dopa	32

3. Methanol/butanol/benzene/water, 4 : 4 : 4 : 1. Develop for 8 h only (it should not run off the end of the paper.)

	$R_F \times 100$
Dopamine	38
Adrenaline	30
Noradrenaline	29
Dopa	12

4. Chloroform/acetic acid/water; 2 : 1 : 1. Separate off the aqueous (upper) layer and use. Develop for 7 h only. (It should not run off the end of the paper.)

	$R_F \times 100$
Dopamine	86
Adrenaline	83
Noradrenaline	82
Dopa	81

Further confirmation is obtained by the action of various drugs. Reserpine when injected into the snail and left for 48 h will remove the dopamine so that no fluorescent spot will be found on the chromatogram.

Dopa, which is the immediate precursor of dopamine, will increase the dopamine content and hence increase the intensity of the spot.

CLEANING UP

The chromatography tank must be thoroughly cleaned out since, unless it is an all-glass tank, the acid will corrode the metal.

BIBLIOGRAPHY

Carlsson, A., Jonasson, J. and Rosengren, E. (1963). Time correlation between the effects of reserpine on behaviour and storage mechanism for arylalkylamines. *Acta physiol. scand.* **59**, 474–477.

McGeer, E. G. and McGeer, W. H. (1964). R_F values of some catecholamines, precursors and metabolites. *J. Chromat.*, **14**, 104–107.

Shore, P. A. (1962) Release of serotonin and catecholamines by drugs. *Pharm. Rev.*, **14**, 531–550.

Smith, I. (1960) "Chromatographic and Electrophoretic Techniques", Vol. 1, 82 pp. Heinemann, London.

19 | A. Thin-layer Chromatography of Amino Acids and Sugars
B. The Snail Nerve-muscle Preparation
C. Perfusion of the Cockroach Leg

G. A. KERKUT and A. SHAPIRA

Department of Physiology and Biochemistry, University of Southampton, England

A. Thin-layer Chromatography of Amino Acids and Sugars

Thin-layer chromatography is a simple, rapid and efficient method of separating different amino acids and sugars.

MATERIALS

The thin layer of adsorbent material is silica gel (Kieselgel G nach Stahl from Merck Chemicals) and is supported on glass plates 7 in. × 4 in.

PREPARATION OF THIN FILMS

The glass plates must be thoroughly washed with detergent and dried before use. They are then arranged as in Fig. 1. The Sellotape both anchors the plates and determines the thickness of the film. The silica gel is applied as a slurry consisting of 2 : 1 distilled water/powder (30 g of powder being required for six plates of the specified size). The water and powder are mixed and then shaken for 30 sec before the slurry is poured on the plates which have been previously cleaned with ether on tissue paper. The slurry is spread to give an even surface using a thick glass rod.

PREPARATION OF THE TANK

A 2 or 3 litre beaker, or a tank supplied by Shandon Ltd for thin-layer chromatography, is lined with Whatman No. 1 filter paper (Fig. 2) and the solvent is poured into the tank, wetting the filter paper at the same time. The volume of solvent should be such that there is about $\frac{3}{4}$ in. of solvent at the bottom of the tank. Lining of the tank ensures that the atmosphere in

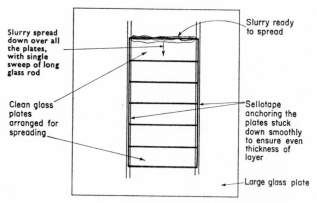

Slurry spread down over all the plates, with single sweep of long glass rod

Clean glass plates arranged for spreading

Slurry ready to spread

Sellotape anchoring the plates stuck down smoothly to ensure even thickness of layer

Large glass plate

Fig. 1. To illustrate (1) arrangement of plates for spreading and (2) spreading.

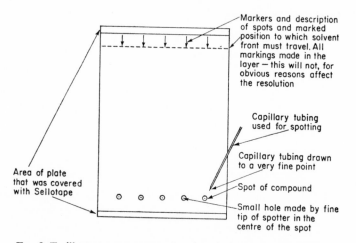

Markers and description of spots and marked position to which solvent front must travel. All markings made in the layer — this will not, for obvious reasons affect the resolution

Capillary tubing used for spotting

Capillary tubing drawn to a very fine point

Spot of compound

Small hole made by fine tip of spotter in the centre of the spot

Area of plate that was covered with Sellotape

Fig. 2. To illustrate appearance of a plate during and after spotting.

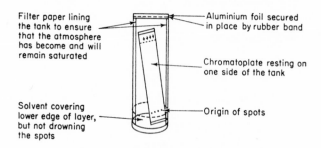

Filter paper lining the tank to ensure that the atmosphere has become and will remain saturated

Aluminium foil secured in place by rubber band

Chromatoplate resting on one side of the tank

Solvent covering lower edge of layer, but not drowning the spots

Origin of spots

Fig. 3. To illustrate the chromoplate in the tank.

the tank will become saturated. The tank is covered with aluminium foil secured in place with a rubber band. Saturation of the tank will take from 30 min to 2 h depending on the solvent used (Fig. 3).

SPOTTING

Compounds are spotted onto the plate with thin capillary tubing (approx. 1 mm internal diameter) drawn out to a fine point. The spots should be as small as possible and the amount of compound should not exceed 10 μg per spot; the volume is usually 0·5–2·0 μl per spot. The spots should be about 1$\frac{1}{2}$ cm from the bottom of the film to avoid immersion of the compounds in the solvent and subsequent loss of the compounds. Six or seven spots can be run on one plate.

FINER TECHNIQUES FOR SPOTTING

Fine capillary tubing is drawn from glass tubing of internal diameter 0·7–0·5 cm. The tubing for spotting is drawn from the capillary tube over a very small flame, the point should be very fine, about 100–200 μ. To spot the compound on a plate, draw up a little in the spotting tube and bring the point of the tube on to the surface of the film, take it away again quickly and a small spot, about 1–2 mm, of the compound will have been deposited on the plate. If this procedure is repeated four or five times in exactly the same place, the spot will hold about 1 μl of the compound, and this is an ideal amount for accurate resolution. Care should be taken to ensure that each of the applications to the spot is quite dry before the next application; if this is not adhered to, the spot will spread and the resolution will be lowered.

DEVELOPMENT

When each spot is completely dry, the plate is ready for development. The plate is placed in the tank quickly to avoid unsaturation of the atmosphere in the tank, and is left to run until the solvent front reaches a pre-determined mark (Fig. 4).

FACTORS INFLUENCING THE R_F VALUE OF COMPOUNDS

The R_F value is defined as the ratio:

$$\frac{\text{distance travelled by compound}}{\text{distance travelled by solvent front}}$$

There are three main factors which influence the R_F value of a compound.

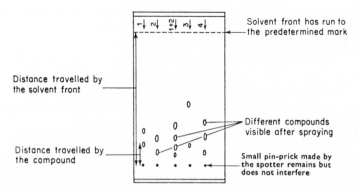

FIG. 4. To illustrate a model plate after developing and spraying.

(1) *Film thickness.* A chromatoplate which has not been evenly spread will yield much lower R_F values than an even thickness of film. Similarly, an even film that is thicker than 250 μ will also render the R_F values too low.

(2) *Atmosphere in the developing tank.* When the atmosphere in the tank is not saturated, the solvent will climb up the film and evaporate; therefore more solvent will pass through the film to carry the solvent front to the pre-determined mark than if the atmosphere were saturated. Hence, the R_F values will be appreciably higher than those obtained under normal conditions. Overdevelopment of a chromatogram is an important source of error in the measurement of R_F values.

(3) *Loading.* If the optimum load per spot, 10 μg, is exceeded, the spots become larger and the R_F values increase progressively.

CHROMOGENIC REAGENTS FOR AMINO ACIDS AND SUGARS

AMINO ACIDS.

Amino acids are detected with ninhydrin in cadmium acetate solution: 12 ml cadmium acetate solution added to 0·25 g ninhydrin (indane-trione hydrate) dissolved in 100 ml acetone.

Cadmium acetate solution
900 ml Distilled water
180 ml Glacial acetic acid
9 g Cadmium acetate

The cadmium acetate solution can be stored as a stock solution, but the ninhydrin should be made up fresh as required.

For colour development place plates at 110°C for 10 min.

SUGARS

Sugars are detected with anisaldehyde solution:

9 ml Ethanol (100%)
0·5 ml Conc. H_2SO_4
0·5 ml Anisaldehyde

For colour development, place plates at 100°C for 20 min.

SOLVENTS FOR AMINO ACIDS (Brenner and Niederwieser, 1960)

1. 96% Ethanol/water (63 : 37)
2. n-Propanol/water (64 : 36)
3. n-Butanol/acetic acid/water (60 : 20 : 20)
4. Phenol/water (75 : 25) + 20 mg sodium cyanide per 100 ml mixture
5. n-Propanol/34% aqueous ammonia (67 : 33)
6. 96% Ethanol/34% aqueous ammonia (77 : 23)

R_F values of the commoner amino acids in these solvents are given in Table I.

TABLE I

R_F values of amino acids in the six solvents listed above

Amino acid	Solvent					
	1	2	3	4	5	6
Alanine	45	40	36	39	41	44
Arginine	06	02	11	17	11	05
Aspartic acid	56	36	29	05	06	08
Cysteic acid	65	55	10	03	18	22
Cystine	39	36	20	16	24	22
Glutamic acid	56	33	27	12	21	26
Glycine	42	30	24	20	31	33
Histidine	30	25	06	32	37	41
Leucine	60	52	48	46	55	60
Lysine	04	02	08	10	16	14
Methionine	58	51	36	47	53	58
Norvaline	48	46	40	44	45	50
Phenylalanine	62	58	43	61	58	53
Serine	48	36	25	20	28	30
Threonine	51	39	26	28	35	36
Tyrosine	67	60	46	48	40	46
Valine	58	46	34	40	48	56

All R_F values expressed as R_F value × 100.

An extract to be analysed for amino acids should be desalted with ethanol if necessary. The 95 % ethanol will take up the amino acids and leave the salts.

Two dimensional chromatography of amino acids is carried out on plates 5½ in. square. The best combination of solvents according to Neiderwieser and Pataki (1960) is n-butanol/acetic acid/water and phenol/water/cyanide.

The R_F value of the spots

No. of spot	R_F value	Corresponds to standard
1	54	Tryptophan
2	30	Alanine
3	27	Glutamic acid
4	23	Serine
5	20	Aspartic acid
6	18	Cystine
7	08	Arginine
8	07	Histidine

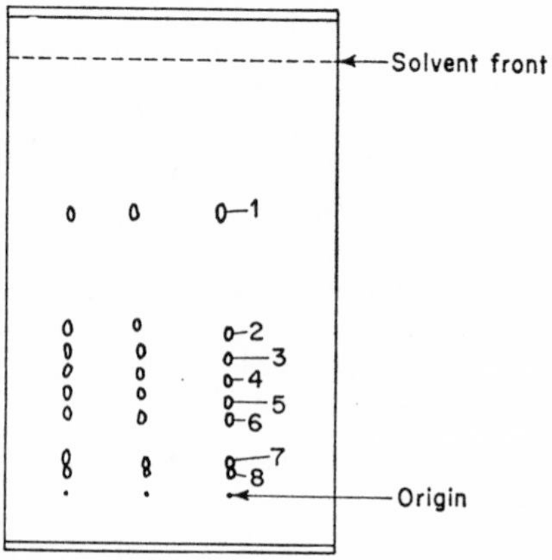

Fig. 5. This is an illustration of the different amino acids that can be separated from a crude extract made from the brain of the common garden snail, *Helix aspersa*. The adsorbent material is silica gel "G"; the solvent is n-butanol/glacial acetic acid/water; and the spray reagent is ninhydrin in cadmium acetate solution.

SUGARS

Plates made in the usual way are pre-run in 0·02 M sodium acetate solution. When the film is saturated with sodium acetate, the chromatoplate is dried at room temperature. After spotting the plate is run in ethyl acetate/iso-propanol/water (26 : 14 : 7). For R_F values of sugars, see Table II.

TABLE II

R_F values for sugars on silica gel layers in iso-propanol/ethyl acetate/water

Sugar	R_F value
Arabinose	20
Fructose	21
Galactose	16
Glucose	17
Lactose	04
Maltose	05
Mannose	19
Rhamnose	59
Ribose	42
Xylose	35

All R_F values expressed as R_F value $\times$ 100.

Using the techniques described it is possible to determine qualitatively the amino acid and sugar content of any unknown system.

FURTHER POINTS ON SPRAYING A DEVELOPED CHROMATOPLATE

The best spray bottles for this purpose are of the type supplied by Shandon Ltd, mainly because they give a fine, uniform spray. A harsh spray will blow the powder off the plate. The spray is driven by air from an "Aerostyle" compressor. Care should be taken to ensure that the reagent is evenly distributed over the plate.

BIBLIOGRAPHY

Brenner, M. and Niederwieser, A. (1960). *Experientia* **16**, 378.
Brenner, M. and Pataki, G. (1961). *Helv. Chim. Acta* **44**, 1420.
Fahmy, A. R., Niederwieser, A., Pataki, G. and Brenner, M. (1961). *Helv. Chim. Acta* **44**, 2022.
Niederwieser, A. and Pataki, G. (1960). *Chimia* **14**, 378.
Nurnberg, E. (1959). *Arch. Pharm.* **292**, 610.
Prey, V., Berbalk, H. and Kausz, M. (1961). *Mikrochim. Acta*, p. 968.
Randerath, K. (1963). "Thin-layer Chromatography." Verlag Chemie and Academic Press, New York.
Stahl, E. and Kaltenbach, U. (1961). *J. Chromat.* **5**, 458.
Truter, E. (1963). "Thin Film Chromatography." Cleaver-Hume Press, London.

B.   The Snail Nerve-muscle Preparation

This is another nerve-muscle preparation that can be adopted to test the action of different drugs on the muscle. It has certain advantages in that the snail is fairly easily come by, the dissection is simple, and the apparatus required for the experiment is minimal.

MATERIALS AND METHODS

The snail, *Helix aspersa*, is put in a beaker containing about half an inch of luke-warm water (about 30°C). This will "wake" the snail up. When it has crawled about half-way up the beaker, it is ready for dissection. The shell is quickly removed with coarse scissors. The snail is then pinned in an extended position on a wax block; one pin going through the head and the other through the mantle and extreme end of the foot (Fig. 6). The first incision is made in the edge of the mantle in line with the centre of the head. The snail is then cut open and the edges of the mantle pinned aside revealing a mass of reproductive organs, the albumen gland, intestine and heart. All this is pinned to one side

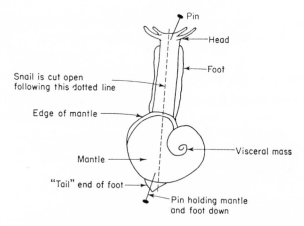

FIG. 6. Diagram of snail pinned to wax block after removal of the shell.

and the buccal mass, pharyngeal retractor muscle and supraoesophageal ganglia can now be seen (Fig. 7).

Cut the intestine from the buccal mass, and carefully cut the buccal mass from the wall of the head. Lift the buccal mass up gently so as not to wrench it from the retractor muscle, or damage the brain. The suboesophageal ganglia can be seen under the buccal mass. Cut the suboesophageal ganglia free with a pair of fine scissors—all the nerves except the two to the retractor muscle will be severed. The buccal mass, brain and most of the retractor muscle should now be free, isolated as a whole from the rest of the animal. Follow the retractor muscle to its end in the coil of the visceral mass, and cut around

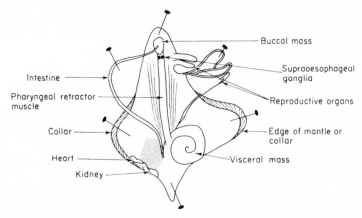

FIG. 7. Illustration to show exposure of pharyngeal retractor muscle, buccal mass and supraoesophageal ganglia.

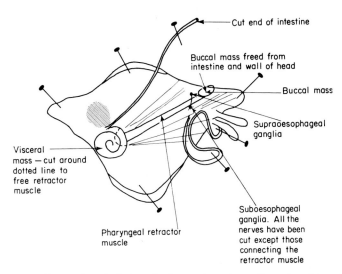

FIG. 8. Illustration to show isolation of suboesophageal ganglia and position of the end of the retractor muscle.

it so as to free the entire preparation, but not cut "short" the retractor muscle (Fig. 8). Having isolated the preparation, place it quickly into a frog bath containing Meng's Ringer. Keep the preparation in position by putting a pin through the buccal mass into the hole in the raised platform in the bath. Tie a piece of cotton round the "tail" end of the retractor muscle and attach the cotton to the hook of the straw lever holder (Fig. 9). The straw lever writes on a kymograph drum. Place a pair of electrodes on the brain gently

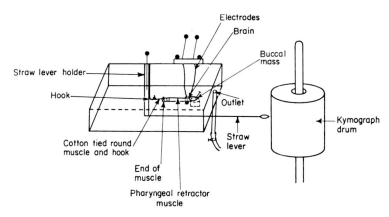

FIG. 9. Diagram to show position of preparation in frog bath and the attachment of the muscle to the straw lever holder.

O

lifting the supraoesophageal ganglia just out of the Ringer solution (Fig. 10). Take great care not to damage the brain or break the nerves; if this happens, the preparation should be abandoned and a fresh one set up. The frequency of shocks delivered to the electrodes should be about 2/min and the intensity adjusted so that the muscle gives a uniform twitch about $\frac{1}{2}$ to 1 in. high for every stimulus. Test solutions may be added as soon as the preparation has

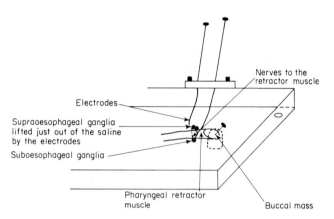

FIG. 10. Diagram of the brain and the electrodes to show how the electrodes are placed on the brain.

"settled down", and their effects on the contractions of the muscle recorded on the kymograph set to move at about 0·05 mm/sec. The preparation should be washed thoroughly after the effect of each application of the drug has been recorded. Washing is done by letting the fluid out of the bath through the built-in outlet, and refilling the bath quickly with fresh saline. This procedure is repeated two or three times for each washing.

Recipe for Meng's Ringer

KCl	0·86 g
NaCl	6·90 g
$CaCl_2.6H_2O$	2·34 g
$NaHCO_3$	2·20 g
$MgCl_2.6H_2O$	6·62 g
Distilled water	2·00 litres

RESULTS

The effect of L-glutamate on the snail pharyngeal retractor muscle can be seen in the trace in Fig. 11. The glutamate was made up in ringer solution, and the dilutions worked out to include the Ringer already in the bath.

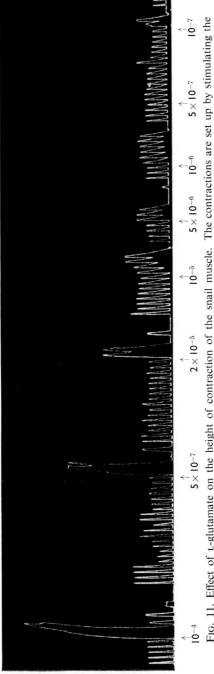

FIG. 11. Effect of L-glutamate on the height of contraction of the snail muscle. The contractions are set up by stimulating the preparation electrically. L-Glutamate at the concentrations indicated on the figure (g/ml final concentration in bath) was then added and produced the greater contractions.

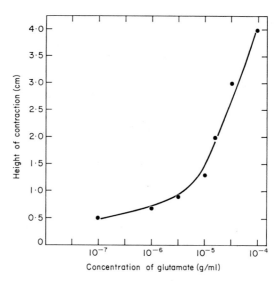

Fig. 12. Graph to show the effect of L-glutamic acid on the pharyngeal retractor muscle.

Figure 12 shows the graph obtained by measuring the height of the contractions on the illustrated trace.

If care and attention is paid to the dissection, there is very little that can "go wrong" in this experiment. Once the preparation is set up it will last up to 24 h, given a short rest periodically.

C.   Perfusion of the Cockroach Leg

This preparation offers a useful method for the assay of different pharmacologically active compounds. The preparation is delicate but relatively simple to set up and it will last for several hours.

MATERIALS AND METHODS

A live, healthy, adult cockroach, *Periplaneta americana*, is pinned to a cork frog board ventral side uppermost (Fig. 13). The mesothoracic legs are removed and the metatarsus of one of the metathoracic legs is cut off. A fine pin bent into a small hook is inserted through the tibia near the cut end (Fig. 14). A piece of cotton which has been previously tied to the pin will lead to a straw writing lever which writes on a kymograph drum. The ventral sternites over the metathoracic segments are gently removed to expose the thoracic ganglia (Fig. 15). A slit is made in the joint between the coxa

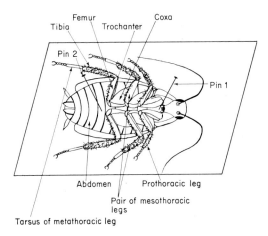

FIG. 13. To illustrate the cockroach pinned on the extreme right-hand corner of the frog board before experimentation is started. Pins 1 and 2 hold the cockroach to the board.

and the thorax with very fine forceps, and a fine nylon cannula inserted in the slit. The cannula, outside diameter 0·037 in., internal diameter 0·030 in., fits tightly into the coxa, and is attached by polythene tubing to a 10 litre aspirator containing 5 litres of Pringle's Ringer (p. 367). The aspirator is placed about 4 ft above the preparation and the pressure of the fluid in the cannula is maintained at 14 cm/Hg by a hand pump (Fig. 16). At this pressure, the fluid will perfuse through the leg at a rate of 2 drops per sec. A pair of electrodes are then placed on the exposed thoracic ganglia (Fig. 17) and shocks

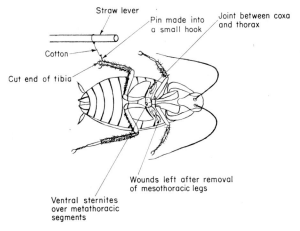

FIG. 14. Diagram to show pin placed through the cut end of the tibia, and the connexion of the pin to the straw lever.

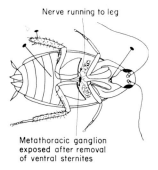

FIG. 15. Illustration of position of the metathoracic ganglion and the nerves to the leg.

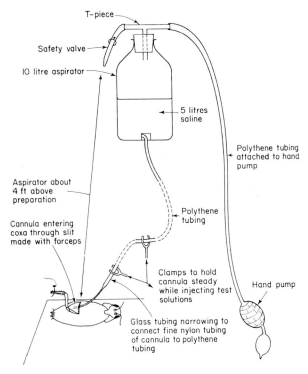

FIG. 16. Diagram to illustrate perfusion system and insertion of cannula in the coxa of the metathoracic leg.

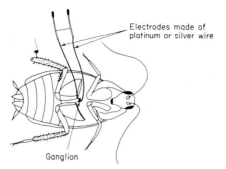

Electrodes made of
platinum or silver wire

Ganglion

FIG. 17. Diagram to show positioning of electrodes on exposed metathoracic ganglion.

are delivered to the electrodes at the rate of one stimulus every 2 sec. The intensity of the stimulus is adjusted so that the leg gives a twitch about 1 cm high for every stimulus. The writing point of the lever is now brought up to the kymograph drum which is set to move at 0·16 mm/sec on a 6 in. cylinder.

Test solutions are made up in saline and injected with a syringe into rubber tubing attached by glass tubing to the polythene tubing (Fig. 18). As the test solution is injected into a constant flow of Ringer it will be diluted by the

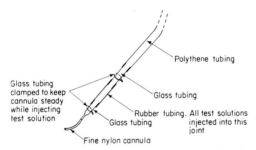

Polythene tubing

Glass tubing
clamped to keep
cannula steady
while injecting
test solution

Glass tubing

Rubber tubing. All test solutions
injected into this
joint

Glass tubing

Fine nylon cannula

FIG. 18. Enlarged diagram of cannula and attachment of cannula to main polythene tubing.

time it reaches the cockroach leg. In order to obtain the required concentration of the compound under study perfusing through the leg, it is necessary to determine the dilution factor involved. This is done quite simply by test injections before the experiment of a dye, such as phenol red. If a known concentration of the dye is injected, the dilution can be measured on an absorptiometer.

Recipe for Pringle's Ringer
45 g NaCl
1·0 g KCl
1·0 g $CaCl_2$
20 g Glucose
5 litres distilled water

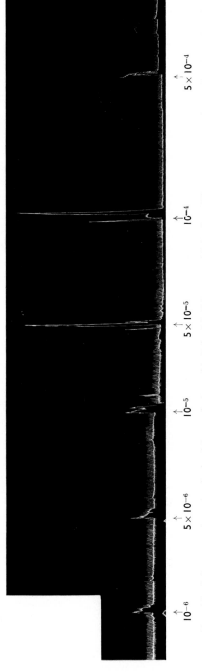

FIG. 19. A kymograph trace obtained by perfusing with Pringle's Ringer and injecting different concentrations of L-glutamic acid into the perfusing system and hence through the cockroach leg.

TROUBLE-SHOOTING

1. Healthy cockroaches must be used for a successful experiment. The animal should not be anaesthesized in any way.

2. Great care should be taken over inserting the pin in the end of the tibia and attaching the thread to the straw lever, or the leg will be pulled off.

3. When the ganglion is exposed, it should be handled as little as possible. Rough treatment could cause damage to the ganglion or sectioning of the nerves. If either of these damages occurred, the preparation would have to be abandoned.

4. Great care must be taken over inserting the cannula into the coxa. The coxa is easily split or separated from the rest of the leg.

5. The rate of perfusion through the leg must be kept constant at no less than 2 drops per sec. The response to electrical stimulation will never be regular if the correct pressure is not maintained, and it would be almost impossible to determine any response to chemical stimulation.

6. Should the leg remain flexed, the preparation should be abandoned and a new one set up.

RESULTS

The effects of many excitatory and inhibitory compounds can be studied. Two drugs can be mixed before injection, and the effect of one upon the other

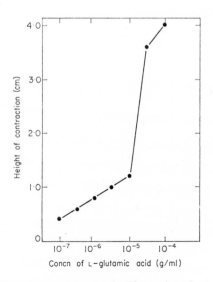

FIG. 20. Response of muscle to L-glutamic acid. Figures for this graph come from measuring the trace in Fig. 19.

P

on the response of the muscle noted. Figures 19 and 20 show a typical trace and dose response curve of L-glutamic acid.

Once this technique has been mastered, the experiment is simple and the results rewarding, requiring no more than patience on the part of the operator.

20 | Physiological Responses to Asphyxia in Animals, Including Man

GEORGE V. PICKWELL

U.S. Navy Electronics Laboratory, San Diego, California, U.S.A.

and

EVERETT DOUGLAS

Scripps Institution of Oceanography, University of California, La Jolla, California, U.S.A.

ANIMALS AND APPARATUS

Virtually any vertebrate or invertebrate of appropriate size for obtaining heart signals and which may be easily handled will prove suitable for these experiments. In the interests of obtaining meaningful comparative data at least one aquatic or amphibious animal, for example a duck, should be contrasted with a more or less comparable terrestrial animal such as a chicken, or a coypu versus a guinea-pig or white rat, a frog versus a toad, and so on.

Any electrocardiograph machine will be satisfactory. For very small animals additional amplification of the heart beat signal may be required, but the authors have not found this necessary with animals the size of rats or even small crabs.

IDEA AND PRINCIPLE

The animal body possesses certain intrinsic defense mechanisms by which it guards itself during times of stress. Among these, few are as readily observed as the adaptations for tolerance to asphyxia, especially in the diving animals. The decline in heart rate upon submergence (bradycardia) is perhaps the most rapid of the asphyctic responses and lends itself easily to investigation.

This reduction signals a general shift, as it were, to emergency measures, such as a reduction of blood flow in all but the most sensitive tissues (Elsner *et al.*, 1963), thus conserving the bodily stores of oxygen for the organs most in need, usually the heart and brain. Rapidity of onset of bradycardia is often an indication of the degree of adaptation possessed by an animal for tolerance to short term asphyxia.

A comparison of electrocardiograph (ECG) records obtained from diving and non-diving animals during periods of submergence may disclose other adaptive advantages possessed by the divers, in terms of total degree of reduction sustained when compared to pre-dive resting levels and quickness of post-dive return to resting levels. For thorough discussions of these and other adaptive responses see Irving (1939), Harrison and Tomlinson (1963) and Scholander (1963a, b, 1964).

Experimental Details

If the animal is to be placed in water unrestrained, the ECG leads must be of suitable length and flexibility. However, for most experiments leads of only a few feet in length are sufficient since the animals will be confined in small enclosures or secured to boards. For the latter method a few strips of adhesive masking tape have proved suitable (see Fig. 1). Care must be taken not to cramp the restrained animal to the point where it encounters respiratory difficulty. Until some idea of the experimental animal's ability to withstand asphyxia is obtained, it is suggested that the periods of submergence be no greater than a minute or two.

Electrodes are easily fashioned from gold-plated fish hooks of small size from which the barbs have been removed. These may be inserted painlessly beneath the skin and taped in place with no bleeding or discomfort to the animal. For human subjects standard ECG electrodes are easiest to use unless the subject is to be entirely submerged, in which case attaching a disk of neoprene rubber cemented atop the electrode to the subject's skin will render the electrode water-tight. The leads may be passed through a hole in the center of the neoprene disk (see Scholander et al., 1962). It is suggested that location of the electrodes be standardized as much as possible—for example, right upper arm (or wing) and left thigh.

Additional measurements may be taken simultaneously with the heart rate, such as blood pressure in human subjects using a standard sphygmomanometer. Other measurements which can be made will be found detailed in various references of the Bibliography (p. 377).

Results

Figure 1 and Tables I and II present results of several actual classroom experiments which illustrate the degree of response which may be expected. Human subjects and other mammals provide interesting points of reference for comparison with lower animals.

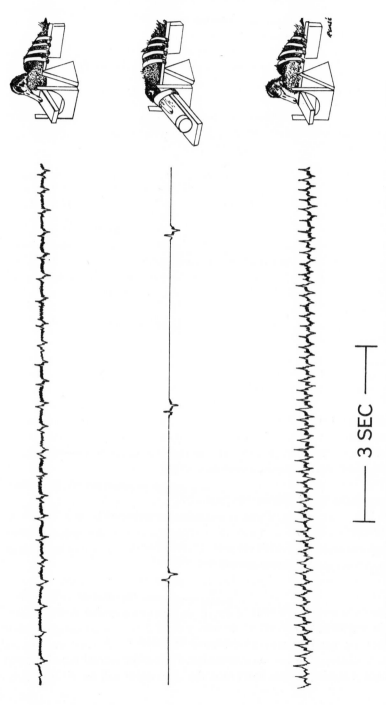

FIG. 1. Heart rate of a male mallard duck before, during and after a 4 min dive. Upper trace, resting rate before dive while strapped to restraining rack; center trace, lowest rate achieved at 3 min of the 4 min dive, bill in tube filled with water; lower trace, immediate post-dive tachycardia upon removal of bill from water.

3 SEC

TABLE I

Apneic diving in man*

	Breath-holding in air			Apneic dive		
Subject	Before	During†	After‡	Before	During†	After‡
A. Heart rate (beats per min)						
M.W. (1)	100	80	90 at 18 sec after first breath	148	80	114 at 21 sec
(2)	110	80	90 at 12 sec	136	76	114 at 20 sec
(3)				100	76	100 at 12 sec
E.D. (1)	86	46	90 at 38 sec	82	48	76 at 18 sec
(2)				94	48	80 at 27 sec
(3)				74	46	
(4)				86	52	70 at 14 sec
B. Blood pressure (systolic/diastolic)						
M.W. (1)				148/98	192/	134/98, 124/96
(2)					172/102	
(3)				140/90	155/110	134/98, 124/96
E.D. (1)				124/80	158/90	
(2)				128/78	164/90	146/80

* All dives were performed while subject, lying comfortably prone, immersed his face in a sink or basin full of water. Dives and breath-holds were all 1 min.

† Figures represent lowest rate attained.

‡ Times are interval from first breath in recovery.

In tabulating the results of his experiment the student should be alert to possible significant adaptive responses of some animals over others. For example, the mallard duck in Table II (see also Fig. 1) exhibits an accelerated heart rate (tachycardia) upon emergence which quickly returns to pre-dive levels. This suggests the ability to rapidly replenish depleted oxygen stores and pay off the accumulated "oxygen debt" resulting from the dive. By contrast, the white rat in Table II exhibits no tachycardia, the heart rate returning more gradually to the pre-dive resting level but showing no immediate post-dive overshoot. This suggests a pay-off of the oxygen debt incurred during asphyxia over a longer period.

Responses which are in part due to excitement, for example the first human subject in Table I, may add confusion and the student is cautioned to handle experimental animals as gently as possible allowing generous pre-asphyctic stabilization periods while taking careful note of all indications of excitement or nervousness. Continuous struggling may be evidence of respiratory distress due to over-restraining. Unless the animal remains quiet and attains a stable pre-dive heart rate, the experiment will be of little value.

TABLE II

Apneic diving in animals other than man

Species	Length of dive (min)	Heart rate (beats per min)		
		Before*	During†	After
White rat (head only immersed)	1	430–440	40	320 at 18 sec 350 at 36 sec 370 at 54 sec 400 at 72 sec
Mallard duck (bill only immersed, see Fig. 1)	1	140–160	46–54	300 at 1 sec 290 at 6 sec 140 at 48 sec
Pacific green turtle (entire body immersed wt 38 lb)	32	29	7	25 at 11 min
California spiny lobster‡	28	60–68	22	61 at 9 min

* Stable resting heart rate.
† Lowest heart rate recorded.
‡ Lobster made anoxic by wrapping in plastic bags and covering with moist sand. Recovery took place in water.

TROUBLE-SHOOTING

If the ECG trace appears fuzzy with no clearly discernible heart beat there are several things to check.

(1) Are the electrodes firmly implanted and making good contact? Generally a standard electrode paste will prove useful in obtaining good contact. The two electrode leads should be taped down in several places either directly to the animal or to the restraining rack or both to insure against loss or loosening of the electrodes by struggling.

(2) Improper grounding of the equipment is a common difficulty, but generally metal plumbing fixtures will provide an adequate ground. Occasionally a metal rod driven a foot or two into moist soil outside the laboratory will remedy the situation and provide a permanent means of grounding electrical equipment.

(3) Occasionally the experimental animal may pick up electrical noise on the ECG circuit by touching some metal fixture which is not itself suitably grounded.

(4) On less frequent occasions fuses in the ECG machine may be blown. It pays to check these periodically and have on hand a supply of spares.

The patient circuit of the machine will take a fuse of perhaps 1/200 amp whereas the power circuit may carry a 6 amp fuse.

(5) It is often wise to check the ECG leads and circuit before connecting to the experimental animal. This is most easily done by grasping one electrode between the thumb and forefinger of each hand while the electrocardiograph machine is running. Should the laboratory floor not be insulated it may be necessary to step upon a wooden box or stool. If the equipment is functioning satisfactorily an ECG trace will be obtained immediately.

CONCLUSIONS

In his laboratory write-up of the experiment the student may wish to include sections of the ECG record which illustrate the phenomena discussed, such as maximum and minimum heart rates achieved by the experimental animals. He should draw conclusions concerning the animal's ability to tolerate short periods of asphyxia based upon rapidity and degree of heart rate response as well as on the general behavior of the animal when confronted with brief asphyxia (for example, does the animal remain quiet, or does it struggle vigorously?). He should attempt to relate these observations and conclusions to what is known of the animal's general physiology and its life history and behavior. For example, given a knowledge of the diving habits of the mallard, why might the post-dive tachycardia shown in Fig. 1 and Table II be of advantage? Answer: divers and "dabblers" while feeding are often observed to submerge several times in rapid succession scarcely allowing time for more than a few breaths between dives. Immediate reduction in heart rate might be evidence for the ability to act quickly to conserve oxygen stores. Rapid pay-off of small oxygen debts would prevent undue stress which might be incurred from a large cumulative debt. The student should become familiar with such terms as apneic, oxygen debt, bradycardia, tachycardia, systolic and diastolic and should employ such terms in his laboratory reports.

FURTHER IDEAS

New or untested species such as different fishes or invertebrates may provide meaningful comparisons and new insight into the problems of asphyxia. Analyses of respiratory and blood gases will present a contrasting manner of viewing the above phenomena and the use of drugs such as atropine, epine-phrine, and acetylcholine should produce another approach which touches upon the neurological control of asphyxia. In all, the interested student will have no problem conceiving various ways to study the physiological adapta-tions involved.

BIBLIOGRAPHY

Anderson, H. T. (1964). Stresses imposed on diving vertebrates during prolonged underwater exposure. *Symp. Soc. exp. Biol.*, **18**, 109–127.

Bond, C. F., Douglas, S. D. and Gilbert, P. W. (1961). Effects of submergence on cardiac cycle and rate in aquatic and terrestrial birds. *Am. J. Physiol.*, **200**, 723–726. [A comparison of ducks and gallinaceous birds among others.]

Berkson, H. (1964). Gas distribution in the Pacific Green Turtle (*Chelonia mydas agassizii*) subjected to prolonged high hydrostatic pressure. Ph.D. Thesis, University of California at San Diego. [Thus far the only study of pressure effects on apneic dive physiology besides that of Scholander, 1940.]

Elsner, R. W., Garey, W. F. and Scholander, P. F. (1963). Selective ischemia in diving man. *Am. Heart J.*, **65**, 571–572. [Reduced limb blood flow in breath-holding and diving graduate students.]

Elsner, R. W., Franklin, D. L. and Van Citters, R. L. (1964). Cardiac output during diving in an unrestrained sea lion. *Nature, Lond.*, **202**, 809–810. [Diving responses during voluntary diving in a trained sea lion.]

Garey, W. F. (1962). Cardiac responses of fishes in asphyxic environments. *Biol. Bull. mar. Biol. Lab., Woods Hole*, **122**, 362–368. [Details of heart rate responses of fishes which habitually leave the water.]

Harrison, J. J. and Tomlinson, J. D. W. (1963). Anatomical and physiological adaptations in diving mammals. *In* "Viewpoints in Biology" (J. D. Carthy and C. L. Duddington, eds.), Vol. 2, pp. 115–162, Butterworths, London. [An excellent review article. Comprehensive coverage of anatomical aspects.]

Irving, L. (1939). Respiration in diving mammals. *Physiol. Rev.*, **19**, 112–134. [The first thorough review of this subject. A classic, and a useful guide to the early literature.]

Scholander, P. F. (1940). Experimental investigations on the respiratory function in diving mammals and birds. *Hvalrådets Skrifter*. No. 22. 131 pp. [The most comprehensive single study undertaken in apneic dive physiology.]

Scholander, P. F. (1963a). Physiological adaptation to diving in animals and man. *Harvey Lect.*, **57**, 93–110. [A good, rather brief summary of the subject and especially the contributions of Scholander and Irving.]

Scholander, P. F. (1963b). The master switch of life. *Sci. Am.*, **202**, 92–106. [An excellent non-technical article. Strongly recommended as a starting point for reading in this field.]

Scholander, P. F. (1964). Animals in aquatic environments: diving mammals and birds. *In* "Handbook of Physiology." Section 4. Adaptation to the Environment (D. B. Dill, ed.), pp. 729–739. American Physiological Society, Washington, D.C. [The most comprehensive review article now available. Includes references to most of the significant work performed in the field of apneic dive physiology to 1963.]

Scholander, P. F., Hammel, H. T., LeMessurier, H., Hemmingsen, E. and Garey, W. (1962). Circulatory adjustment in pearl divers. *J. appl. Physiol.*, **17**, 184–190. [Diving responses of professional Trochus shell divers in North Australia.]

21 | Intestinal Absorption of Glucose, *in vivo*

X. J. MUSACCHIA

Department of Physiology, University of Missouri, Columbia, Missouri, U.S.A.

Background and Principles

A primary function of the intestine is absorption of nutrients. Glucose is one of the most common products of digestion and most readily absorbed by all areas of the small intestine.

The following experiment will provide a technique for the demonstration of absorption of glucose from the lumen of the intestine. In this experiment a solution of known glucose concentration is placed in the lumen of the small intestine, and after a period of time the lumenal contents are collected and the amount of remaining glucose is determined. The difference in concentration, from the start of the experiment until its termination, will indicate the amount of sugar absorbed. The amount of sugar can be determined by calculation as either the difference, "before" and "after" concentrations, or as an amount absorbed per unit of tissue per unit of time.

There are two aspects of this experiment which are pertinent to an understanding of the phenomenon of intestinal absorption. (1) The hamster is alive during the experiment, thus the physiological features measured are being witnessed in a living system. (2) The concentration of glucose used (not more than 100 mg%) is less than the average range of blood sugar levels in this animal (usually from 140 to 200 mg%, and higher). This should suggest to the student that glucose is moving from a compartment, the intestinal lumen, through the intestinal cells and into the blood-stream against what appears to be a concentration gradient. It has been shown by numerous investigators that, *in vitro*, active transport of glucose is a common feature of the intestinal epithelium (Crane, 1960; Wilson, 1962; Wiseman, 1964) and it is reasonable to assume that the same mechanisms are operative *in vivo*.

This then is a basic exercise which will provide the student with an opportunity to develop some familiarity in elementary surgical manipulations using an animal under anesthesia. The hamster, *Mesocricetus auratus*, is a hardy animal and is recommended for this experiment.

MATERIALS AND METHODS

A colorimeter or photometer to measure color intensity of solutions.

A dissecting or surgical kit with one or two scissors, forceps, and scalpels for opening the abdominal wall, to manipulate the intestine and to remove the segments at the end of the experiment.

A 10 ml syringe attached to polyethylene or rubber tubing is used to wash and rinse the intestine of its lumenal contents.

A 5 ml syringe and No. 22 hypodermic needle is used to introduce the test solution into the intestinal lumen.

A 1 or 2 ml syringe and No. 23 hypodermic needle is used to inject sodium nembutal (30–40 mg/kg) intraperitoneally, i.e. if this is the anesthetic of choice.

A large wide mouth vessel of about 1 liter or 2 quart capacity with ether soaked cotton may be used to initiate anesthesia. A common 50 ml beaker with ether soaked cotton is used as a nose cone to maintain the animal under anesthesia during the experiment.

Ordinary cotton thread is used for ligatures.

Graduated centrifuge tubes or comparable vessels may be used for collection of fluid at the end of an experimental run.

Reagents for sugar analysis are commonplace and the methods are numerous, usually each laboratory has its preference. One of the best known references in this area is the method of Nelson and Somogyi (Nelson, 1944). The student is referred to standard laboratory texts dealing with procedures and methods.

One solution which is essential for studies of living mammalian tissue is the classic Krebs-Ringer bicarbonate (KRB) solution (Umbreit et al., 1964). The directions for making the solution follow.

The various salts are dissolved in distilled water to a volume of 100 ml. More concentrated stock solutions can be made as needed (e.g. 5 × concentrated). (N.B. If concentrated stock solutions are used, appropriate dilutions must be made before mixing the various solutions together.)

A. 0·90% NaCl   (0·154 M) = 0·9 g/100 ml
B. 1·15% KCl   (0·154 M) = 1·15 g/100 ml
C. 1·22% $CaCl_2$ (0·11 M) = 1·22 g/100 ml
D. 2·11% KH_2PO_4 (0·154 M) = 2·11 g/100 ml
E. 3·82% $MgSO_4.7H_2O$ (0·154 M) = 3·82 g/100 ml
F. 1·30% $NaHCO_3$ (0·15 M) = 1·30 g/100 ml (gas this with CO_2 for 1 h)

B through E are stable for months in the cold. A and F do not have to be stored in the cold.

To prepare the Krebs-Ringer bicarbonate solution, the following volumes of the above solutions are mixed:

ml
A. 100
B.   4
C.   3
D.   1   (This solution is stable in the cold for several days)
E.   1
F. 21
───
130 ml KRB

Before use, the solution is gassed with 95% O_2/5% CO_2 for 10 min, to maintain a pH range 7.0 to 7.4.

PREPARATION OF THE ANIMAL

A small mammal, such as the hamster, can be anesthetized with nembutal (30–40 mg/kg intraperitoneally) or with ether (merely place the animal in a vessel with ether soaked cotton or gauze) until it becomes limp.

The hamster should be fasted for 24 h. This ensures an intestinal "steady state" and allows the emptying of most of the chyme and other intestinal residues.

The anesthetized hamster is placed on its back on a board or dissecting pan so that the ventral surface is accessible. The limbs are gently stretched and can be fastened with cords, clamps or tape. There is no need to shave the ventral surface.

A mid-line abdominal incision is made through the skin and muscle layers in order to expose the viscera (Figs 1 and 2). Ligatures are placed at the pyloric-duodenal and ileo-caecal junctions (Fig. 3).

The intestine is cut about 1 cm below the pyloric-duodenal ligature, and about 1 cm above the ileo-caecal ligature. At the duodenal end the syringe tube attachment is made and the 10 ml syringe, previously filled with warm (37°C) KRB solution (sugar free), is used to gently flush and clean the intestine. The flushing solution and intestinal contents issue from the opened ileal end and can be collected in a small vessel. The intestine can be gently pressed with thumb and forefinger, moving from the duodenal area distally towards the ileal area. These procedures are intended to clean the gut lumen of digestive remnants, secretions and other sundry lumenal contents. (The flushing and cleaning procedures can be deleted if the laboratory time periods are short; however, one must realize that dilution and other forms of chemical interactions might take place with ordinary lumen contents.)

Sets of two ligatures each are placed at least 5–6 cm apart, only one of each is tied shut, and a number of segments are thus isolated (Figs 3 and 4).

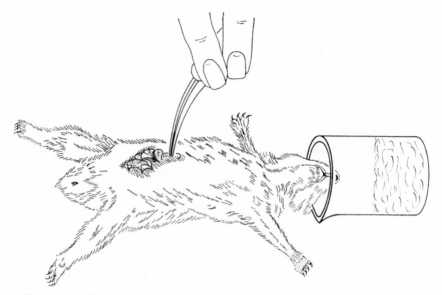

FIG. 1.—A midline abdominal incision is made through the skin and muscle layers in order to expose the viscera. The animal is under anesthesia (beaker with ether-soaked cotton).

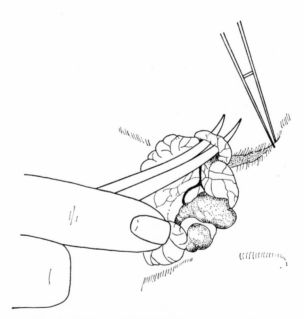

FIG. 2. The duodenal area of the intestine is lifted with a forceps.

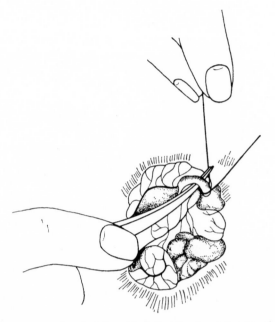

FIG. 3. Ligatures are placed at the pyloric-duodenal and ileo-caecal junctions.

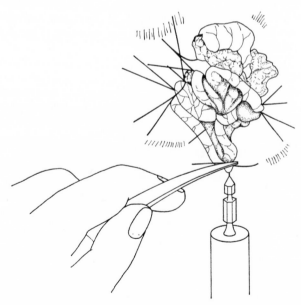

FIG. 4. Sets of 2 ligatures each are placed at least 5 to 6 cm apart, only one of each is tied shut before the second tie is made. The segment is filled with test solution from a syringe and 21 gauge needle.

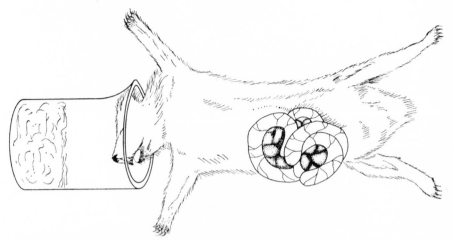

FIG. 5. The filled segments and viscera are exposed (N.B. keep moistened with cotton swabs soaked in 37°C KRB solution). The animal remains under light ether anesthesia.

Each segment is independently filled with a measured amount, 1 or 2 ml, of the test solution (KRB + glucose). This is done with the 5 ml syringe and No. 22 hypodermic needle. The needle is held inside the intestinal lumen as the segment is filled and the remaining loosely placed ligature can be tightened as the needle is withdrawn (Fig. 4). With practice, the entire procedure should take about 10 min. The filled segments (Figs 5 and 6) and

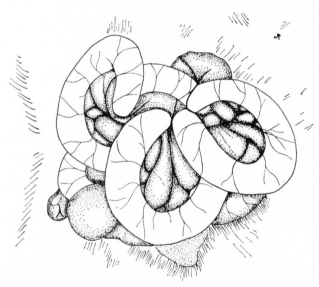

FIG. 6. An enlarged view of the filled segments.

exposed viscera are kept moistened with cotton swabs soaked in 37°C KRB solution.

After a period of time, e.g. 30 min, each segment is freed from its mesenteric connections (Fig. 7) and the lumenal fluid is collected in a centrifuge tube or comparable vessel (Fig. 8). The benefit of using a graduated centrifuge tube is in being able to determine if water was also absorbed. For example, if

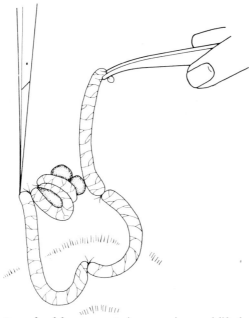

FIG. 7. Segments are freed from mesenteric connections and lifted with a forceps.

2 ml of solution is placed in a particular segment and only 1·6 ml is collected after 30 min, approximately 0·4 ml was absorbed. Ordinarily in 30 min, in hamster intestine the amount of fluid absorbed is only 0·01–0·08 ml, and this may be considered negligible.

After the fluid is collected from the segment an aliquot is taken for glucose determination. The empty segment may be weighed (for wet weight values) and dried at 100°C for 24 h (for dry weight values).

DETERMINATION OF CONCENTRATION OF SUGAR

Sugar determinations can be made using one of various procedures, for example the Nelson and Somogyi method utilizes the familiar reactions of oxidation of glucose in boiling alkaline solution by a reduction of the cupric ion to the red precipitate of cuprous oxide. The next step is a reaction with arsenomolybdate (Nelson's chromogenic reagent) which results in a blue colored solution. The intensity of the blue color is proportional to

R

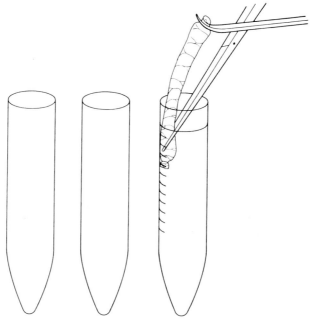

Fig. 8. Lumenal fluid is collected from each segment. Collection vessels are centrifuge tubes or comparable vessels.

concentration of sugar. A colorimeter or photometer can be used to measure the intensity of the colored solution.

A series of standards, i.e. known concentrations of D-glucose, are made by dissolving known amounts: 25, 50, 100 or 150 mg/100 ml in KRB or distilled water. Typically, at the end of a 30 min run the concentration of sugar remaining in the intestinal segment (hereafter referred to as the *unknown*) can be measured as follows:

$$\frac{\text{Optical density of } unknown}{\text{Optical density of } standard} \times \text{concentration of } standard$$

$$= \text{concentration of } unknown$$

Subtract the concentration of the *unknown* from the concentration of the solution used in the start of the experiment and the difference indicates the amount of sugar absorbed in 30 min.

A relationship of the efficiency of the different areas of the intestine can be made by the following calculation.

$$\frac{\text{Concentration of } unknown \times \text{volume of solution}}{\text{Weight (dry* or wet) of tissue}} = \text{amount/g/30 min}$$

Thus one can obtain the amount of sugar absorbed/g of tissue/30 min.

* Dry weight can be obtained by drying at 100°C for 24 h.

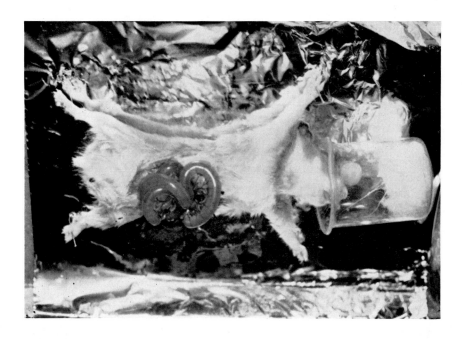

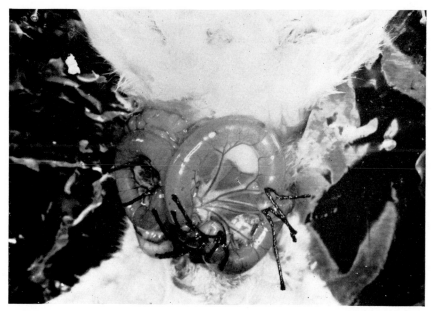

FIGS. 9 and 10. Photographs of filled individual intestinal segments. (The segments were made to protrude out of the body cavity for purposes of demonstration).

Sample calculations:

$$C_u = \text{concentration of } unknown$$
$$C_s = \text{concentration of the } standard$$
$$\text{O.D.}_u = \text{optical density of the } unknown$$
$$\text{O.D.}_s = \text{optical density of the } standard$$
$$\frac{\text{O.D.}_u}{\text{O.D.}_s} \times C_s = C_u$$

Concentration of *unknown* × volume of *unknown* = total amount sugar present in a given volume of solution. This calculation is made for the sugar solution at the onset of the experiment and at the termination. The difference in the amount of sugar = amount of sugar absorbed. e.g.

$$C_u = (\quad)$$
$$C_s = 100 \text{ mg}\% \frac{0\cdot25}{0\cdot50} \times 100 = 50 \text{ mg}\% = C_u$$
$$= 50 \text{ mg}/100 \text{ ml or } 0\cdot5 \text{ mg/ml}$$
$$\text{O.D.}_u = 0\cdot25$$
$$\text{O.D.}_s = 0\cdot50$$

If there was 1 ml fluid in each sac, then 1 ml × 0·5 mg/ml = 0·5 mg total sugar present.

This experimental procedure can be refined and expanded to test and measure individual effects of drugs, by adding compounds to the KRB + glucose solution, or by treating the animal before a typical test run. For example, inhibition of glucose absorption can be demonstrated by adding to the KRB + 100 mg% D-glucose, phlorizin 5×10^{-4} M.

The effects of fasting and starvation can be readily tested by removing food for periods of 12–72 h.

These and many other experimental methods can be introduced, depending upon the interest of the investigator. Some details of experiments and experimental results have been recently published (Musacchia and Bramante, 1966).

REFERENCES

Crane, R. K. (1960). Intestinal absorption of sugars. *Physiol. Rev.*, **40**, 789–825.
Musacchia, X. J. and Bramante, A. V. (1967). Proceedings of the Third International Symposium of Mammalian Hibernation. Oliver and Boyd, Edinburgh.
Nelson, N. (1944). A photometric adaptation of the Somogyi method for the determination of glucose. *J. biol. Chem.*, **153**, 375–380.
Umbreit, W. H., Burris, R. H. and Stauffer, J. F. (1964) "Manometric Techniques," p. 305. Burgess, Minneapolis.
Wilson, T. H. (1962). "Intestinal Absorption," p. 263. Saunders, Philadelphia.
Wiseman, G. (1964). "Absorption from the Intestine," p. 560. Academic Press, London.

22 | The Consumption of Oxygen by the Whole Animal

P. STANBURY

School of Biological Sciences, University of Sydney, N.S.W., Australia

ANIMALS

Toads, lizards, chicks, mice, etc.

APPARATUS

Glass jar with a wide mouth
Rubber bung to fit
Laboratory stands
Metal gauze or fly-wire
Glass tubing
Rubber tubing
Clamps for rubber tubing

Two tin cans, one of which is a close fit inside the other (see Fig. 1). The tins should be open at one end. The larger tin should have a piece of metal tubing soldered through a hole in the closed end so that the tube extends (inside) the length of the tin. In the other direction the tube should project about 2 in. outside the tin. The smaller tin should have a strip of centimetre graph paper pasted on the outside and a hook soldered on the outside of the closed end.

CHEMICALS

Soda lime.

PRINCIPLE OF THE EXPERIMENT

Animals consume oxygen. The oxygen used is combined with hydrogen, obtained from the oxidation of foodstuffs, to form water. During this combination there is an associated release of the energy originally contained in the foodstuffs; the energy released is immediately trapped and transferred to the energy store of the animal.

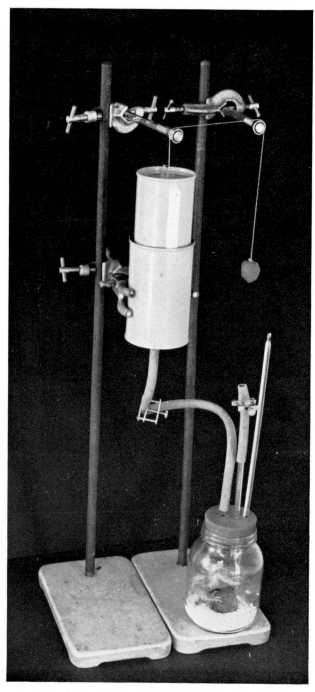

Fig. 1. A home-made respirometer.

The harder an animal works, the more energy is required, and so the more oxygen. For example, a man resting uses approximately 0·2 ml $O_2/g/h$, whereas a man working uses nearly 4 ml $O_2/g/h$.

Oxygen consumption also varies according to (1) temperature, (2) nutrition, (3) body weight, (4) stage in life cycle, (5) sex, and (6) hormonal and environmental effects.

The above differences in oxygen consumption are differences between individuals of the one species, but of course different species also consume different amounts of oxygen. This is due partly to the variables mentioned above and also to the inherent differences in the biochemical makeup between species.

The idea of this experiment is to demonstrate, with a simple respirometer, the differences in oxygen consumption between species and between the individuals of a species.

EXPERIMENTAL DETAILS

Set up the apparatus as in Fig. 2. Fill the larger tin (R) with water and suspend it by means of a clamp and stand about 18 in. above the bench. Moisten the metal tube S and push on to it a length of rubber tubing. Fit the smaller tin (J) into the larger and allow the air trapped (in P) to escape through the rubber tubing. The smaller tin will come to rest almost completely enclosed by the larger. Tie a piece of cotton on to the hook (O), at the end of the smaller tin. Drape the cotton over two lightly greased glass rods (M and L) and attach plasticine to the other end of the cotton (K). The weight

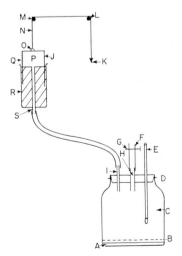

FIG. 2. A diagrammatic representation of the respirometer (for further explanation, see text).

of the plasticine should be such that the smaller tin just sinks through the water, thus slowly expelling the air in P.

Cover the bottom of the wide-mouthed jar (C) with soda lime (A). Arrange a piece of metal gauze (B) above the soda lime so that the experimental animals cannot touch the lime. Through three holes in the rubber bung (D) push (moistened or greased first) a thermometer (E) and two short lengths of glass tubing (I and H). To one of the lengths of glass tubing connect the free end of the rubber tubing attached to the larger tin of the respirometer. To the other length of glass tubing attach a short length of rubber tubing (F). Place around the rubber tubing a screw-clamp (G).

Place the animal (or animals) in the wide-mouthed jar. Insert the rubber bung in the mouth of the jar after making sure that the screw-clamp (G) is open. Raise the smaller can of the respirometer until it is about seven-eighths out of the larger can. Close the screw-clamp G, and note the time, the temperature, and the reading on scale Q.

As the animal uses the oxygen contained in the respirometer and in the glass jar, the inner can of the respirometer will fall and this will be indicated on the scale Q. Remembering that only one-fifth of the air in the apparatus is oxygen, allow the inner can of the respirometer to fall by a convenient amount (say from 0·25 to 2·5 cm), and then note the time, temperature and reading on the scale as accurately as possible. Open the screw-clamp G and remove the rubber bung so that a fresh supply of air reaches the animal.

The experiment should be repeated to obtain duplicate readings. Then experiment with (1) animals of the same species but of different weight, and (2) different species.

SAMPLE RESULTS

The inner can fell in 15 min	1·1 cm
Diameter of the tin	6·0 cm
Volume of oxygen used	$\pi r^2 h$
	3·14 × 9 × 1·1 ml
Weight of animals	65·7 g
O_2 consumed per h per g	$\dfrac{3·14 \times 9 \times 1·1 \times 60}{65·7 \times 15}$ ml = 1·9 ml

TROUBLE-SHOOTING

If, after several minutes, no oxygen appears to have been consumed, try checking the following.

(1) Is the counterbalance weight K too heavy? Is the cotton stuck at M or L? Both of these will prevent the small can from falling.

(2) Is there any water trapped in the rubber tube linking the respirometer with the glass animal-chamber?

(3) Is air leaking into the apparatus? If you think there is, try greasing the suspect areas with petroleum jelly. Or put the glass jar under water.

(4) Is the soda lime fresh? The object of the soda lime is to absorb the carbon dioxide breathed out by the animal.

(5) Is the animal under investigation one which may stop breathing for short periods?

FURTHER EXPERIMENTS

In your experiment you should have found that small animals use more oxygen per unit weight than large ones. How does (a) temperature, (b) sex and (c) light affect the rate of oxygen consumption of individuals of similar weight of the same species? How could the apparatus be improved.

BIBLIOGRAPHY

Prosser, C. L. and Brown, F. A. (1961). "Comparative Animal Physiology". Saunders, Philadelphia. [On pp. 157–166 agents that modify oxygen consumption by intact animals are discussed. On p. 158 there is a table of comparative oxygen consumption.]

Spector, W. S. (Ed.) (1961). "Handbook of Biological Data". Saunders, Philadelphia. [A larger table of respiration rates may be found on p. 261.]

23 | Measurement of the Respiratory Rate of a Small Terrestrial Animal

W. A. L. EVANS

*Department of Zoology, University of Wales,
Cardiff, Wales*

MATERIALS

1. Suitable insects such as larvae or adult flour beetles, *Tenebrio molitor*, or fully grown blowfly larvae.

2. A Dixon-Barcroft constant pressure manometer with mercury in the side limb and Krebs manometer liquid in the U-tube. This manometer liquid has the following composition:

Evans Blue	0·1 g
Sodium iodide	5·0 g
Liquid detergent	1·0 ml
Water	Up to 100 ml

3. 10% Potassium hydroxide and filter paper strips 3 cm wide.

4. A constant temperature water bath at 25°C.

THE PRINCIPLE OF THE CONSTANT PRESSURE MANOMETER

This constant pressure manometer (Fig. 1) presents a useful method of measuring the oxygen consumption of small, fairly active terrestrial animals. The flasks F_1 and F_2 are fully immersed in a constant temperature water bath. The inner tubes of these flasks contain equal volumes of 10% potassium hydroxide plus small rolls of filter paper which protrude about 5 mm out of the tube. Flasks F_2 and F_1 are connected to limbs B and A of the manometer respectively, but between F_1 and A a graduate limb is interposed. The level of the mercury in the side limb can be adjusted by means of the screw S. By turning taps T_1 and T_2 the manometer system is closed to the atmosphere. Animals are placed in flask F_1 only.

At the beginning of the experiment taps T_1 and T_2 are closed when the flasks have attained the temperature of the water bath. During the respiratory process of the animals in the flask F_1 oxygen is inspired and carbon dioxide expired. In F_1 the expired CO_2 is absorbed by the potassium hydroxide so that in the right-hand side of the apparatus there is a decrease in gas pressure

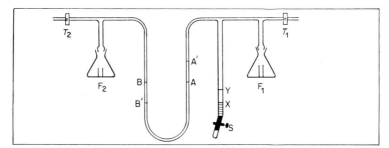

FIG. 1. Diagrammatic representation of the Dixon–Barcroft manometer.

due to the loss of inspired O_2. This is shown by the movement of liquid in the manometer from A to A' and from B to B' since the gas pressure in the left-hand side of the apparatus remains at atmospheric pressure. There is only very slight upward movement of the mercury in the graduated limb. The volume of gas change can be measured directly by adjusting the level of the mercury in the graduated limb by means of the screw, so that the level of liquid in the manometer limbs is the same, i.e. at A and B. The measured upward movement of mercury X to Y, to restore the pressure in the right-hand side of the apparatus to atmospheric, gives the volume of gas change.

The volume change so measured represents the oxygen intake at atmospheric pressure and the temperature of the gas in the graduated limb. In order to make true comparisons of oxygen intake, which may be measured under different conditions of temperature and pressure the volume change, i.e. the reading in the side limb, must be converted into volume changes at S.T.P.

To convert the measured changes into volumes at S.T.P. use the general gas equation

$$\frac{P_1 V_1}{T_1} = \frac{P_2 V_2}{T_2}$$

where P_1 is the atmospheric pressure minus the water vapour pressure; V_1 is the volume change (side limb readings) measured in μl; T_1 is the temperature of the side limb (centigrade gas temperature $+ 273°$); P_2 is the pressure of dry air at 1 atm, 760 mm mercury; T_2 is the absolute temperature $273°$ (i.e. $0°C$); and V_2 is the volume at S.T.P.

EXPERIMENTAL PROCEDURE

1. Identify the animal provided.
2. Make sure you understand and know how to use the apparatus.
3. Fit up the control flask and experimental flask with a single roll of filter paper and 0·3 ml 10% potassium hydroxide.

4. Weigh about six animals and place them in the experimental flask making sure they do not touch the caustic potash.

5. With the taps open completely immerse the flasks in the water bath.

6. Allow the air in the flasks to attain the temperature of the water bath (approx. 20 min). Adjust the mercury in the side limb to a suitable zero point at the bottom of the side limb and then close the taps simultaneously. Note the temperature of the water bath.

7. Record the volume changes in the side limb every 10 min for 90 min after adjusting the liquid in both limbs of the U-tube to the same level by means of the screw.

8. Plot the curve of volume change against time and from its slope obtain the average change in volume per hour. Calculate the best value for the slope by the method of least squares (see below). Compare the curves obtained by drawing a line by eye through the experimental points with the regression line.

9. Correct the average volume change per hour for the apparatus constant, which takes into account inaccuracies in the side-limb scale. Convert the corrected volume change to the equivalent change under standard temperature and pressure conditions and after taking into account the weight of animals, find the O_2 consumption per gram per hour.

RECORD OF AN EXPERIMENT

Date: 4/2/66

Species: *Tenebrio molitor*, larvae

Weight of 7 animals	$= 0.713$ g
Water bath temperature	$= 25°C$
Side limb (air temperature)	$= 14°C$
Barometric pressure	$= 762$ mm
Water vapour pressure at $14°C$	$= 12$ mm
Respirometer correction factor	$= 1.11$

Manometer readings

Clock time	Time (min)	Side-limb reading (ml)	Side-limb vol change (μl)
10.00	—	0.95	—
10.10	10	0.87	80
10.20	20	0.79	160
10.30	30	0.72	230
10.40	40	0.65	300
10.50	50	0.57	380
11.00	60	0.50	450
11.10	70	0.43	520
11.20	80	0.35	600

Calculation of the result:

From the time/manometer volume change plot the slope, estimated by eye, gives an average volume change of 7·5 μl per min.

Volume change per hour corrected for the apparatus constant $= 7\cdot5 \times 1\cdot11 \times 60$ μl.

Applying the gas equation to determine the equivalent change at S.T.P.,

$$\frac{(762 - 12)(7\cdot5 \times 1\cdot11 \times 60)}{287} = \frac{V_2 760}{273}$$

V_2, the corrected volume change per hour $= 469$ μl

Volume change per gram of animal $\quad = \dfrac{469}{0\cdot713} = 658$ μl

Respiratory rate of *Tenebrio* larvae $\quad = 0\cdot66$ ml/g/h.

A SHORT NOTE ON DRAWING THE BEST STRAIGHT LINE THROUGH A SERIES OF POINTS, WHICH INDICATE A LINEAR RELATIONSHIP, BY THE METHOD OF LEAST SQUARES

In the equation $Y = a + bX$, the plot of Y against X gives a straight line with slope b. The interception on the Y axis is at a, but if the straight line passes through the origin then a is zero, which means of course that $Y = bX$. Assuming X is the independent variable and Y the dependent variable (this means in practice that X can be measured very accurately whilst there is a possibility of sampling errors in the measurement of Y), then the best straight line to be drawn through a series of points is the one in which the sum of the squares of the distance of the points from the line, along the Y axis, is a minimum (see Fig. 2).

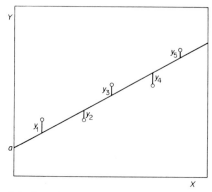

FIG. 2. The best straight line drawn through a series of five points with $y_1^2 + y_2^2 + y_3^2 + y_4^2 + y_5^2$ a minimum, or Σy^2 is a minimum. The line so drawn is known as the *regression line* of Y on X, symbolized y; the slope b is the regression coefficient.

To obtain the regression coefficient is quite straightforward and can be calculated from the X and Y values. It can be shown that the regression coefficient, or slope, is equal to $\Sigma xy/\Sigma x^2$ where x and y are the deviations of X and Y from the means of the values of X and Y (M_X and M_Y). The data are tabulated and computed as shown in Table I.

TABLE I

Arrangement of data for calculation of the regression coefficient or slope for the time/manometer volume change values given in the previous experiment record
N.B. Zero values for X and Y are not used

| | | | Deviations | | |
| | | x | y | | |
X	Y	$(X - M_x)$	$(X - M_y)$	x^2	xy
10	80	−35	−260	1 225	9 100
20	160	−25	−180	625	4 500
30	230	−15	−110	225	1 650
40	300	−5	−40	25	200
50	380	5	40	25	200
60	450	15	110	225	1 650
70	520	25	180	625	4 500
80	600	35	260	1 225	9 100
Sum 360	2 720			4 200	30 900
Mean 45	340				

$$\text{Regression coefficient, or slope} = \frac{\Sigma xy}{\Sigma x^2}$$

$$= \frac{30\ 920}{4\ 200}$$

$$= 7\cdot38\ \mu\text{l/min.}$$

TO CALCULATE THE POSITION OF THE REGRESSION LINE

The regression coefficient, b, for the regression of Y on X is calculated from the deviations x and y from the mean values of $X_1 X_2 X_3 \ldots$ and $Y_1 Y_2 Y_3 \ldots$ respectively. The point corresponding to the value of M_X (mean value of X's) and M_Y (mean value of Y's) can be regarded as the *origin for the regression line*, and the regression line must pass through this point. Given the calculated values M_X and M_Y and the slope b (regression coefficient) it is clear that the regression line can be drawn, by measuring off abscissa and ordinate values from the origin for the regression line to give a slope value b. Note, however, that it is not really necessary to draw a graph since the regression coefficient gives the average volume change per minute which is the value required to calculate the result of the respiratory rate experiment.

FURTHER EXPERIMENTS

The measurement of oxygen uptake of animals or tissue suspensions in this kind of manometer at different temperatures can give data for the determination of the temperature coefficient, Q_{10}, for the respiratory rate. It is advisable to use the same group of animals at the different temperatures. If only two temperatures are used then the Q_{10} can be calculated from the equation

$$Q_{10} = \left(\frac{R_2}{R_1}\right)^{10/T_2 - T_1}$$

where R_1 and R_2 are the respiratory rates at temperatures T_1 and T_2 respectively. Alternatively, if several temperatures are used then Q_{10} can be obtained from the plot, log respiratory rate/temperature since log Q_{10} = slope × 10. Note that if the same animals are used only relative values for the respiratory rate are required for the calculation.

BIBLIOGRAPHY

Dixon, M. (1951). "Manometric Methods", 3rd ed. Cambridge University Press, London.

Index

A